Instrument Technology

Volume 2

Dedicated to
Mother

Instrument Technology
Volume 2

ON-LINE
ANALYSIS INSTRUMENTS

E. B. JONES
B.Sc., F.Inst.P., F.Inst.M.C.

NEWNES–BUTTERWORTHS
LONDON   BOSTON
Sydney–Wellington–Durban–Toronto

THE BUTTERWORTH GROUP

ENGLAND
Butterworth & Co (Publishers) Ltd
London: 88 Kingsway, WC2B 6AB

AUSTRALIA
Butterworths Pty Ltd
Sydney: 586 Pacific Highway, NSW 2067
Also at Melbourne, Brisbane, Adelaide and Perth

SOUTH AFRICA
Butterworth & Co (South Africa) (Pty) Ltd
Durban: 152-154 Gale Street

NEW ZEALAND
Butterworths of New Zealand Ltd
Wellington: 26-28 Waring Taylor Street, 1

CANADA
Butterworth & Co (Canada) Ltd
Toronto: 2265 Midland Avenue, Scarborough, Ontario M1P 4S1

USA
Butterworth (Publishers) Inc
Boston: 161 Ash Street, Reading, Mass. 01867

First published in 1956
Second impression 1960
Third impression 1963
Fourth impression 1967
Fifth impression 1968
Sixth impression 1971
Second edition published in 1976
by Newnes–Butterworths

ISBN 0 408 00198 4

© Butterworth & Co (Publishers) Ltd 1976

Photoset by Amos Typesetters, Hockley, Essex

Printed and bound in England by
Redwood Burn Ltd., Trowbridge and Esher

PREFACE

The aim of most manufacturers is to obtain a desired quality and quantity of products at a minimum cost, and to realise this aim a great deal of money, ingenuity and effort is being devoted to the design and development of instruments which will measure the quality of the products of a process. Quality is the combination of a number of simple physical properties, and in order to ensure that the product has the desired quality, instruments of the types described in this volume are used.

As with Volume 1, the selection of material has been difficult, but the aim has been to give as complete a picture as possible while emphasising the more important and the more common types of on-line analysis instruments.

As far as possible instruments have been classified according to the physical principle upon which the measurement is based, but this has not always been possible where the measurement is in effect an automated laboratory method.

As in Volume 1, SI units have been used. It has not always been possible to give the B.A.S.E.E.F.A. classifications where the instruments have an American National Electrical Code Certification, but an indication of the approximate equivalent British classification has been given. It is important, however, to realise that the classifications are not identical, as certain gases are covered by a classification in one code but may not be included in the approximate classification in the other code.

It is hoped that this volume will cover the appropriate portion of the Instrument Technician courses of the City and Guilds of London, and courses established by the various industrial training boards and other educational establishments. The usefulness of the book is not limited to examination candidates, and it is expected that chemists, instrument and chemical engineers and others will find a great deal of useful information between its covers, which will help them solve problems that occur during their training and daily work.

Routine laboratory analysis is rapidly being replaced by on-line analysis instruments. As increased reliance is placed on on-line instrumentation, particularly when the results of such instruments are fed into elaborate control systems, the accuracy and reliability of the measurements must be maintained at a very high level, otherwise the cost of off-specification products and loss of production will become increasingly heavy.

At this time there is a grave shortage of highly skilled technicians who can ensure that industry gets the full benefit of the available on-line analysers. It is hoped that this book will contribute to reducing this shortage while drawing the attention of industrial management to the benefits available from the rapidly expanding availability of on-line analytical techniques. This book cannot hope to cover all the techniques at present available or in the course of development, but it is hoped that the reader's appetite will be so whetted that he will be encouraged to study the subject more widely and deeply.

The author wishes to express his appreciation of the considerable help received from the makers and users of instruments, and his colleagues past and present, and the publishers for their ready cooperation in the preparation of the book. The sources of material where known are gratefully acknowledged, but the author hopes he will be forgiven if any acknowledgement due has been overlooked.

In conclusion, the writer acknowledges with gratitude the assistance of his wife in undertaking the typing and the multitude of other tasks associated with this work.

Holywell   E. B. JONES

CONTENTS

INTRODUCTION

The importance of analysis instruments increases daily as the complexity and variety of the materials made by man increase. Many substances until recently unknown are now produced in increasing quantities. Their production often requires the use of very carefully controlled plants in which it is necessary to control not only the pressure, flow and temperature of the process materials but also their chemical composition, density, viscosity and humidity and a wide range of other properties.

In the past the control of these variables has been in the hands of chemists who from time to time withdrew samples from the process and analysed them. This is often a lengthy process in spite of the fact that the methods of analysis adopted give results in the minimum of time. A great deal of manpower is employed and the results of the analysis are not immediately available. The tendency, therefore, is to install instruments which give immediate and continuous indication, record and control of the product quality.

Quality is a combination of a number of simple physical properties, and in order to ensure that the product has the desired quality it is necessary to measure these properties, preferably on-line.

On-line quality measurement involves the measurement of the properties of the product at the point of production as opposed to removing samples from the process from time to time and analysing them in a laboratory. On-line quality measurement has many advantages and although the capital cost of the analysis instruments and associated equipment may be high, this is off-set by higher product quality, improved production and reduction in labour.

The use of on-line quality measuring instruments may require a high degree of skill on the part of the technician whose duty it is to service the equipment, as this type of instrumentation may have a high degree of sophistication.

Use of continuous analysis has greatly increased safety in plants where an inflammable or toxic atmosphere may be present. By the use of an instrument which directly measures the concentration of flammable or toxic substance in the atmosphere and sounding an alarm or initiating emergency action when the situation warrants it, the level of safety in the plant may be greatly increased.

In the chemical and petroleum industries a wide range of analyses are made on-line either for monitoring and controlling the product quality, or where necessary in order to provide a quality over-ride on process controllers. In problems such as the production of finished petrol to a specification which involves the satisfaction of a number of physical qualities such as octane number, boiling range, Reid vapour pressure, density, etc., the problem of control is more complex. If the petrol is produced by in-line blending using digital volumetric blenders as described in Volume 3, then varying the ratio of the constituent components will in general influence more than the product quality. In order continuously to calculate the influence of the change of quality constituents it is necessary to use a computer.

Where the quantity of product involved is large, and the computer can be programmed to optimise the production so as to produce on-specification petrol at the minimum cost, the cost of the equipment may be recovered in a sufficiently short time to make the installation profitable.

A wide range of analysis instruments is being developed to monitor continuously the wastes from process plants, whether they be solid, liquid or gaseous, so that atmospheric pollution may be reduced to a minimum.

In order to ensure the efficient use of fuel in boilers and furnaces it is usual to measure the oxygen content of the flue gas and use the value to control the desired value setting of the air-to-fuel ratio controller.

The usefulness of other on-line analysers will become obvious as one reads the book.

1

SAMPLING SYSTEMS

Any form of analysis instrument can only be as effective as its sampling system. Analysis instruments are out of commission more frequently owing to troubles in the sampling system than for any other cause, and time and care expended in designing and installing an efficient sampling system is well repaid in the saving of servicing time and dependability of instrument readings. The object of a sampling system is to provide a truly representative sample of the solid, liquid or gas which is to be analysed, at an adequate and steady rate, and conduct it without change to the analysis instrument, and all precautions necessary should be taken to ensure that it does this. Before the sample enters the instrument it may be necessary to process the sample to the required physical and chemical state, i.e. correct temperature, pressure, flow, purity, etc., without removing essential components. It is also essential to dispose of the sample and any reagent after analysis without introducing a toxic or explosive hazard. For this reason the sample, after analysis, is where possible returned to the process at a suitable point, or a suitable disposal system designed.

Analysis instruments sample the process material in a variety of ways. Sampling may be continuous, or intermittent, when the sample is known as a batch sample. A batch sample may consist of either a snap sample taken from the process or an average sample collected from the process over a period of time. In order that the batch sample may truly represent the process stream the rate of sample collection may be arranged to be proportional to the rate of flow in the process line from which the sample is collected.

Obtaining a representative sample at the instrument

It is essential that the sample taken should represent the mean composition of the process material. If the process sample is solid in sheet form it is necessary to scan the whole sheet for a reliable measure of the state of the sheet, e.g. in thickness, density or moisture content measurement, a measurement at one point is insufficient to give a representative value of the parameter being measured.

If the solid is in the form of granules or powder of uniform size a sample collected across a belt or chute and thoroughly mixed will give a reasonably representative sample. If measurements of density or moisture content can be made on the solid while it is in a vertical chute under a constant head, packing density problems may be avoided. Variable size solids are much more difficult to sample and specialist works on the subject should be consulted. When sampling liquids, unless a pipe length of say 200 pipe diameters exists between the point of adding the constituents and the sampling point, a suitable method of agitating and mixing the liquid should be installed. Using a mixer in the line has the advantage that the sampling time will be reduced because the time taken for the sample to flow the 200 pipe diameters will be almost eliminated. In sampling process gases no difficulty arises. It is usually necessary for the purpose of the process to ensure that the gases are mixed, and if any doubt exists a turbulent zone may be introduced in order to produce thorough mixing. In sampling flue gases in a large flue, particularly one collecting gases from several boilers, stratification may occur and the composition of the gases may vary from one point to another. In these circumstances one of the following methods, which are given in order of preference, should be adopted:

1. Select a site for the sampling point at which the flow is likely to be turbulent at all times, e.g. in flue gas sampling, four flue-diameters downstream of a damper or valve.

2. If necessary introduce a source of turbulence. If a turbulent source cannot be produced, install several sampling tubes and analyse the gas from each point in turn, or draw off samples at the same rate and thoroughly mix before analysis.

3. If the flow conditions in the duct are substantially constant, a point may be found which gives a sample representative of the mean composition of the gas. This point may be found by sampling the gas at a number of points on cross traverses of the duct as described in 'Method of use of pitot static tubes', page 187, Volume 1.

4. When mist or dust content of a gas is to be measured the sample must be withdrawn under iso-kinetic conditions, i.e. the sample tube must face into flow and the velocity of the sample into the tube must be the same as that of the flowing gas, as change in direction or velocity of the sample could cause separation of the constituents.

It is essential when sampling gases to ensure that no air leaks into the sampling system, and that no constituent of the gas mixture diffuses out or is absorbed between the sampling point and the analysis instrument.

Care should be taken to arrange conditions so that no chemical reaction takes place between the constituents of the gas sample, or between the constituents and the material of the sampling line. For example, iron and copper tubing should not be used for carrying gases containing carbon monoxide and oxygen, for iron and copper oxide catalyse the oxidation of carbon monoxide. At temperatures above 550°C iron also catalyses the dissociation of water vapour, and will reduce carbon dioxide to carbon monoxide with resulting errors in the final analysis.

Parts of the analysis equipment

The complete analysis equipment consists of: (a) the sampling tube which is used to withdraw the sample from the pipe or flue; (b) the sampling line which carries the sample from the sampling tube to the analysis instrument; (c) the analysis instrument.

Most commercial instruments are designed to operate at or near atmospheric pressure. Process fluids are often at a pressure which is very different from that of the atmosphere. It is therefore necessary to provide:

1. Where the gas or liquid is about or below atmospheric pressure, an aspirator or pump which draws off a sample of the process fluid and passes it through the instrument. The aspirator or pump may be before or after the instrument, depending upon the nature of the instrument.

2. Where the gas or liquid is above atmospheric pressure, a suitable let-down valve or capillary tube which reduces the pressure to a value a little above atmospheric pressure so that there is just sufficient pressure difference to cause the sample to flow through the instrument.

In addition, filters for dust and soot removal, water seals for the drainage of condensate, relief valves for protecting the sampling system from excessive pressure differences, cooling systems for hot gases, drying chambers, or other sample conditioning equipment must be provided between the sampling point and the instrument as required.

Reduction of time lags to a minimum

In any measuring instrument, particularly one which may be used with a controller, it is desirable that the time interval between the occurrence of a change in the process fluid and its detection at the instrument should be as short as possible consistent with reliable measurement. In order to keep this time interval to a minimum in analysis instruments the following points should be kept in mind.

1. The distance between the analysing instrument and the sampling point should be kept as short as possible. Where long sampling lines cannot be avoided the velocity in the line should be as high as possible. A high velocity may be obtained by withdrawing from the sample point a much larger sample than that required by the instrument. This large sample flows past the instrument, which withdraws the required sample through a short length of narrow tube, and the excess, if harmless, may be allowed to escape to atmosphere. If it is dangerous or valuable it may be fed back into the plant at a point at a lower pressure.

2. Pipes, valves, filters and sample conditioners should have the smallest capacity possible without introducing an unduly large resistance to the flow of the sample, and lutes and separators should be installed in 'dead' ends.

3. The sample if it is a gas should be filtered and travel to the instrument at the lowest possible pressure, as the mass of gas in the lines, filters, etc., depends upon the pressure as well as upon the volume of gas in the system. When sampling high pressure gas, the pressure reducing valve should be at the end of the sampling line away from the instrument. Unfortunately it is necessary to filter the gas at high pressure to prevent the accumulation of solid matter in the reducing valve.

Prevention of blockage due to corrosion on the sampling pipes or deposits in the pipes

Blockage of sampling pipes may occur owing to: corrosion of the sampling pipe itself; deposits within the pipes as the result of evaporation of liquid containing dissolved solid; the condensation of sublimable solids. Troubles due to these causes may be kept to a minimum by observing the following points:

1. Where possible the sampling system should be constructed from materials which are known to resist the corrosive constituents of the fluid which is being analysed.

2. All dust, soot or any other solid matter should be removed as soon as possible from the sample. In the first place, the amount of solid matter carried by the sample into the sampling tube may be reduced to a minimum by making the inlet as large as possible in order to reduce the gas velocity, and arranging that the inlet faces downstream in the duct. Gas entering the sampling tube is compelled to change its direction of motion completely. The particles of solid having a larger mass than the gas molecules will have a greater inertia and are less likely to enter the inlet than the gas molecules. Solid particles which do enter may be removed by means of filters.

3. The corrosive constituents or deposit forming gases should, if possible, be removed from the sample by the use of suitable chemical absorbents. For example, when sampling gases from high sulphur bearing fuels the sulphur dioxide may be removed by passing the gas through a wash bottle containing strong hydrochloric acid. This acid absorbs very little carbon dioxide. Renewal of the acid must be made at intervals which depend upon the amount of sulphur dioxide present.

4. To prevent the condensation of liquids in a gas sampling line, the temperature should be kept above the dew point. Deposition of moisture causes troubles other than those due to the moisture itself, by causing dust and other solid matter to accumulate on the inside of the pipe. When this solid matter dries out it is often difficult to remove. In some cases the gas which is being sampled may be dried by the use of a suitable solid drying agent. This also reduces the risk of corrosion, for the corrosive action of many gases is considerably reduced when the gas is dried.

5. Large variations of the ambient temperature of the sampling line should be avoided as this causes condensation and re-evaporation of vapours in the gas sampling line, or crystallisation of solids in lines carrying liquids containing dissolved solids. Lagging or even heating of sampling lines may be necessary in some cases to prevent condensation or deposition of solids.

6. In all cases where solid deposits may be formed in the pipes, facilities for rodding and washing out should be provided. All pipes likely to block should run in straight lengths with crosses at all changes of direction. A T connection for a hose should be provided near the instrument and cocks should be provided on all drain points and lutes and on an outlet near the site of the sampling point. Washing should be carried out in the direction opposite to that of the gas flow. This method, though washing sediment up-hill, ensures that the pipe is full of liquid.

7. It is often possible to duplicate the sampling system in troublesome applications so that one system is in operation while the other is back-flushed or cleaned.

Sampling systems will be described under two main headings:

Sampling for gases
Sampling systems for liquids

The sampling systems for gases will be divided into two sections:

Systems for sampling gases which are at atmospheric pressure or below, and
in particular systems for flue gas sampling.
Systems for gases at pressures above atmospheric pressure.

1.1 SAMPLING SYSTEMS FOR GASES

1.1.1 Sampling gases which are at, or slightly below, atmospheric pressure

The two most common applications of analysis to gases from sources at or
slightly below atmospheric pressure are in atmospheric pollution monitoring
and in the measurement of the products of combustion.

Figure 1.1 illustrates the type of system used to monitor the atmosphere of a
number of plants in which a gas may be present under certain circumstances at

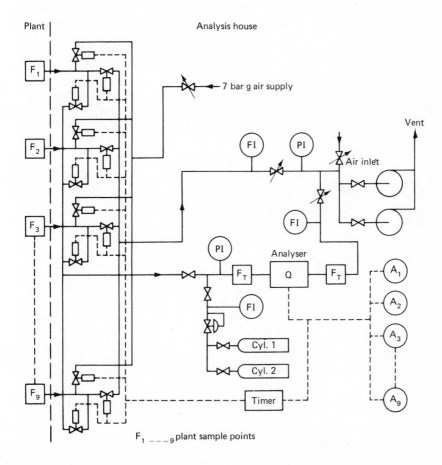

Figure 1.1   *Monitoring of carbon monoxide in air*

toxic levels. In such applications it is often sufficient to use a timer to operate valves in such a way that while the atmosphere of the plants is continuously sampled in order to reduce the sampling time, a sample of gas from each system is diverted to the analyser on a time cycle. If any sample reaches a toxic limit an alarm would be initiated. Provision is shown for calibrating the instrument when necessary with air containing known amounts of the contaminant so that the instrument may be checked at two points bracketing the critical value.

The products of combustion may be measured for two reasons. In the case of boilers and heating furnaces the products of combustion are monitored in order to ensure that the fuel-to-air ratio is such as to produce the most economic use of the fuel. In the case of sulphur burners, blast furnaces and other applications where the products of combustion are used, it is essential to know the composition for process control purposes.

Sampling of gases in the flue from a boiler, kiln or furnace requires a carefully designed system if the time spent on maintenance is to be kept within reasonable limits and the sample reaching the instrument is to be representative of the true composition of the process stream.

The system must be designed so that blockage of the sampling system owing to soot, dust and tar is avoided and provision is made where possible to purge lines clean on a regular basis. The materials in contact with the process gases must be carefully chosen to keep corrosion to a minimum and to ensure they do not react with the sampled gas.

The problem of choosing a suitable sampling system is complex but a very wide range of possibilities are available to solve the problem. The choice is governed by a number of factors such as the temperature of the sampled gas, whether or not its dew point is above ambient temperature, whether it contains other constituents which if allowed to condense out would cause erroneous results on analysis, whether reactions will take place between elements of the sampled gas if it is kept hot, whether the gas contains substances which would interfere with the measurement of the relevant substance, and whether the gas is very dirty. All these problems and others may be solved if certain features of the system are given careful consideration.

1.1.1.1   THE SAMPLING POINT

The sample of gas analysed must be a representative one at all times. The sampling point must therefore be located in the gas main, flue or process vessel in a position in which it is in the main gas stream and not in a backwater. When gas is sampled from a large flue, care must be taken to avoid positions where the gas is stagnant or where the gas velocity is less than that in the main stream. Positions near dampers, orifice plates and economisers where dead spaces may be expected should be avoided, and so should positions on or near bends where the distribution of gas velocities and densities may vary with the rate of gas flow. Again, where several flues join up with the main flue, the distribution of velocities across the flue may vary as one or other of the subsidiary flues is shut off, so that a position which is good on one occasion may be completely unsatisfactory at other times.

Boiler flue gases are analysed for two reasons:

1. Combustion control; in which case the sample should be withdrawn from a point just downstream of the point at which combustion is complete, e.g. at the boiler outlet.

2. For the detection of air leaks; in which case the samples may be withdrawn from any convenient points downstream of that used for combustion control. For example, in order to detect air leaks in the economiser, the gas may be analysed before entering and on leaving the economiser.

In all cases the essential requirements for obtaining a representative sample must be observed.

1.1.1.2 THE SAMPLING TUBE

Sampling tubes should be strong enough to withstand both mechanical and thermal shock. There should be no chemical reaction between tube and flue gases as this reduces the life of the tube and interferes with the accuracy of the analysis owing to the changes brought about in the sample gas. The tube should not be porous or absorbent to any constituent of the gas, or catalyse chemical reactions between constituents of the gas.

Simple sampling tubes or probes may be of three types:

> Uncooled metal tubes
> Water cooled metal tubes
> Refractory tubes.

1. *Uncooled metal tubes.* Mild steel or wrought iron tubes, usually about 25 mm diameter, are used but these materials should not be used at temperatures above 300°C as oxidation is likely to occur at higher temperatures. Certain alloy steels may be used for temperatures up to 1100°C where there is no likelihood of chemical reactions taking place between constituents of the gas. The life of an alloy steel tube is largely dependent upon the conditions prevailing, and the recommendations of the tube manufacturers should be sought when choosing a tube for a particular use.

2. *Water cooled metal tubes.* Water cooled tubes are used to prevent possible chemical reaction between components of the flue gas during its passage through the sampling tube. This precaution is particularly necessary if the flue gases contain combustible components and the gas temperature is high enough to cause further reaction, with or without the catalytic assistance of the material of the tube. The construction of a typical tube is shown in *Figure 1.2.* In order to cool the gas effectively the diameter of the gas sample tube is kept as small as possible consistent with freedom from choking.

3. *Refractory tubes.* Refractory tubes have not the mechanical strength of metal tubes but they are not attacked by the sampled gas and may be used at a much higher temperature than metal tubes. The materials used for these tubes are fused silica, porcelain, aluminous porcelain, mullite or recrystallised alumina.

Silica tubes can be used indefinitely at temperatures below 900°C, but embrittlement owing to devitrification occurs at higher temperatures, the rate of devitrification increasing with rise in temperature. The maximum temperature to which these tubes should be exposed even for short periods is 1500°C. Ash particles often flux with silica, causing deterioration of the tube. Silica tubes may be protected against fluxing, mechanical shock or distortion by binding with asbestos yarn and enclosing in a sheath of heat resisting alloy steel; a few centimetres of tube is allowed to protrude at each end. Cracking and devitrification is more easily detected in transparent silica tubes than in the translucent type.

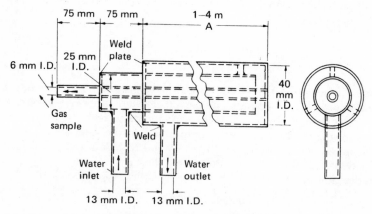

Figure 1.2   Water cooled sampling tube (BS 1756, Methods for the sampling and analysis of flue gases)

Glazed porcelain tubes are normally satisfactory up to 1400°C but are also subject to fluxing troubles. Aluminous porcelain tubes are more suitable for continuous use at temperatures up to 1500°C.

Mullite tubes are more resistant to fluxing than porcelain and are suitable for continuous use up to 1700°C.

Recrystallised alumina tubes are inert to those fluxes likely to occur in combustion gases and are suitable for continuous use up to 1900°C. Borosilicate glass may be used up to 450°C.

The use of refractory tubes for sampling high temperature gases has been greatly reduced by the use of water cooled, water washed probes, but they cannot be used when water-soluble gases are being measured.

In order to prevent condensation, particularly where the gases to be analysed may condense out, the probe, filter and even the whole of the sampling system may be electrically or steam heated.

1.1.1.3   FILTERS

Filters may be fitted inside or outside the flue. The external filters have the advantage that they are easily inspected and cleaned. The internal filter, however, protects the sampling tube from choking and is particularly suited to cases where the relative humidity is low, the flue-gas temperatures high (about 250°C) and oxidising conditions which will burn off the soot deposited on the filter occur at intervals.

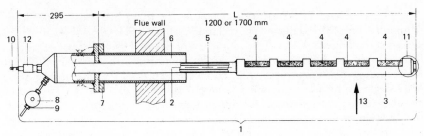

1. Gas sampling probe
2. Heat resistant steel
3. Supporting pipe (Sicromal)
4. Filter cartridges
5. Heating rod
6. Bushing tube
7. Mounting flange
8. Valve
9. Gas sampling line
10. Connection cable
11. Ceramic filter screw connection
12. Tuchel plug
13. Flow direction of the flue gas

(a)

Flue wall
or duct Hole sufficiently
large for withdrawal
of whole assembly

Dust shield
facing gas flow

To aspirator
and cooler

Tapered packing
piece

Filter

Extension pipe long
enough to place filter
in main gas stream

Wall
sleeve

Flange

Slope at least
1 in 12

Removable plug for
'rodding out' and
taking test samples

To catchpot or lute

(b)

Lagging
40 mm thick

To aspirator
and cooler

To catchpot or lute

Gap

10 mm iron pipe long
enough to hold filter
in best position

Filter

A ———————— A

Baffle

Flow

Section on AA

(c)

Figure 1.3   (a) Heated gas sampling probe suitable for flue gases up to 500°C and 4 bar pressure (Courtesy Hartmann and Braun) (b) Installation of sampling tube and filter—filter horizontal (c) Installation of sampling tube and filter—filter vertical

1. *Internal filters.* These are cylindrical in form and are constructed from Alundum Aerolith unglazed porcelain, carborundum or asbestos cloth, suitably supported. The construction is shown in *Figure 1.3(a)*. All metal fittings used to hold the filter and its mountings must be capable of withstanding the temperature and corrosive nature of the flue atmosphere. Mild steel may be used up to 600°C and stainless steel up to 900°C. The side of the filter facing the gas flow is usually protected by a suitable dust shield and the junction between filter and tube must be dust-tight. A sampling tube and filter are mounted as shown in *Figure 1.3(b)*, and should slope downwards in the direction of gas flow with a slope of at least 1 in 12 (some manufacturers advocate 1 in 6), so that any moisture formed owing to condensation drains away from the filter and is collected in the catchpot or lute.

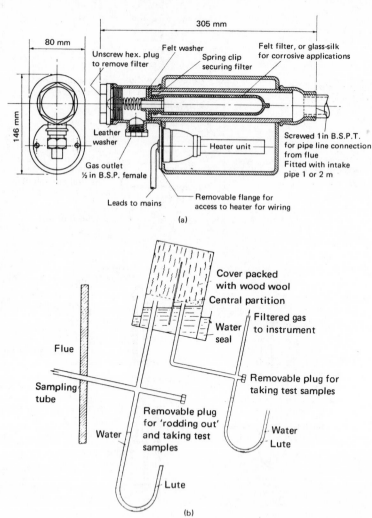

Figure 1.4   (a) Heated type soot filter (b) Arrangement of 'top hat' filter and lutes

Vertical mounting of the filter should be avoided where possible, but if it cannot be avoided, the vertical sampling tube should be carefully lagged and a baffle fitted to encourage a flow of gas through the annular space around the sampling pipe *(Figure 1.3(c))* so that no condensation takes place in the tube and no moisture drains back into the filter.

Care must be taken to see that the hole in the flue wall is large enough to allow the whole assembly to be withdrawn for inspection and cleaning, and the piping should be designed with a view to ease of cleaning. Removable plugs should be fitted where necessary to facilitate 'rodding out'. Internal filters of Alundum, unglazed porcelain or carborundum may be cleaned by blowing the dirt back into the flue. Arrangements may be made so that the sampling tube may be detached from the rest of the installation and connected to a suitable supply of compressed air. Care must be taken, however, to see that the pressure of the air is not sufficient to burst the filter or produce leaks in the sampling tube.

2. *External filters.* As they are easily inspected and maintained, external filters are often used. They consist of airtight vessels containing asbestos wool, glass wool, slag wool or wood wool.

Where the sampling pipe has to be mounted vertically in the flue, or in other cases where condensation at the filter causes difficulty, a heated soot filter is used. The gas is filtered through a thick felt cylinder and an electrical heating element is mounted in the body of the assembly so that the whole filter is kept hot enough to prevent condensation *(Figure 1.4(a))*. It is usually easier to maintain the necessary temperature if the whole assembly is very carefully lagged.

A very convenient form of external filter, known for obvious reasons as a 'top hat' filter, is illustrated in *Figure 1.4(b)*. It consists of a metal cylinder closed at one end and fitted with a central partition which extends almost to the top. The cylinder is packed with wood-wool filtering material, which is cheap and easily renewed, and placed open end downwards in an outer dish of water. When the filter is used in a hot position it is often necessary to arrange an overflow and a constant slow feed of water into the sealing dish in order to make up the water lost by evaporation.

A convenient type of filter for process gases is shown in *Figure 1.5(a)*. It is absolutely leak-proof and has a large filtering capacity. Where required to handle corrosive gases it may be made of stainless steel, monel, Hastelloy or other material suitable for the application. Likewise the filtering medium must be tailored to the application, a wide range of materials being available, such as asbestos, glass or Terylene wool, granulated p.v.c., p.t.f.e. or polypropylene, or where necessary molecular sieves which as their name suggests are very selective in what they absorb; care must be taken, however, that no significant component is absorbed. Substitution or cleaning of the filtering medium may be carried out without disconnecting the filter from the line. The filter shown has a maximum operating pressure of 10 bar and a maximum operating temperature of 90°C.

Replaceable cartridge filters are also very common, consisting of metals, alumina, silica or paper depending upon the application. By-pass filters are also common and take a variety of forms. The simplest form consists of a T piece. The main flow is directly through the main tube, in which a filtering tube of ceramic or other material of the required porosity is fitted. The sample

14

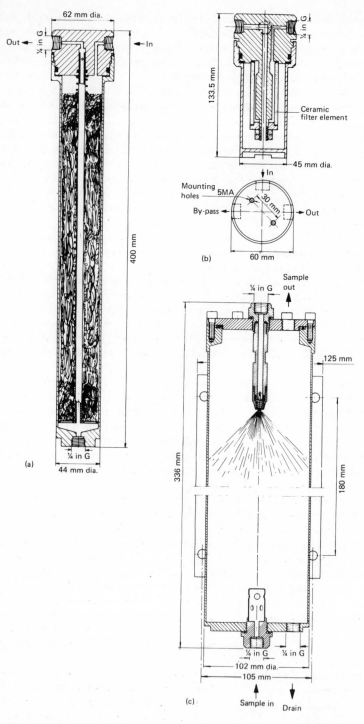

Figure 1.5 (Courtesy Carlo Erba) (a) Primary filter (b) By-pass filter (c) Wet scrubber

diffuses through the filter and leaves by the side connection. As the flow is directly through the main tube the filter is self-cleaning. Another form of this type of filter is shown in *Figure 1.5(b)*. This may be constructed in material suitable for the application and contains a ceramic filtering element having a porosity of 100 μm, and the filter is capable of withstanding an operating pressure of 25 bar and a temperature of 90°C.

Another method of removing solids from gaseous samples, particularly from cracking processes in the petroleum industry, is the wet scrubber, an example of which is shown in *Figure 1.5(c)*. The solids are removed from the up-flowing sample by a spray of clean water, free from entrained gases, while a level regulator permits the complete removal and discharge of the trapped products.

1.1.1.4 WATER TRAPS

Many gases, and in particular flue gases, may contain water vapour often at a relatively high vapour pressure. As these cool while flowing through the sampling line this water vapour condenses, producing water which must be removed from the sampling system. Many instruments are sensitive to the presence of water vapour in the sample and it is necessary to dry the gas. Other instruments require the sample to be saturated with water vapour at a lower temperature than that of the instrument. In this way the gas may be made to contain a definite amount of water vapour without danger of the vapour condensing in the instrument.

Water may be removed by the use of:

lutes, catchpots, chemical driers, centrifugal separators.

1. *Lutes.* Where the difference in pressure between the gas sample and the atmosphere is small, a 'lute' forms a convenient automatic method of removing condensate from the sampling line. Two forms of lute are shown in *Figures 1.4(b)* and *1.6(a)*, both functioning as U tubes. One form of lute, shown in *Figure 1.4(b)*, consists of a U tube having one limb longer than the other; the longer limb is connected to the sampling tube and the other is open to the atmosphere. The U tube is initially filled with water. The difference between the levels of the water in the two limbs is an indication of the difference between the pressure of the gas and atmospheric pressure. As condensate is collected, the level rises in both limbs until it reaches the top of the open limb when it will overflow into a drain beneath the lute. Where there is any danger of solid matter collecting in the lute and blocking the U tube, the second form, shown in *Figure 1.6(a)*, is used. It consists of a 'vertical' tube dipping into a tall vessel. As in the case of the U tube, liquid will collect in the vessel until it overflows.

2. *Catchpots.* Where the difference between the pressure in the sampling line and atmospheric pressure is too large to be conveniently accommodated by a lute, a catchpot or drain bottle *(Figure 1.6(b))* with a drain cock at the bottom, is installed in the gas line. These do not function automatically and must be drained at intervals; the length of the interval will, of course, depend upon the wetness of the gas. With a very wet gas the catchpots would require frequent

attention so it is usual for a level controller automatically to discharge the contents when a predetermined level is reached.

The auto-change lute illustrated in *Figure 1.6(c)* is a very useful device, which in addition to acting as a catchpot, indicates when a filter requires renewal. Two sampling parts each complete with filter are used. Gas normally enters by tube T_1 until the pressure drop across No. 1 filter increases by an amount equivalent to the head of liquid H, when gas enters by tube T_2. Bubbling in of gas through T_2 gives a clear indication that No. 1 filter requires renewal.

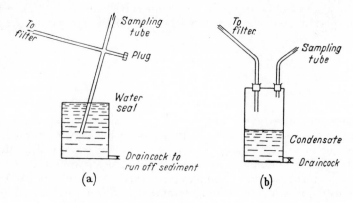

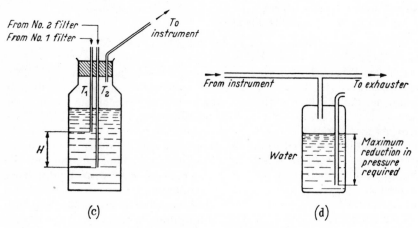

Figure 1.6   (a) Lute or water seal (b) Catchpot or drain bottle (c) Auto-change lute (d) Vacuum relief

3. *Chemical driers.* Where a dry sample is required, a drying vessel containing an absorbing material, such as calcium chloride, alumina or silica gel, may be installed between the catchpot or lute and the instrument. Calcium chloride has the disadvantage that it dissolves in the water collected and forms a paste which may block the sampling line. Silica gel has the advantage that it may contain a colouring material which indicates some renewal is necessary and then it may be reactivated, but it must not be used in cases where it would absorb the measured gas.

Where the gas contains an acid mist this must be removed by a suitable filter before the driers. This usually consists of a large ceramic cylinder closed at the lower end contained in a glass container. As the gas passes from the outside to the inside the ceramic cylinder prevents the passage of the acid, which collects at the bottom of the outer vessel which should be emptied periodically. If the gas contains sulphur trioxide this should be removed by bubbling through 98.9% sulphuric acid, which will remove it together with any moisture.

4. *Centrifugal separators.* The degree of sample preparation before analysis depends upon the source of the gas sample and the type of analyser. Washing, filtering and drying by simple means is adequate in the case of many analysers but more elaborate instruments such as chromatographs, paramagnetic meters and infra-red analysers require that all entrained liquid be removed. This may be carried out by the centrifugal separator shown in *Figure 1.7*. It consists of an air-driven turbine in the base magnetically coupled to the four-bladed rotor in the upper section. Air at 0.5 bar is fed into the air supply connection to operate the turbine. The sample is fed through the inlet into the separation chamber at the bottom of the rotor. Any liquid in the sample will, when rotated with the sample, tend to move in a straight line so that it will be deposited on the glass walls of the chamber where it will drain downwards and be carried away by the by-pass stream out through the by-pass outlet. The liquid-free sample is drawn from the top of the chamber through the dry sample outlet to the analyser. The wetted parts of the equipment are stainless steel and the maximum working pressure is 4 bar, the air flow being 2 m³/h.

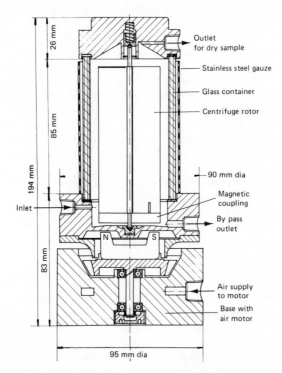

Figure 1.7   Centrifugal separator (Courtesy Carlo Erba)

1.1.1.5   VACUUM RELIEFS

If for some reason a blockage occurs at a sampling point, the aspirator is likely to draw in air through the water traps and vitiate the sample. This may be prevented by fitting an excess vacuum relief of the form shown in *Figure 1.6(d)* between the instrument and the aspirator.

1.1.1.6   HEAT EXCHANGERS

Where the temperature of the sampled gas is different from that at which it is analysed, it may be necessary to use a heat exchanger to cool or heat the sample. The exchanger consists merely of a suitable length of small bore tube, say 4 mm i.d., 6 mm o.d., of appropriate material long enough to provide the required exchange surface, either straight or coiled, contained in a vessel of the required heat exchange medium. To cool the sample the medium is usually water at the appropriate temperature. For heating, hot water or steam may be used. Electrical heating may also be used, applied directly or heating air which is blown over the equipment. In the equipment shown in *Figure 1.8* the shell has a maximum working pressure of 10 bar, the straight tube of 15 bar and the coiled tube 35 bar.

1.1.1.7   GAS-LINES; MATERIALS, LAYOUT, TESTING AND MAINTENANCE

Sampling lines should be made of materials which do not corrode in the presence of the sampled gas, for corrosion not only shortens the life of the line, but may cause changes in the composition of the gas. A variety of materials is used. Mild steel may be used on non-corrosive services above the dew point of the sampled gas but lines of glass, glass-lined, or stainless steel are to be preferred. For temperatures below 75°C polythene may be used; hard rubber may be used below 70°C and p.v.c. below 50°C; but care must be taken when using flexible pipes to see that they are supported to prevent sagging. Where the gas handled is corrosive, glass, Hastelloy or acid resistant hose may have to be used.

Gas lines should run downwards at a slope of at least 1 in 12 away from the sampling point towards the instrument, where any liquid which has formed may be collected in a lute or catchpot. If a rising section of the line cannot be avoided, the rise should be as short and as steep as possible, and a lute or catchpot installed at the lowest point as shown in *Figure 1.4(b)*.

Before use, the complete sampling system should be tested for leaks. This can be done by blocking off all points in the system communicating with the atmosphere and reducing the pressure in the system by means of an aspirator. When the pressure has been reduced to a steady value, there should be no sign of any gas passing through a bubbler unit installed just before the aspirator. Rubber stoppers should be used where required and not cork stoppers, which are often porous.

The cleaning of all sampling systems should be carried out at regular intervals; the length of the interval can only be found by experience of the individual installation.

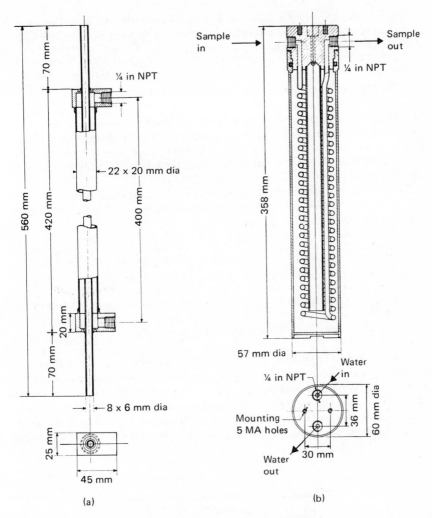

Figure 1.8   Heat exchangers (Courtesy Carlo Erba)

Lines should preferably be cleaned by the use of rods or wire rope, or by washing out with water or other solvent depending upon the nature of the sediment. Where compressed air is used for blowing out sampling tubes the system should be such that the sampling line must be disconnected before the hose can be connected, and the maximum pressure must be limited by the use of a suitable reducing or relief valve.

Filters should be cleaned regularly; the condition of the filter at the time of cleaning can give valuable information of its suitability and upon the correctness of the siting.

Lutes and drain points should be inspected regularly in order to check for blockages, leaks and correct liquid level. When the lines are flushed out, each drain point should be opened in turn to clear any blockages.

In addition to testing for leaks the line should be tested for flow. Disconnect at the sampling point, and with the aspirator drawing air, test for flow with a bubbler (or a lighted match) at the open end.

1.1.1.8 DEVICES FOR OBTAINING THE GAS SAMPLE

In certain circumstances the natural pressure drop in a main may be used to draw a sample through the analysing instrument by installing the instrument in a by-pass to a section of the main. In some cases the flow through the instrument may be brought about by installing a suitable orifice in the main and connecting the sampling lines to the usual taps.

The pressure at the sampling point in steam boilers, kilns, furnaces, etc., is usually a little below atmospheric and some form of aspirator or pump is necessary to withdraw the sample.

Five methods of withdrawing the sample are in common use:

1. The fluid-operated laboratory pattern filter pump or ejector.
2. The water-operated 'tail pipe' type of aspirator.
3. The water-operated 'tee-piece' type of aspirator.
4. Venturi type aspirator, operating on the natural draught of the system.
5. Motor operated mechanical displacement pumps of the reciprocating piston, rotary piston and diaphragm types.

1. The laboratory pattern filter pump type aspirator or ejector is illustrated in *Figure 1.9(a)*. When used to draw gas through the instrument as shown in *Figure 1.10(a)* it may be operated by water, compressed air or steam; but when used to force gas through the instrument as shown in *Figure 1.10(b)*, air-free water only may be used. It is suitable for withdrawing gas from a main where the gas pressure may be as low as 0.3 bar. If compressed air is used with this

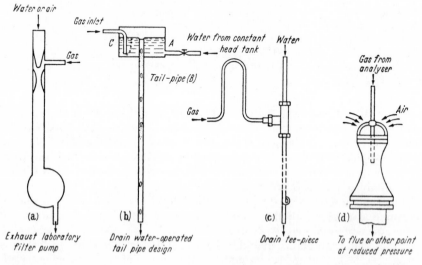

Figure 1.9   (a), (b) and (c) Typical aspirator and exhaust pumps (BS 1756) (d) Venturi operated aspirator

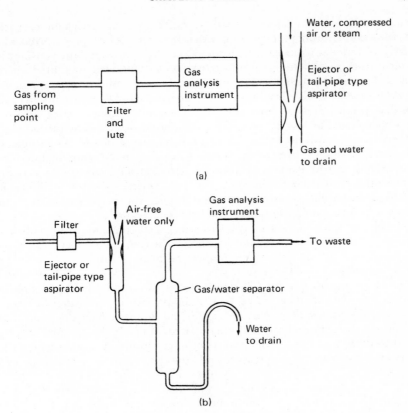

Figure 1.10   Arrangements for sampling with ejector or aspirator (a) Pressure in instrument less than atmospheric pressure (b) Pressure in instrument greater than atmospheric pressure

form of aspirator, a bubbler unit should be connected in the sampling line to give warning of any air flowing back along the line. Air may flow back along the line if there is an obstruction in the exhaust of the aspirator.

When it is required to deliver gas to the instrument at a pressure above atmospheric, or where the gas sampled is toxic or inflammable and must not be released to the atmosphere near the instrument, it is necessary to use the ejector as shown in *Figure 1.9(b)*. The gas–water mixture is fed into a separator which consists of a chamber having two outlets. As the velocity of the mixture is reduced when it enters the chamber, the gas rises to the top outlet and the water overflows through the tube at the bottom. The pressure of the gas delivered to the instrument will depend upon the difference between the level of the water in the chamber and the level of the opening of the overflow pipe. The relationship between the flow of water and the bore of the overflow pipe is rather critical and the use of a constant head tank to maintain a constant flow is desirable. The flow may be as much as 140 litre/h.

2. The 'tail-pipe' type of aspirator is illustrated in *Figure 1.9(b)*. This type is very simple to use and requires less water than the filter pump type but it will not produce as great a reduction of pressure (about 0.25 bar max.). The actual reduction of pressure produced depends upon the length of the tail pipe B and

is usually equivalent to about 1.3 m of water. Water enters the chamber A and overflows into the tail pipe carrying with it gas from the inlet pipe C. About 27 litre/h of water is required, which should be clean, substantially constant in temperature, and should be supplied from a constant head tank fitted with a ball valve and installed a metre or more above the aspirator. The use of the tank ensures a bubble-free supply. A restrictor should be used to give the necessary flow. It is essential that the amount of water flowing into the chamber should be less than that which can be carried away by the tail pipe, otherwise water will rise in the chamber and flow back through the gas inlet C and may get into the instrument or driers installed in the sampling line. The gas analysis instrument may be installed in the top of the chamber A as in the Cambridge Katharometer, in which case the gas enters the unit by diffusion; or the aspirator may be used to draw gas through the instrument in the same way as the filter-pump aspirator is used in *Figure 1.10(a)*.

3. The 'tee-piece' type aspirator works on exactly the same principle as the tail-pipe type. It has the advantage that it can be constructed very easily from standard pipe fittings and tubing, but the gas analysis instrument cannot be mounted on this type of aspirator.

4. The venturi aspirator is illustrated in *Figure 1.9(d)*. The reduction in pressure at the throat of the venturi is about twice the pressure difference between the atmosphere and the gas in the flue to which the venturi is connected. It is cheap, both in original cost and in maintenance, and may be used to draw a sample through an instrument from a gas main where the difference between the gas pressure and atmospheric pressure is less than 75 mm water gauge.

5. In certain installations, for example the Marine Type carbon dioxide measuring equipment, and where the gas pressure is less than 0.3 bar, it is necessary to use a pump to withdraw the gas sample. A large variety of motor operated pumps are used for fluid sampling but an essential feature of the design of such a pump is that the parts which come into contact with the process fluid should not be corroded by it. The difficulty of designing suitable corrosion-resisting valves is often overcome by using pumps which do not require the use of valves. Where the pump produces a pulsating flow it is necessary to fit a pulsation damper to ensure that the gas flow through the instrument is steady. The reduction in pressure produced by the pump should be measured and controlled at a value which produces the correct flow through the instrument, or the flow should be measured and controlled. Devices which are used to produce a steady purging rate in purge systems of pressure measurement may also be used to produce a steady flow of gas through an analysis instrument. Owing to their high initial cost and maintenance mechanical pumps are only used where the cheaper alternative methods are unsuitable and their design must be such that air is not introduced through the gland.

1.1.1.9   SAMPLING HOT AND DIRTY GASES

The problem of sampling hot and dirty gases is greatly reduced by the use of the water-washed sampling system. Gas entering the BS EN58 B stainless steel sample probe is thoroughly mixed with cold water by means of a water spray facing either against the direction or in the same direction as the sampled gas flow. For use on high temperature applications above 650°C and below 1760°C the probe should be water cooled as well as being washed. The external end of the sampling tube is connected directly to the inductor which is an enlarged cylindrical section of the sampling line containing a tangential nozzle through which clean cold water at 0.7 bar is sprayed at 1 litre/min, thus reducing the temperature of the gas and washing out dust and dirt from the sampling line.

The water source must be reliable and never fall below the minimum pressure required to maintain the necessary rate of flow. The water-washed, water-cooled system consumes about 14 litre/min. The introduction of water into the line at the point at which the gas temperature is reduced to the dew point ensures that all solids are immediately flushed away, thus preventing the plugging which would occur on a dry line. As the temperature of the gas has been reduced flexible polyethylene tube may be used for the sample lines provided the temperature does not exceed 43°C, when rubber based plastics pipe may be used up to a temperature of 77°C. In designing the piping system run it is important to avoid hot surfaces so as to keep the temperature of water and sample lines as low as possible.

A water-washed or water-washed, water-cooled type of sampling tube must never be installed in a hot zone without first ensuring that the water is flowing.

Figure 1.11(a) shows the complete installation, while *Figure 1.11(b)* shows the water-washed, water-cooled type sampling tube. *Figure 1.11(c)* shows the inductor fitted to the reverse water spray sampling tube, installed on a system where the water spray must not enter the process.

Dry type sampling tubes may be installed at any angle from the horizontal to 60° from the horizontal, sloping up from the sample entry.

Water-washed, (water-cooled or not) type sampling tubes should be installed sloping up from the sample entry at an angle of from 30 to 60° to the horizontal as shown in *Figure 1.11(b)*. This prevents the return of an excessive quantity of spray water with the gas, or the formation of a steam pocket in the cooling jacket. Where the water spray must not enter the process the slope of the sample tube is reversed so that it slopes downwards from the sample entry at 10–30° to the horizontal, as shown in *Figure 1.11(c)*.

All tubes extending more than 1.5 m into the duct must be supported by welding into the duct a length of heavy pipe or tubing through which the sampling tube is inserted, or an angle iron on which it may rest. Without adequate cooling, carbon steel will not stand temperatures above 426°C.

The gas pump, washer and separator trap are assembled on a single mounting plate as shown in *Figure 1.11(d)*.

The centrifugal pump draws water from the reservoir and forces it through an orifice at one end of the aspirator. The jet of water thus created draws in the gas and washes it. The jet is then broken up by an assembly of baffles in the disintegrator at the other end of the aspirator recovery tube. This arrangement mixes the water and gas thoroughly so that when the gas and water disengage in the separator trap all dirt particles are drained off with the wash water, and the clean gas passes up the sample line to the filter and heater assembly and hence to the analyser.

The assembly should be as close as possible to the sampling point and below the level of the inductor so that the sampling lines slope continuously down to the pump. The make-up water to the washer should be at least 5°C below

24

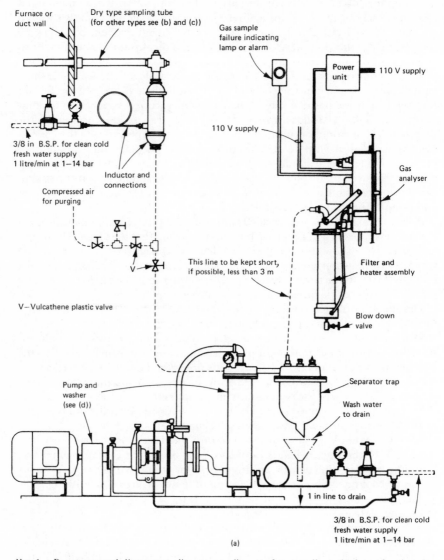

Furnace or duct wall

Dry type sampling tube (for other types see (b) and (c))

Gas sample failure indicating lamp or alarm

Power unit

110 V supply

110 V supply

Gas analyser

3/8 in B.S.P. for clean cold fresh water supply 1 litre/min at 1−14 bar

Inductor and connections

Compressed air for purging

This line to be kept short, if possible, less than 3 m

Filter and heater assembly

V−Vulcathene plastic valve

V

Blow down valve

Pump and washer (see (d))

Separator trap

Wash water to drain

1 in line to drain

3/8 in B.S.P. for clean cold fresh water supply 1 litre/min at 1−14 bar

(a)

Note 1.   Do not run sample lines or water lines near or adjacent to furnace walls or other hot surfaces in such a manner as to increase the gas sample or water temperature.

Note 2.   Sample line between inductor assembly and gas pump and washer must be sloped continuously down with no horizontal runs or vertical drops; also sharp or short radius bends must be avoided.

Note 3.   Analyser to be as close as possible to sampling point where ambient temperature will not be above 43°C and location free from vibration. Every extra 7.5 m of connecting tubing creates approximately 5 s lag.

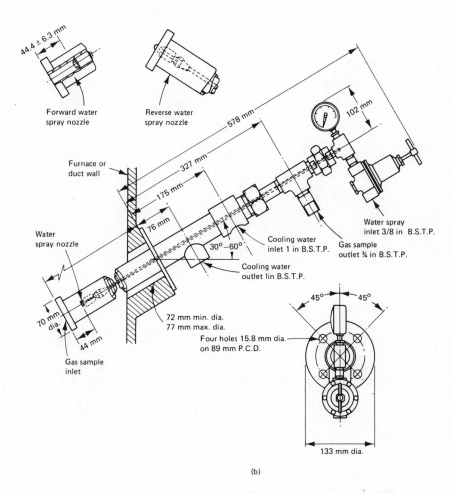

44.4 ± 6.3 mm

Forward water spray nozzle

Reverse water spray nozzle

578 mm

327 mm

175 mm

102 mm

Furnace or duct wall

76 mm

Water spray nozzle

30°–60°

Cooling water inlet 1 in B.S.T.P.

Gas sample outlet ¾ in B.S.T.P.

Water spray inlet 3/8 in B.S.T.P.

Cooling water outlet 1in B.S.T.P.

70 mm dia.

44 mm

Gas sample inlet

72 mm min. dia.
77 mm max. dia.

Four holes 15.8 mm dia. on 89 mm P.C.D.

45°   45°

133 mm dia.

(b)

Figure 1.11   Sampling systems for hot gases (Courtesy Bailey Meters and Controls Ltd.) (a) Schematic layout (b) Water-washed, water-cooled type sampling tube (c) Inductor fitted to reverse water spray sampling tube (d) Gas pump, washer and separator trap

26

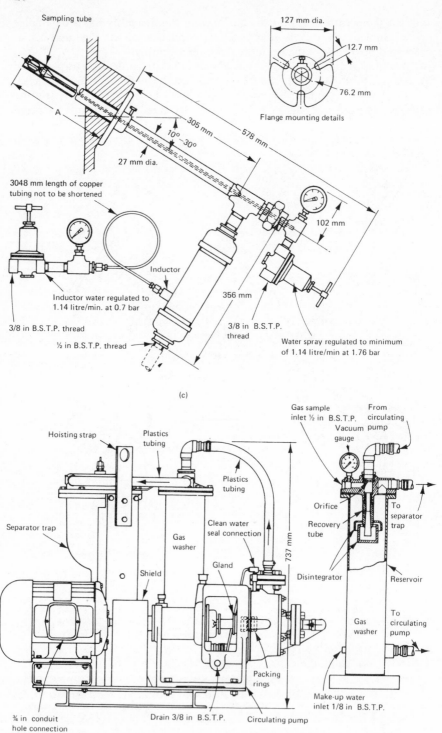

Sampling tube

127 mm dia.

12.7 mm

76.2 mm

Flange mounting details

A

305 mm

578 mm

10° 30°

27 mm dia.

3048 mm length of copper
tubing not to be shortened

102 mm

Inductor

Inductor water regulated to
1.14 litre/min. at 0.7 bar

356 mm

3/8 in B.S.T.P. thread

3/8 in B.S.T.P.
thread

½ in B.S.T.P. thread

Water spray regulated to minimum
of 1.14 litre/min at 1.76 bar

(c)

Gas sample
inlet ½ in B.S.T.P.

From
circulating
pump

Vacuum
gauge

Hoisting strap

Plastics
tubing

Plastics
tubing

Orifice

To
separator
trap

Separator trap

Clean water
seal connection

Recovery
tube

Gas
washer

Shield

Gland

Disintegrator

Reservoir

737 mm

Packing
rings

Gas
washer

To
circulating
pump

Make-up water
inlet 1/8 in B.S.T.P.

¾ in conduit
hole connection

Drain 3/8 in B.S.T.P.

Circulating pump

(d)

ambient temperature so that the gas leaving the assembly has a dew point below ambient. If this is not possible, condensation in the analyser is prevented by the use of the heater in the filter assembly.

Under no circumstances should the motor be started unless the trap is full of water and a flow of wash water of 1 litre/min established.

The separator trap is fitted with a weight loaded relief valve to prevent the analysis instrument being over-pressured. By handling a relatively large quantity of gas (between 60 and 90 litre/min) the sampling system delivers a sample to the analyser in a very brief time, ensuring the minimum of transport lag in the resultant analysis.

The amount of maintenance required will depend upon the severity of the conditions, but with particularly dirty sampling conditions it is advisable to carry out the following:

Daily

(a) Clean sampling probe either by rodding out (for dry probes) or by blowing compressed air in other cases to ensure that the sampling tube passage is free.

(b) Check inductor water pressure, sampling tube cooling water, and spray water where applicable, and ensure reliable and continuous water supply.

(c) Check and ensure make-up water supply to washer unit and pump water seal.

(d) Check that float in separator trap is functioning satisfactorily.

Weekly

Check filter in analyser and clean it by blowing back with compressed air. Replace as necessary

Monthly

(a) Check that pump motor is running satisfactorily.

(b) Check that there are no leaks in pump sealing gland, and replace packing if necessary.

Twice yearly

(a) Check and replace float in separator trap if necessary.

(b) Check function of washer and clean orifice as necessary.

Yearly

(a) Check motor bearings and grease as necessary. See motor maker's handbook for replacements.

(b) Check and replace pump packing as necessary.

(c) Check pump bearings and lubricate as necessary. See maker's handbook.

Steam ejector probe

Another method of extracting a sample of hot dirty gas is to use the steam ejector illustrated in *Figure 1.12*.

Dry steam passed down the inlet tube is turned through 180° in the probe head and is ejected through a small jet at the throat of a venturi tube. The reduction of pressure so created at the throat of the venturi causes sample gas to be drawn into the probe. The steam and gas at a positive pressure pass out of the probe and down the sample line where wash water is added. The mixture then passes into a separator where the water separates out, and the washed gas sample passes to a cooler where further mixture passes to the drain. The gas sample passes up into conditioning blocks where the sample is heated above the dew point and filtered through a 0.3 μm filter before entering the analysis instrument.

The advantage of this system is that the steam flow cools the probe but keeps it above the dew point, avoiding condensation in the probe. The high velocity of the steam jet provides a cleaning action and as the pressure in the sampling line is above atmospheric pressure any leak would be to atmosphere rather than of air in.

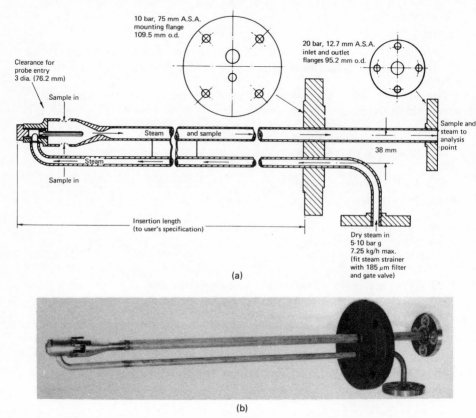

(a)

(b)

Figure 1.12   Steam ejector probe (Courtesy Servomex Controls Ltd.) (a) Schematic (b) Actual

In order to avoid condensation in the probe the steam temperature should be above the dew point of the flue gas. For most applications steam at 5 bar and a temperature of 152°C is adequate. For higher flue gas temperatures the size of the jet is increased to increase the steam flow at the same inlet pressure.

The probe length may be anything from 0.5 to 5 m and a flow of 2.5 litre/min of cooling water at a maximum temperature of 40°C is required. If the length and temperature demand it the probe should be suitably supported.

1.1.2 Sampling gases which are above atmospheric pressure

Where the pressure of the gas to be sampled is less than 0.1 bar above atmospheric pressure, and the gas is not toxic or inflammable, a lute will suffice to regulate the pressure of the gas to the instrument. Where the pressure is less than 70 bar, all that is required is an automatic reducing valve and a lute. It is advisable to fit some form of flow indicator or measurer, or a flow control device to ensure that the gas flows through the instrument at a steady rate. After passing through the instrument, the gas may be allowed to escape, or if it is toxic or inflammable, returned to the process at a point where the pressure is sufficiently low.

Where the pressure is greater than 70 bar the pressure of the gas must be reduced by means of a high pressure fine-adjustment valve, and the low pressure side fitted with a relief valve and a lute. In some cases it is necessary to fit two needle valves in series, or a needle valve and a capillary tube, in order to regulate the pressure. The pressure reducing device should be fitted as near to the sampling point as possible. In the interests of safety the entire system up to the lute controlling the low pressure should be capable of withstanding the maximum pressure of the source. Relief valves are not considered reliable and are not recommended as a means of protection against pressure in this type of installation. The instrument may be given additional protection by connecting it to the sample line by means of rubber tubing. The type of layout used is illustrated in *Figure 1.13*.

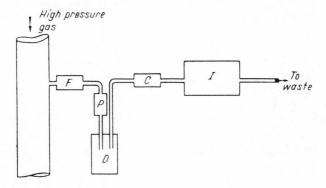

F   *Filter having as small a volume as possible consistent with efficient filtering*
P   *Pressure-reducing or let-down valve, heated if necessary*
D   *Drain bottle to collect condensed vapour*
C   *Flow meter and regulator or flow controller*
I   *Analysis instrument*

Figure 1.13   Sampling system for high pressure gas: instrument at about atmospheric pressure

When the pressure on a gas is reduced, the gas expands and does external work and its internal energy also decreases. The gas therefore cools, and when the reduction in pressure is large the cooling effect may be quite considerable. This cooling effect will condense vapour contained in the gas and may even freeze the condensed vapour and the gas itself. It is therefore necessary, in many cases, to heat the pressure reducing valve to prevent condensation or freezing which would produce a blockage.

A sampling line containing gas at high pressure will contain a very much larger mass of gas than a line full of gas at low pressure. If the time taken for a sample to travel from the sampling point to the instrument is to be kept small, it is necessary to install the instrument as near to the sampling point as possible. In order to prevent the pressure reducing valve from becoming blocked, however, it is essential to filter the gas before its pressure is reduced. The filtering materials used include glass wool, slag wool (Stillite), paper and various cloth fabrics, some of special weave. The filtering material must be such that it will remove even very small particles which would block up the small-bore holes of needle valves and capillary tubes.

Filters containing shredded polythene have been found to act as electrostatic precipitators. The flow of gas past the polythene shreds causes them to acquire an electrostatic charge so that they attract to themselves the dust particles which would otherwise pass through the filter. Owing to the fact that the insulating properties of polythene are not impaired by moisture, this method has been found to be successful even with moderately moist gases.

It is usually very difficult to reduce the pressure of the very small volume of high pressure gas required by the analysis instrument. It is therefore found easier to let down a sample which is considerably larger than that required by the instrument and withdraw the required sample from this.

Where the gas being sampled is toxic, and the analysis installation can be made strong enough to withstand the gas pressure, the system shown in *Figure 1.14* may be used. An orifice plate is fitted in the gas main and produces a pressure difference which causes the gas to flow through the instrument.

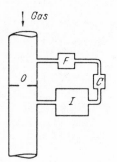

F Filter having as small a volume as possible consistent with efficient filtering
C Flow meter and regulator or flow controller
I Analysis instrument
O Orifice plate to induce flow through the instrument

Figure 1.14   Sampling toxic gases: instrument is at same pressure as the process gas. Pressure must not be greater than the safe pressure for the instrument, filter and flow controller

When gas is sampled in order to measure the dust content, or when steam is sampled in order to measure the solid content, the sampling tube should be arranged to face into the stream. Gas or steam should enter the sampling tube at the same velocity as that in the undisturbed stream. If the velocity of sampling is different from the undisturbed velocity of the gas, the gas must move across the stream; and the solid particles, having a larger mass than the gas or steam particles, are liable to lag behind, so that the sample withdrawn may not contain a truly representative number of solid particles. In fact, the sampling of a mixture of two phases is one of the most difficult sampling problems.

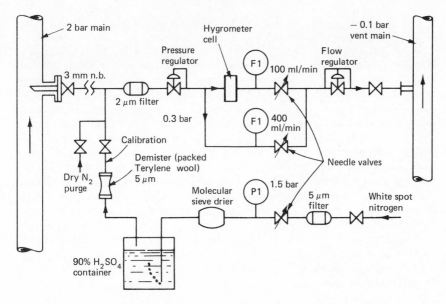

Figure 1.15   Measurement of water in corrosive gas

Figure 1.15 shows a typical system for measuring a component of a corrosive gas mixture at a pressure above atmospheric.

1.1.2.1   MAINTENANCE AND TESTING

The remarks already made about the maintenance of sampling lines, filters, lutes and drain points apply equally to those used in these systems. Lines may be tested for leaks, in a similar manner to that already described, by sealing off the line and applying an appropriate air pressure through a bubbler. Leaks may be located by painting the joints with soap solution, when the presence of bubbles makes the position of the leak obvious. Where the gas in the line is neither toxic nor inflammable the examination of the sampling lines for small leaks is not necessary.

1.2   SAMPLING SYSTEMS FOR LIQUIDS

Much of what has been said about the sampling of gases applies equally to the sampling of liquids. As with gases, it is essential to obtain a truly representative sample so that it is usual to fit some form of agitator in a vessel from which a sample is to be withdrawn. Because of the difficulty of withdrawing a representative sample, the tendency is where possible to adopt methods of analysis which do not require the sample to be withdrawn from the process vessel, e.g. use the immersion or dip type assembly to measure pH; or to arrange, as in the case of pH and electrical conductivity measurement, for the measurement to take place in a pipe along which the process liquid flows.

Where the liquid is free from suspended solids, a system similar to that shown in *Figure 1.14* may be used.

In the measurement of the pH value of precipitates or slurries which tend to clog the electrode system, the process liquid must be continuously recirculated. *Figure 1.16* illustrates some sampling systems which have been successfully employed. *Figure 1.16(a)* illustrates a method of sampling paper stock which prevents clogging of the electrodes. *Figure 1.16(b)* illustrates a method used for sampling a viscous paste; a baffle plate and adjustable weir ensure continuous sampling. *Figure 1.16(c)* illustrates the use of a cone shaped orifice to separate the measured solution from paper stock; the orifice may from time to time be flushed with water. *Figure 1.16(d)* shows a jet of water impinging on the electrodes to keep them free from precipitate. The effect of the water upon the pH value must, however, be known. *Figure 1.16(e)* illustrates the extraction of a small portion of corrosive liquid by means of compressed air; the sample is taken to a remotely situated electrode system.

Where the pH value of a viscous or hot liquid is required, it is possible to bleed off a sample and dilute and cool it to a manageable condition, provided the pH of the diluted or cooled sample bears a constant relationship to that of the original solution.

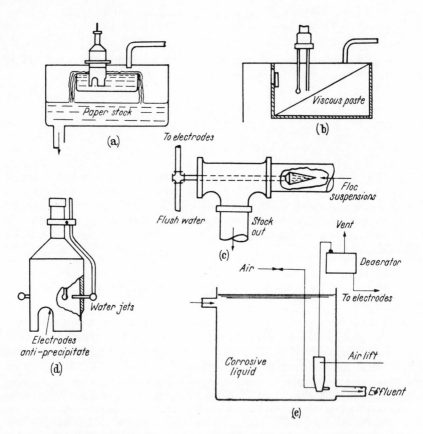

Figure 1.16   Some electrode sampling devices (Courtesy Electronic Instruments Ltd.)

Controller
pH Recorder
Feeder of treatment material
Immersion-type pH electrode assembly
Untreated liquid
Treated liquid
Agitator
Baffles
Treatment basin
Settling basin

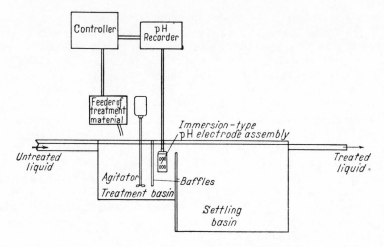

Figure 1.17 Treatment of liquids

In the treatment of water in order to precipitate suspended organic matter it is necessary to control the pH value of the liquid. The pH value of the water may be measured by installing an immersion type pH electrode assembly in the position shown in *Figure 1.17*. A similar arrangement may be used for the treatment of waste pickle liquor in the steel industry.

When sampling a liquid from a process line, e.g. the finished product in an in-line blending petrol plant, it is necessary to have a carefully designed sampling system.

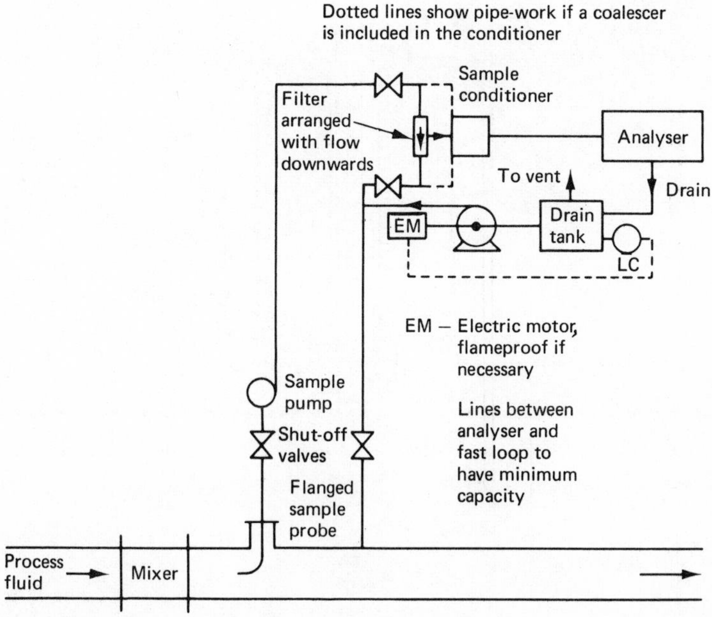

Dotted lines show pipe-work if a coalescer is included in the conditioner
Sample conditioner
Filter arranged with flow downwards
Analyser
To vent
Drain
Drain tank
EM
LC
EM – Electric motor, flameproof if necessary
Lines between analyser and fast loop to have minimum capacity
Sample pump
Shut-off valves
Flanged sample probe
Process fluid
Mixer

Figure 1.18 Sampling system for liquids

Before removal from the process line the liquid components should be thoroughly mixed to ensure a representative sample. If any doubt exists an in-line mixer may be installed. This may consist of from four to six curved vanes arranged in such a way that consecutive vanes produce rotation of the liquid stream in opposite directions so that in passing through the vanes the liquid is intimately mixed. Alternatively, the pipe section may be enlarged and an impeller fitted, driven by an electric or pneumatic motor, rotating with its axis at right-angles to the flow, thoroughly to mix the liquid. To increase the chance of the sample being representative it is removed from the centre of the pipe, as shown in *Figure 1.18,* where the velocity is greatest. The lines to the analyser should be as short as possible but if necessary a fast loop should be designed with a pump to circulate the process liquid past the analyser, the actual sample being taken off from the appropriate connection of an in-line or by-pass filter. The sample after passing through the analyser may be collected in a suitable vessel and pumped back into the return line at intervals determined by a level controller.

Sample preparation equipment such as filters, heat exchangers, etc., will in general be similar to that for gases, but one new problem arises in removing free water or steam contained in hydrocarbon streams flowing to the analyser. It is essential in gas chromatography to remove water completely from the

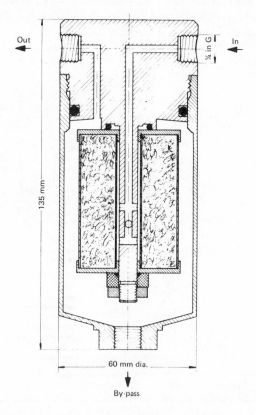

Figure 1.19   Filter coalescer (Courtesy Carlo Erba)

sample and this may be achieved by the use of the filter coalescer shown in *Figure 1.19*. In passing from the inside of the coalescer, consisting of silanised glass wool, the diffused water is slowed down so forming droplets which when they reach the outer surface drain downwards, as the water is denser than the hydrocarbon. Thus the water falls to the bottom and is carried away by the by-pass stream while the dry sample flows upwards and out. In order that the water removing properties of the device are not prejudiced, a filter should be fitted upstream if the sample contains solids, and the inlet sample temperature must be kept below 40°C.

2

MEASUREMENT OF DENSITY OR SPECIFIC GRAVITY

Instruments for the measurement of density are divided into two sections:

Instruments for measuring the density of liquids
Instruments for measuring the density of gases.

2.1   INSTRUMENTS FOR MEASURING THE DENSITY OF LIQUIDS

The measurement of density or specific gravity of a liquid may be accomplished by similar means to those employed in the indirect methods of measuring levels.

The pressure due to a column of liquid is equal to the product of the depth and the weight per unit volume. In level measurement it is assumed that the weight per unit volume is constant so that the pressure produced by the column is a measure of the level. In density measurement, the depth is maintained constant so that the pressure produced by the column is a measure of the density. The weight of a given volume of liquid is equal to $g \times$ the product of the volume of the liquid and its density. The weight of a fixed volume of liquid will, therefore, be a measure of its density. A weighing tube may be employed, provided it is always kept full of liquid, when the weight of liquid in the tube will be directly proportional to its density.

The upthrust on a body which is immersed in a liquid is equal to the weight of fluid displaced, and so will be equal to $g \times$ the product of the volume and density of the liquid displaced. If the weight of the immersed body is less than the weight of liquid it displaces when completely immersed, the body will float and the weight of liquid displaced will be equal to the weight of the floating body. The floating body must be free to rise or fall with the change of density of the liquid. It will then adjust itself so that the product of the weight per unit volume and volume of the liquid displaced is equal to the weight of the floating body. As the weight of the floating body is fixed, the product, Density of liquid $\times$ Volume of liquid displaced = Constant.

∴ Density of liquid = Constant/Volume of liquid displaced

This is the principle of the simple hydrometer and of the recording hydrometer.

If the displacer is arranged so that it is always completely immersed in the liquid, the upthrust will be equal to the product of g, the volume of the displacer and the density of the liquid. The upthrust on a given totally immersed displacer will therefore be a measure of the density of the liquid in which it is immersed.

The instruments for measuring density and specific gravity of liquids may therefore be classified under the following headings:

1. Static-pressure-operated mechanisms, including gas purge systems
2. Weighing tube types
3. Buoyancy types:
   (a) Recording hydrometer
   (b) Totally immersed displacer type
4. Acoustic resonance type.

2.1.1   Static-pressure-operated mechanisms

The pressure due to the liquid at any point in a liquid is equal to $g \times$ the product of the depth of the point below the surface and the density of the liquid. The pressure due to a fixed depth of liquid is therefore a measure of the density of the liquid. This pressure may be measured by any of the methods described in Section 2.2 of Chapter 2 in Volume 1, provided that the level of the liquid can be maintained constant. Probably the simplest method is to employ a gas purge system (usually an air purge) as illustrated in *Figure 2.1*. Where the sampling system is at atmospheric pressure the arrangement shown in *Figure 2.1(a)* may be used. The sampling container provides a constant depth of liquid, and the pressure due to the liquid above the bottom of the stand pipe is measured by feeding a supply of compressed air, or gas, into the stand pipe at a constant rate. The rate of flow of gas must be kept constant, as any excessive irregularity may cause erratic results in the density measurement. The rate of flow may be measured by means of a simple bubbler as shown in the figure, or by means of a flow measurer of the rotameter type, and the valve adjusted to give the required flow. Alternatively it may be kept constant by replacing the valve and flow measurer by a resistance in the form of a length of capillary tubing, by using a constant differential gas purge valve, or by using a Pneumerstat. The pressure of gas in the stand pipe will build up until it is equal to that due to the liquid above the bottom of the stand pipe. The choice of purge gas will depend upon the nature of the process liquid. This topic is discussed in Volume 1.

The pressure of the purge gas is measured by a pressure gauge suited to the range of pressure to be measured and sensitive enough to show small changes of pressure. It may be a liquid manometer, a bell type instrument, or a form of bourdon tube. In the assembly used in *Figure 2.1(a)* a diaphragm assembly is used. On the dial are marked two scales, one, S1, showing the total pressure and the other, S2, the portion of the pressure due to the specific gravity of the liquid being above unity. This second scale may be calibrated in terms of density, specific gravity, or any other convenient hydrometer units.

Where the level of the liquid must be allowed to vary, or where the sampling device cannot be maintained at atmospheric pressure, the arrangement shown in *Figure 2.1(b)* is used. Two stand pipes are immersed in the liquid so that the

38

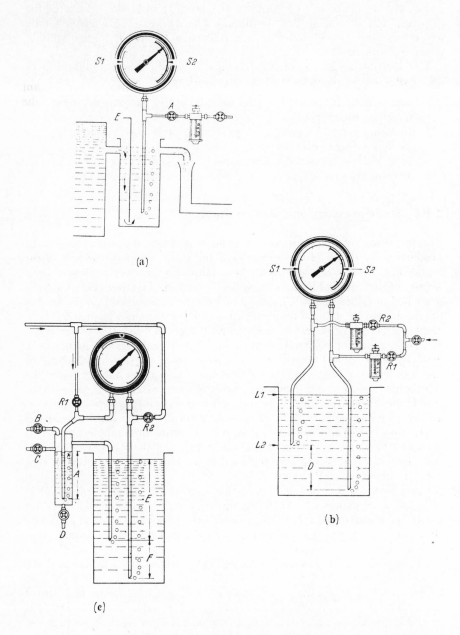

Figure 2.1   Stand pipe methods (Courtesy Negretti and Zambra Ltd.)

lower end of one is at a depth D below the end of the other, and so that the level of the end of the shorter stand pipe is below the minimum level of the tank liquid. Gas is fed to both stand pipes, at rates which are constant, small, and equal to each other, through the restrictions R1 and R2, the difference between the pressures built up in the pipes being measured by a suitable differential pressure gauge. This pressure difference is equal to the pressure due to a column of liquid of depth D, and is shown on scale S1; while the portion of the pressure due to the changes in specific gravity above some fixed value is shown on scale S2.

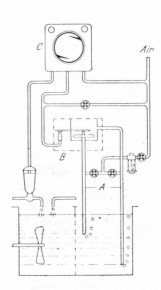

Figure 2.2   Control system using a
pneumatic amplifier
(Courtesy Negretti and Zambra Ltd.)

Where it is required to measure small variations of specific gravity the arrangement shown in Figure 2.1(c) is used. In this arrangement, a pressure equivalent to that of reference liquid of length A, in addition to that due to a column of tank liquid of depth E, is applied to one side of the differential pressure gauge; while a pressure equal to that due to a column of tank liquid of depth $(E + F)$ is applied to the other side. The gauge measures the difference between the pressure due to a column F of tank liquid and that due to a column A of reference liquid of fixed density. If the reference liquid is water, and the length A is equal to the length E, there will be no difference of pressure at the indicator when the density of the tank liquid is the same as that of water, i.e. when its specific gravity is unity. The scale of the differential pressure gauge may, therefore, be calibrated to indicate specific gravity above unity, and the whole of the scale used to indicate the changes of specific gravity.

In addition, if the reference liquid has a coefficient of expansion of the same order as that of the tank liquid, the instrument may be arranged to indicate the specific gravity of the tank liquid at some fixed temperature.

The level of the reference liquid must be maintained constant. If the liquid is volatile, the level will tend to fall owing to evaporation. The loss of liquid must be made up by providing a small but continuous flow of liquid through the reference chamber. To avoid the difficulty of loss of liquid owing to evaporation, mercury, or oil having a very low vapour pressure, may be used as the reference liquid. As mercury has such a high specific gravity, great care must be taken to ensure that the level in the reference chamber is correct, as a small error in the level of the mercury will cause a large error in the indication of the instrument.

In the measurement of small variations of specific gravity, the differential pressure produced by the differential stand pipes may be amplified by means of a pneumatic amplifier. The resulting amplified pressure may then be used to operate an indicator, recorder or controller. The controller may control the flow of diluent into the tank, or control the heat output of the system employed to evaporate the tank contents to the required concentration. A control system using a pneumatic amplifier is shown in *Figure 2.2*. This operates on a similar principle to the servo-operated pressure mechanism described in Volume 1. The pressure of the air controlled by the air escape valve will depend upon the difference between the pressure of the air inside and outside the capsule, i.e. upon the difference in pressure between the ends of the stand pipes. This pressure is directly proportional to the density of the liquid.

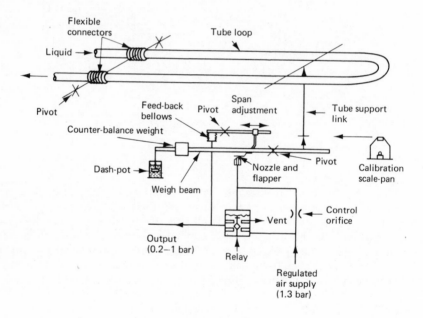

Figure 2.3   Schematic diagram of Mk. 5 density meter (pneumatic transmission) (Courtesy G.E.C.—Elliott Process Instruments)

2.1.2   Weighing tube types

A continuous weighing type of density meter is shown in *Figure 2.3*. The meter consists of a tube loop which is pivoted about flexible connectors and supported on a weigh beam. The process liquid flows through the tube loop and is weighed continuously by the force balance system which produces an output air pressure of 0.2–1.0 bar, linearly related to the liquid density. Where the process liquid contains solids, the flow rate in the tube loop is maintained high enough to prevent their deposition.

In operation the counter-balance weight is so positioned that balance is achieved. When the weight of the tube loop increases, due to an increase in density of the process liquid, the weigh beam tends to turn in a clockwise direction, raising the flapper and thus allowing more air to escape from the nozzle. The resulting decrease in pressure on top of the diaphragm in the relay allows the valve spool to rise, thus increasing the pressure in the feed-back bellows and output connection. The pressure in the feed-back bellows will increase until sufficient extra force is applied to the weigh beam through the pivoted transmitter arm, to restore the original balance. The tube loop is in effect continuously balanced and its movement, which is damped by the silicone fluid dashpot, does not exceed a few seconds of arc. Since the area of feed-back bellows and lever lengths involved are fixed, the increase in pressure required to restore balance will be directly proportional to the increase in density of the process liquid. The output air pressure will therefore be a measure of the density of the liquid flowing in the tube loop, and may be transmitted to an indicator, recorder or controller, the receiver of which has a range of 0.2–1.0 bar.

To calibrate the density meter for a given range the span is set by moving the rider along the transmitter arm and the zero adjusted by moving the counter-balance weight. Moving the rider towards the transmitter arm pivot will increase both the force acting at the rider and the lever length at which this force acts on the weigh beam. Thus, for the 0.2–1.0 bar output a greater weight change can be balanced, i.e. the span of the meter is increased. In order to facilitate calibration without passing a sample of known density through the tube loop, a calibration scale-pan is provided. With the tube loop empty and the scale-pan hanging from the weigh beam, weights corresponding to top and bottom points of the required range can be applied. These weights are calculated from the 'density 1.0 kg/dm^3 equivalent' for the meter, determined at the factory; this being the weight required to simulate a liquid having a density of 1.0 kg/dm^3 flowing through the meter. Thus, although the meter is set to a specified range before leaving the factory, it can be adjusted on site to any span between 0.02 and 0.5 kg/dm^3. The meter is usually used for liquids having a density of 1.6 kg/dm^3 or less, but special models may be obtained for higher densities and greater spans.

There is also a model giving an electrical output signal linearly related to the density of the process fluid. This is achieved by replacing the pneumatic system with an electronic one. The nozzle and flapper are replaced by detector coils and an intercepting vane. The position of the vane, which is attached to the weigh beam, governs the amplitude of oscillation in the coils which form part of a transistorised oscillator circuit. The oscillation is amplified and converted into a direct current which is the output signal. This current is fed into a pot-coil, which replaces the pneumatic feed-back bellows, thus producing the required feed-back force on the weigh beam.

In the standard model, the tube loop is made of 25 mm diameter stainless steel tube and the flexible connectors are stainless steel bellows. For use on chemical plants, the tube loop may be ebonite and the connectors butyl rubber; or a glass tube loop with p.t.f.e. (polytetrafluoroethylene) connectors may be used. In the food industry where a smooth hygienic bore is required, or in applications where a slurry would otherwise block the bellows convolutions, rubber connectors or bellows lined with silicone rubber can be used.

Little maintenance is required apart from span and zero checks. The tube loop is readily removable for cleaning. The sensitivity is 0.5% of the span and repeatability and linearity ±0.25% of the span. The accuracy for spans of 0.03–0.5 kg/dm³ over the working pressure range is ±1% of the span.

A change of process fluid temperature causes a change of 7×10^{-6} kg/dm³ per °C, but the effects of ambient temperature change are negligible. Works calibration ensures that the density indication is not affected by working pressure changes within the specified range.

2.1.2.1 INSTALLATION

As the meter will detect a weight change of one part in 10^5, the location and environment of the meter should be carefully considered in order to obtain accurate trouble-free operation. Standard tube loop bores of 22.9 and 35.6 mm are available through which all, or part, of the process liquid can be passed.

Where possible the meter should be installed in a by-pass so that it may be serviced without disturbing the flow of process liquid. To ensure that no stress or vibration is transmitted to the meter through the pipework the connections should be made with flexible connectors. The support of the meter should also be arranged so that it is not subject to vibrations.

A slurry should be circulated through the meter at a velocity of at least 2.1 m/s in order to prevent the deposition of solids. For clean liquids a high velocity is only necessary at start-up to clear the air from the tube loop, the recommended minimum velocity being 1 m/s. Once the air is cleared the velocity can be reduced to a value consistent with the response time requirement.

For service with liquids at elevated temperature, temperature compensation can be applied by a device which applies a force to the measuring system equal to that produced by the temperature change.

2.1.3 Buoyancy types

2.1.3.1 RECORDING HYDROMETER

A hydrometer floating freely in a liquid will always adjust itself so that the weight of the liquid it displaces is equal to the weight of the hydrometer. When the density of the liquid in which it floats is reduced, the hydrometer will sink further into the liquid until equilibrium between the upthrust and the floating weight is again attained. When the liquid density increases, the hydrometer rises. The position of the hydrometer is, therefore, a measure of the density, or the specific gravity, of the liquid in which it floats.

In the recording hydrometer, an inductance bridge is arranged to detect the position of a hydrometer floating in a sample of the process liquid. The level of the liquid in which the hydrometer is floating is maintained constant as is the rate of flow of the liquid through the hydrometer chamber. The level of the liquid in which the hydrometer floats is fixed by the level of the hydrometer overflow point, and the rate of flow is decided by the difference in levels of the constant head overflow point and the hydrometer overflow point.

2.1.3.2   TOTALLY IMMERSED DISPLACER TYPE

Instruments of this type are similar to those described in Section 2.1.3.1 in that they measure the upthrust on a body; but instead of allowing the body to float, the displacer is always completely immersed so that the upthrust is directly proportional to the density of the liquid.

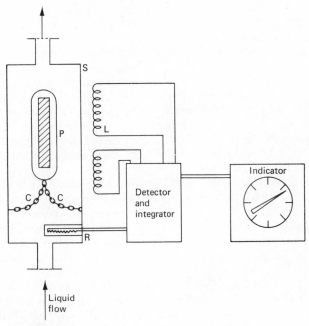

S *Sampling chamber*
L *Linear variable transformer*
P *Plummet with metal core supporting chains, C*
R *Resistance thermometer bulb*

Figure 2.4   Densitrol density indicator (Courtesy Princo Instruments Inc.)

In the Princo Densitrol density indicator shown in *Figure 2.4*, the upthrust on the displacer or plummet is counterbalanced by the weight of the plummet and platinum–iridium calibrating chain. The plummet is so weighted that, at the middle of the density indicating range, it will support half the weight of the chain with the reference points supporting the other half. As the density of the liquid increases, the increased buoyancy of the plummet causes it to rise. In rising, the plummet will take up a greater portion of the weight of the chain. It will continue to rise until the increased portion of the weight which it now supports is equal to the added buoyancy. When the density of the liquid decreases, the upthrust on the plummet is reduced and the plummet will sink so that a greater portion of the weight of the chain is taken by the reference points. It will continue to sink until equilibrium is again attained.

Thus, for each value of the density within the range of the plummet–chain assembly, the plummet will take up a definite position which is a measure of the density of the liquid. The plummet contains a ferromagnetic core which alters the inductance between the primary winding and the two opposed halves of the secondary winding of a differential transformer as the plummet rises or falls. The output of the transformer is, therefore, an indication of the position of the plummet and after rectification this signal together with the signal from a resistance thermometer are combined in a solid state integrator to produce a temperature corrected output signal of -5 to $+5$ mV with an impedance of 300Ω. This signal can be used as the input into a standard millivolt recorder, controller or data acquisition system calibrated in terms of the density of the liquid.

The design of the plummet assembly and the transformer is such that the instrument scale is linear, and the same instrument may be used for a number of ranges by using interchangeable chain–plummet reference point assemblies. The plummet and the sampling chamber may be made from a wide range of materials such as glass, brass, stainless steel, Monel or any other machinable material. The measuring chamber may be designed to withstand static pressure up to 34.5 bar. When constructed in glass it will withstand pressures up to 8.6 bar; when made of metal the normal design will withstand pressures up to 10.3 bar.

The instrument may be designed for use at any temperature between $-60°C$ and $+230°C$. A Teflon lined version with the Teflon plummet is available, and an explosion proof version of both transmitter and integrator is available.

The normal maximum operating temperature is 110°C but a special coil is available extending the operating temperature to 230°C. The maximum operating pressure is 14 bar, but metal plummets are limited to 2.8 bar, and glass bodies to 3.5 bar.

The span of the instrument can be between 5 kg/m³ and 200 kg/m³ anywhere in the range 500–3500 kg/m³, but other ranges are available.

The accuracy is $\pm3\%$ of the span or ±0.2 kg/m³, whichever is the greater, and sensitivity is 0.5% of the span. A zero setting control is fitted in the sensor chamber enabling the instrument to be set in the field with an accuracy at the calibration point equal to the accuracy of the measuring standard itself.

The flow rate and permissible variation is determined by the viscosity of the measured liquid. For liquids with a viscosity less than 50 cP at the operating temperature, the permissible flow rate is 0.4–2.0 dm³/min.

Where the operating temperature is reasonably steady, the scale is calibrated in terms of density at the operating temperature. Where the ambient temperature fluctuates, manual or automatic temperature compensation may be applied, or the liquid entering the sampling chamber may be maintained at a constant temperature by means of a thermostatically controlled heater.

The instrument is used to indicate continuously, and to record and control the density of flowing process liquids in pulp, paper, textile, food, petroleum and chemical industries.

The Sangamo specific gravity meter shown in *Figure 2.5(a)* employs an electrical force balance system to weigh a plummet which is housed inside the lower portion of an epoxy probe and completely immersed in the liquid. The plummet, which is spherical, is made of a special ferrous alloy heavily gold plated to protect it from corrosion and has a density slightly greater than the maximum of the process liquid, so that it always tends to sink. It is prevented from doing so by the attraction of the magnetic field of a suspension solenoid situated directly above it *(Figure 2.5(b))*. The position of the plummet is detected by two search coils fed with a high frequency a.c. supply which, through the circuitry shown in *Figure 2.5(c)*, adjusts the current in the solenoid to maintain the plummet centrally between the coils in a liquid of given density. Any movement of the plummet relative to the search coils results in a correcting change in the current through the solenoid to restore the position of the plummet relative to the search coils. The current through the solenoid is therefore a measure of the force required to support the plummet, i.e. proportional to the difference in density between the plummet and the supporting liquid.

This current is also passed through a highly stable resistor so that the voltage across the resistor is a measure of the solenoid current. Range and span controls are provided, the range control being used to vary the level of the stabilised reference voltage which is connected in opposition to the voltage across the resistor, and the span control to vary the sensitivity of the 'voltage comparison' network.

The main electronic circuits associated with the meter are mounted in a robust aluminium head, flange mounted on the stem. All electrical parts in the vicinity of the process liquid are potted in epoxy resin, ensuring safety when measuring inflammable liquids. All electronic circuits associated with the

(a)

Figure 2.5   Sangamo specific gravity meter (Courtesy Sangamo Controls Ltd.) (a) Meter with sampling tank and plummet removed

46

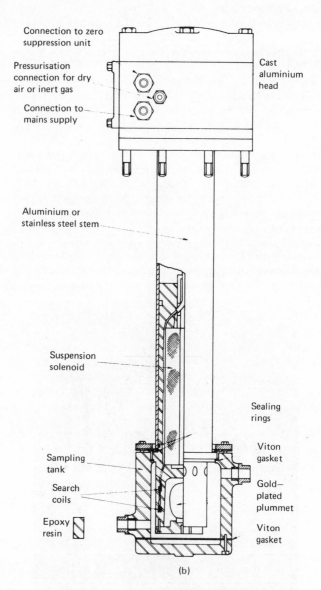

Connection to zero
suppression unit

Pressurisation
connection for dry
air or inert gas

Connection to
mains supply

Cast
aluminium
head

Aluminium or
stainless steel stem

Suspension
solenoid

Sealing
rings

Viton
gasket

Sampling
tank

Search
coils

Gold—
plated
plummet

Epoxy
resin

Viton
gasket

(b)

Figure 2.5(b)   Section showing arrangement of probe

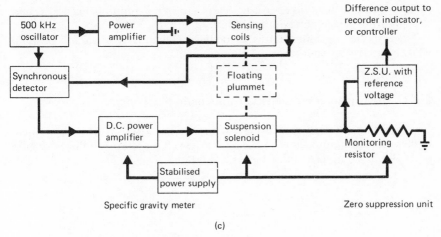

Figure 2.5(c)   Circuit diagram

'range' and 'span' control use solid state components mounted on printed circuit boards and mounted in a separate unit, the zero suppression unit. Pressurisation connections are fitted to both meter head and zero suppression unit, enabling them to be pressurised with air or inert gas rendering them safe to use where an explosive hazard exists.

All instruments are fitted with a 'spider' at the bottom of the probe to maintain the plummet within the influence of the solenoid and search coils when the current is switched off. With the spider fitted, flow rates past the probe of up to 68 litre/h can be tolerated for liquids up to viscosity of 1 cP.

The instrument can be used with one plummet to measure densities over a range of 400 kg/m^3 from the plummet density downwards. As the instrument is basically measuring only the difference in liquid and plummet densities called the plummet density difference (p.d.d.) the best results are obtained when the p.d.d. is small but not less than 0.03. The basic accuracy of the instrument is better than 0.1% p.d.d. under controlled temperature conditions, enabling a density to be measured with an accuracy better than 1×10^{-4} with a set span of 1×10^{-2}.

Temperature variations can affect this figure due to:

Head: measurement error $\pm 0.01\%$ p.d.d. per °C maximum.
Probe: -0.02% p.d.d. per °C due to change in solenoid temperature.
Plummet: $+0.04 \text{ kg/m}^3$ per °C due to plummet expansion.

As the liquid usually expands about ten times this amount the effect of the plummet expansion may often be ignored.

A positive temperature coefficient infers the instrument will read high with increasing temperature. Where the density at a fixed reference temperature is required a temperature compensation may be used. This unit measures the liquid temperature by means of a platinum resistance thermometer and applies a correction for temperature to the output of the instrument.

The instrument specific gravity span may be between 0.01 and 0.4 and the range 0.4 to 2.0, the fluid operating temperature maximum being 170°C and the operating pressure maximum 14 bar.

The accuracy of calibration is ±0.0001 specific gravity or ±0.5% of span, whichever is the greater error.

2.1.4   Measurement of density by acoustic resonance

Several forms of density measuring instruments are based on the measurement of the resonant frequency of an oscillating system, be it a tube filled with fluid or a cylinder completely immersed in a fluid.

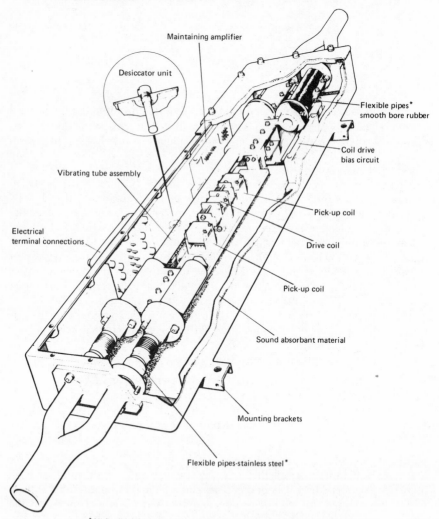

*All flexible pipes are either stainless steel or rubber depending on application

Figure 2.6   Acoustic density meter (Courtesy The Solartron Electronic Group)

The principle of the Solartron density meter is shown in *Figure 2.6*. The sensing element consists of two parallel tubes carrying the process liquid which are resonated at their natural frequency of oscillation.

A fully encapsulated solid state amplifier, magnetically coupled to the tubes, maintains them in vibration and also provides the output signal. The frequency of oscillation of the tubes is dependent upon the mass of the tubes, which in turn is dependent upon the density of the liquid filling them. Thus, any change in density will produce a change in frequency. In short, the density meter is a hollow tuning fork filled with the measurement liquid. The output from the meter is a frequency modulated signal, which is detected and converted to a direct density reading by an associated read-out unit, thus enabling the density to be monitored and controlled.

A twin-tube design of this instrument provides continuous on-stream measurement of density. The flow through the tubes can be in either direction, or the liquid can be at rest.

The meter is constructed of an ultra-stable high nickel alloy giving extremely good long term stability—alloys of this type were originally developed for manufacturers of tuning forks. The instrument is assembled so that it is immune to vibration and can be mounted at any angle. Vertical mounting is preferred as this prevents solids being deposited on the tube walls and air bubbles from being trapped. It is extremely robust and easy to maintain, its straight-through construction giving ease in inspection. It has flexible coupling tubes at the ends ensuring that it can be readily flanged into an existing pipeline system.

Platinum resistance thermometers can be mounted at each end of the instrument so that a correction can be made to refer the density reading to a specific temperature.

Accuracy

The density range of the meter is unlimited, the transducer requiring no adjustment for changes in liquid density, although it may be desirable to make adjustments in the read-out system in order to select a more suitable density span. The instrument's design achieves high accuracy, as variables such as pressure, viscosity, flow rates, etc., have an almost negligible effect. The absolute accuracy is mainly defined by the accuracy of calibration and on standard instruments this is better than 0.0001 kg/dm^3 over a density range of 0.6–1.6 kg/dm^3.

The dimensions of the vibrating tube are chosen so that the frequency of oscillation changes by about 20% for a density change from 0 to 1 kg/dm^3. Linearisation can be introduced within the read-out system, but if the required density span is small, linearisation is not necessary.

Repeatability

The repeatability of measurement is in $0.000\,03$ kg/litre: the instrument has no hysteresis effect, and evaluation tests at the National Physical Laboratory confirm this figure.

Stability

In the absence of corrosion and deposition the instrument's ability is such that the calibration will not drift by more than 0.0002 kg/litre per year. It is therefore important to ensure that the materials of construction are suitable for the process liquid. If necessary the vibrating tube may be gold plated to increase its resistance to corrosion.

Calibration

Each instrument is calibrated using two standard points: the instrument empty (air density approximately 0.0012 kg/litre) and the instrument filled with purified water (density approximately 0.998); from these two recordings the complete density/output frequency relationship can be obtained. Further check points are made to verify this relationship, using as the standard an instrument which has been calibrated by the N.P.L.

Flow rate

The instrument has an extremely small flow rate coefficient. For water, the error introduced when the flow rate is increased from zero to 4500 litre/h is about 0.000 03 kg/litre. The instrument may be designed to be suitable for process pressures from 10 to 70 bar and process temperatures of from $-30°C$ to $+100°C$.

Maintenance

The instrument is very robust and requires little maintenance. The tube may be cleared either with cleaning liquid or mechanically by removing the Y pieces and using a push rod. Visual inspection of the tubes is also easy, since the flow path is straight through the instrument. A desiccator is used to dry the air inside, and thus prevent condensation forming on the vibrating tubes. When saturated this desiccator is removed and dried out or replaced. To check the calibration it is only necessary to confirm the frequency reading for a liquid of a defined density. If the reading is within the tolerance the complete calibration will be correct. In most cases the easiest check point is when the instrument is empty and clean, i.e. 0.0012 kg/litre, the density of air. Recalibration of the instrument is carried out by taking readings of two liquids of different densities. From these two readings the complete frequency/density relationship is obtained. Generally the two liquids are air and pure water, since the densities of these are well defined.

Intrinsic safety

Provided the meter is installed with barrier units in the conductors between the safe and hazardous areas (as shown in *Figure 2.7*) the equipment meets the requirements of BS 4683, Group 11A, B and C.

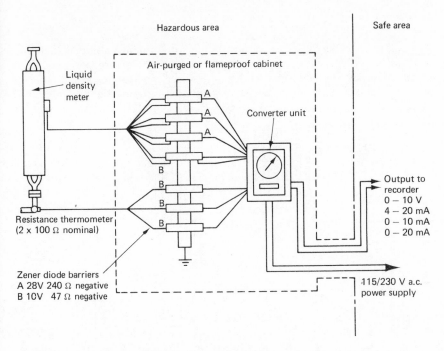

Figure 2.7   Installation of Solartron liquid density meter in a hazardous area
(Courtesy Associated Octel Co. Ltd.)

In the alternative design used for liquids, gases and cryogenic fluids, shown in *Figure 2.8*, the transducer consists of a thin cylinder surrounded by the process fluid, and set into circumferential oscillation at its resonant frequency by the electromagnetic field produced by the 'drive coil'. The frequency of oscillation is detected by the 'pick-off' coil and the oscillation maintained by the amplifier, which also provides the 5 V peak-to-peak pulse frequency signal to the digital density converter. The periodic time T of the oscillation is related to the density of the fluid by the equation

$$d = d_0[(T/T_0)^2 - 1]$$

where d = Density of the measured fluid in kg/m^3
d_0 = Meter constant in kg/m^3
T = Periodic time of the output signal in μs when the density is d
T_0 = Periodic time of the output when the oscillation takes place in a vacuum.

In the converter the frequency is compared with that of a quartz crystal oscillator. The difference signal suitably processed is fed to a frequency-to-voltage converter whose output is linearised to compensate for the non-linear relationship between periodic time and density and forms the converter output which is a measure of the density.

The instrument body is made of EN 58 J stainless steel designed for pressures up to 700 bar and the reading is unaffected by pressures up to the

52

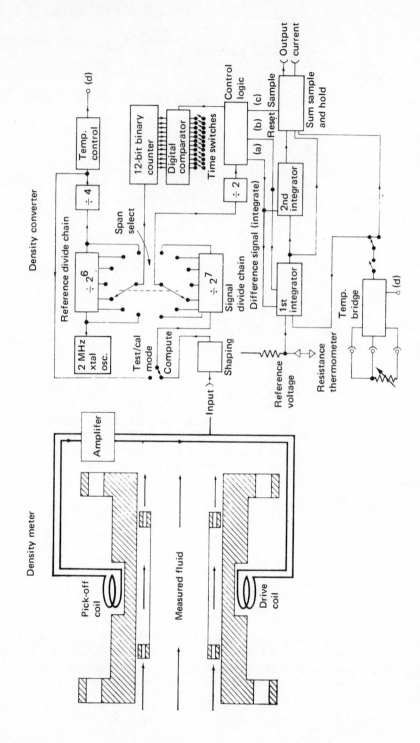

Figure 2.8 Density meter and converter (Courtesy Joram Agar and Co. Ltd.)

body design pressure. Viscosity changes have no effect up to a viscosity of 20 cP. The temperature coefficient per °C of the meter is shown below:

	Ni Span C Spool	FV 520 B Spool
Gas density meter	<0.003 kg/m^3	<0.07 kg/m^3
Liquid density meter	<0.01 kg/m^3	<0.2 kg/m^3

The sensitivity is such that the periodic time changes by 1 μs for a density change of 4.2 kg/m^3 in liquids and 0.5 kg/m^3 in gases. The accuracy of the meter is:

Liquids	$\pm0.1\%$ of the range, ±0.5 kg/m^3
Gases	$\pm0.1\%$ of the range, ±0.005 kg/m^3

and the repeatability and hysteresis are better than 0.01% of the range.

The minimum operational span is 10 kg/m^3 for liquids and 0.8 kg/m^3 for gases. Four operating temperature ranges are available:

Ni Span C Spool	$-270°C - +75°C$ or $-20°C - +75°C$
FV 520 B Spool	$-20°C - +200°C$ or $+100°C - +400°C$.

When used for gas density measurement the body temperature must be maintained at the fluid operating temperature. When it is required to relate the density to a fixed temperature a correction may be applied for the temperature as measured by a platinum resistance thermometer.

The instrument is used in conjunction with flow meters to obtain mass flow measurements.

Installation

The sensor is mounted so that liquid flow is vertically upwards and gas flow is vertically downwards and the flow through the meter should not be greater than 1 m/s in the case of liquids, or 3 m/s in the case of gases.

The meter may be installed in a by-pass with isolating valves and suitably lagged in with the main flow line to ensure the fluid in the meter is at the same temperature as the line fluid.

By installing approved barriers in the connections between the converter located in a safe area and the detector located in the hazardous area, the meter may be rendered intrinsically safe.

Another density meter operating on the same principle but employing a sensor of a different physical form is the ITT densitometer. The sensor consists of a probe installed in the line which contains the flowing fluid, thus ensuring that the measurement is taken at the working temperature and pressure. The probe consists of a sensing vane symmetrically positioned across a supporting cylinder. The method of maintaining and detecting the frequency of oscillation, and the relationship between the frequency and density, are similar to other oscillatory systems.

Probes suitable for liquids, gases and cryogenic fluids are available, the maximum operating pressure being 80 bar and the operating temperatures from 0 to 120°C for the liquid and gas probe and -200 to $+120°C$ for the cryogenic version.

The probe specifications are:

	Gas	Liquid
Density range	0–80 kg/m³	320–1200 kg/m³
Span adjustment	8–80 kg/m³	100–320 kg/m³
Zero adjustment	0–72 kg/m³	320–1100 kg/m³
Temperature sensitivity per °C	0.07 kg/m³	0.11 kg/m³
Frequency	2.4–3.2 kHz	3–5 kHz

The transmitter may be located up to 800 m from the probe and the precision of the system as a whole is ±0.1% of the span.

2.2 INSTRUMENTS FOR MEASURING THE DENSITY OF GASES

2.2.1 The density balance

Owing to the fact that the density of a gas is very small, an instrument depending upon weighing and designed to measure changes in gas density must be very sensitive to small changes of weight if accurate results are to be obtained. As the density of hydrogen is much less than that of other common gases, an instrument of this type does, however, provide a convenient method of determining the concentration of hydrogen in a gas mixture. The instrument consists of a large glass globe suspended from a very sensitive weigh beam in a chamber maintained at a constant temperature. The gas mixture is passed through the chamber and any movement of the weigh beam owing to changes in gas density is transmitted to the pen or pointer of the recorder by means of a magnetic coupling.

Another gas density meter based on measuring the upthrust on a displacer is illustrated in *Figure 2.9*. The force on the displacer is counterbalanced by an electromagnet and maintained in the null position by the force generated by the flow of current in the electromagnet coil.

The float is carried at one end of a beam pivoted on flexure pivots so that change in apparent weight of the float causes angular rotation of the beam which is detected by a differential transformer type detector and associated electronic circuits operating at 50 kHz. The rectified 50 kHz signal controls the d.c. current applied to the electromagnet to restore balance. The size of this d.c. current, which has a range of 10–50 mA, is directly proportional to the density of the gas. Instruments are available to cover density ranges from 0–16 to 0–480 kg/m³ at pressures up to 172 bar and ambient temperatures of −20 to +60°C. The instrument operates from a 25–45 V d.c. power source and the accuracy claimed by the manufacturer is ±0.25% span. A thermometer pocket is provided adjacent to the gas inlet so that the gas temperature may be measured.

As the accuracy will be dependent upon the attitude of the beam, care must be taken to ensure that its mounting position is correct. Ferrous metals in close proximity will also influence the reading, so site calibration may in certain cases be advisable. Span adjustment is achieved electrically by zero adjustment and is mechanical by moving a mass along the beam. Masses representing 50 and 100% change of span are provided which can be hung from a groove at one end of the beam so that field calibration can be carried

1. Float
2. Pivot
3. Counterweight
4. Vent
5. Coil cover
6. Closure pin
7. Plug-in circuit board

(a)

Span adjustment

Power supply

Amplifier

Restoring coil

Differential
transformer
null position
detector

Fluid
inlet

Float

Pivot
(flexures)

Zero
(adjustment)

Baffle

Outlet

(b)

Figure 2.9 Gas density meter (Courtesy UGC Industries Inc. USA) (a) Instrument removed from pressure housing (b) Principle of operation

out. In common with all delicate instruments this one should be handled with care to ensure the flexure pivots are not damaged.

A similar instrument with provision for venting out gases may be used for liquid density measurement.

A pneumatic density transmitter giving a 0.2–1 bar output and having a maximum range of 880 kg/m³ is also available. This instrument has a guaranteed accuracy of ±0.25% of the scale range.

3

MEASUREMENT OF HUMIDITY

The measurement and control of the humidity of the air in factories and stores is frequently of great practical importance.

Air which is not saturated with water vapour is capable of absorbing moisture from materials with which it is in contact, thus causing evaporation and a consequent drying of the materials. Also, certain materials have the power of absorbing moisture from the air, so causing an increase in the moisture content of the material and a corresponding decrease in the moisture content of the air. These two considerations may seriously affect the resulting product of certain processes unless a state of equilibrium between atmosphere and process material is maintained.

In all textile industries, especially in those dealing with the manufacture of wool and cotton, it is important to maintain a high level of humidity in the atmosphere, not only to keep up the weight of the material, but also to prevent electrification of the strands.

Colour printing requires the relative humidity to be kept within very narrow limits, usually in the neighbourhood of 60%. If the relative humidity is allowed to vary beyond the critical limit, the paper alters in dimensions, and the alteration is not constant along a cross fibre. Where several colours are to be superimposed, with an ink-drying interval between each printing, any such alteration has a serious effect on the appearance of the finished product.

The drying of wood, leather, paper, celluloid, artificial resins, lacquers, glues, films and starches requires careful humidity control so that alteration of the texture and shape of the product may be avoided; whilst in the desiccation of foods such as eggs, fruit, meat, etc., the colloids and vitamins must not be disturbed and the swelling properties must be preserved. The successful storage of meat, fruit and eggs often depends upon the control of the amount of water vapour present.

The importance of humidity to bodily comfort is being increasingly realised. Cold and heat can be endured without great discomfort if the humidity of the air favours the appropriate bodily reaction.

The state of the humidity of a gas is usually expressed in terms of the 'absolute humidity,' or of the 'relative humidity'.

The absolute humidity of a gas is defined as a mass of water vapour present in a unit volume of the gas, and is usually expressed in grams per cubic metre.

The definition of 'relative humidity' has already been given in Volume 1, but for convenience it is repeated here:

$$\text{Relative humidity} = \frac{\text{Mass of water vapour present in a given volume of gas}}{\text{Mass of water vapour necessary to saturate the same volume of gas at the same temperature}}$$

$$= \frac{\text{Pressure exerted by the vapour}}{\text{Saturation vapour pressure at the given temperature}}$$

$$= \frac{\text{Saturation vapour pressure at the dew point}}{\text{Saturation vapour pressure at the given temperature.}}$$

The instruments used to measure the humidity of a gas are called hygrometers.

In the laboratory, the humidity of a gas may be determined by absorbing the water vapour contained in a known volume of the gas by passing it through a weighed drying tube containing a suitable dehydrating agent such as phosphorus pentoxide, or pieces of pumice stone soaked with concentrated sulphuric acid.

The amount of moisture in a solid may also be obtained gravimetrically by weighing a sample before and after drying.

Very dry gas is required for many industrial processes. Dry nitrogen, helium or argon are used in transistor manufacture, as the presence of moisture causes decay of the semiconductor material. Presence of moisture in natural gas will cause the formation of hydrates which will freeze above 0°C, causing valve failure. Moisture in hydrogen used as a feed stock to catalytic reformers in the oil industry will cause deterioration of the catalyst. Air for purging instruments must be dry to prevent corrosion. Many industrial gases used as feed stocks must be dry to prevent corrosion or other interference with the process. For example, the presence of moisture in the ethylene feed gas produces a weak polythene. In the metallurgical industry, the moisture content of feed and blanketing gases must be kept to a minimum. Thus the measurement of moisture in a wide range of industrial gases has become vital and on-line analysers have been developed for this purpose.

The methods of measurement of humidity which are used in industry will be described under the following headings:

1. Dew-point methods
2. Wet- and dry-bulb hygrometers
3. Hair hygrometers
4. Electrical methods.

3.1   DEW-POINT METHODS

The quantity of moisture required to saturate a given volume of air or gas will depend upon the temperature of the air or gas. When moist air is cooled, a temperature is reached when the moisture present is sufficient to saturate the air. Further cooling will cause some vapour to be deposited on surrounding objects in the form of dew, and the temperature at which this deposition takes place is called the dew point for the sample of air. The first hygrometers produced were designed to estimate the dew point. When the dew point is known, the partial pressure of the moisture in the original sample of air is known, since this is equal to the saturation vapour pressure at the dew point. The value of this vapour pressure may be obtained from the temperature graph (Volume 1, *Figure 3.34*) for water vapour. The value of the saturation vapour pressure for the working temperature may be obtained from the same graph, and hence the relative humidity may be calculated.

Regnault's hygrometer provides a suitable laboratory method of producing local cooling of the air in order to estimate the dew point. It consists of two similar tubes A and B, the upper portions of which are made of glass, while the lower portions consist of highly polished silver thimbles. Sufficient ether is placed in tube A to fill the silver cap, and a thermometer dips into the ether. By means of two tubes, air is bubbled through the ether, which evaporates and becomes cooled. The liquid is well stirred by the bubbling air, thus ensuring that thermometer, ether and silver cap are at the same temperature. Dew forms on the silver cap as soon as the air in contact with the cap is cooled down to its dew point. The temperature at which the silver cap becomes clouded by a thin film of moisture is noted. The flow of air is then reduced to one bubble every 5 or 10 s. The rate of evaporation will be considerably reduced, and the temperature of the ether will begin to rise; but the bubbles will continue to stir the liquid. The temperature at which the moisture disappears is observed, and the mean of the temperatures at which the moisture appears and disappears is taken as the dew point. The thermometer in bulb B indicates the normal air temperature. The apparatus should be observed through a sheet of glass which protects the tubes from the disturbing effects of the observer.

Griffiths* devised a modification of this apparatus for use in cold stores. The silver cap is replaced by a nickel plated copper block, cooled by the brine in circulation which is used to obtain the low temperature of the stores. The temperature of the block is measured by a thermometer inserted near its surface. This hygrometer is used in a similar way to Regnault's hygrometer.

3.1.1   Thermo-electric dew-point hygrometer

The dew-point indicator shown in *Figure 3.1* is used to make continuous automatic measurements of dew points down to 45°C below ambient temperature.

The method is based on detecting the presence of water particles on the mirror when it is cooled, by means of a photo-sensitive resistor. The mirror is cooled by means of a thermo-electric cooling unit which uses the Peltier effect to produce cooling. It is well known that a current is produced across the junction of dissimilar metals when the junction is heated. The converse is also true. The junction will be heated or cooled when a current is passed through the junction. A current in one direction will produce a heating effect, whereas if the current is reversed a cooling effect will be produced.

A lamp operating from a stabilised power supply provides a light source of constant intensity, and this is focused on to a metallic mirror. The angle of incidence of the light beam is adjusted so that when the mirror is clear the reflected beam does not fall on the photo-sensitive resistor. Under this condition, which only occurs when the temperature of the mirror is above dew point, the amplifier supplies current to the cooling unit so that the temperature of the mirror is depressed.

As the temperature of the mirror approaches dew point, dew rapidly forms

*Griffiths, 'Discussions on Hygrometry', *Proc. Phys. Soc.*, 34, XXV (1922).

on its surface and causes some of the incident light to be scattered. Some of the scattered light is focused on to the photo-sensitive resistor, which changes its resistance inversely with the intensity of the light falling on it. The change in resistance alters the amplitude of the input signal to the amplifier, and the amplifier responds by reducing the amount of current fed to the cooling unit. The variation of the mirror temperature, between the point at which dew just starts to form and the point at which the mirror becomes heavily misted, is only 0.5°C. The system stabilises the temperature of the mirror within this 0.5°C range, and within 0.25°C of the true dew point.

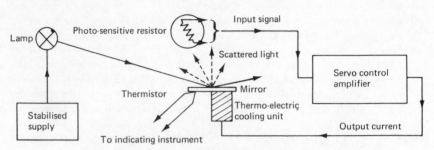

Figure 3.1   Thermo-electric dew-point hygrometer (Courtesy Salford Electrical Instruments Ltd.)

The temperature of the mirror is monitored by a thermistor and an indication of the dew point is obtained on the meter in the control unit. The output current of the meter bridge may, if required, be recorded and used as the input signal to automatically controlled drying or humidifying systems.

The accuracy of the dew-point measurement is ±1.5°C and the output is 0–10 mV. Gas stream connections are provided to the detector unit for metal pipe and at a temperature of 25°C and atmospheric pressure the rate of gas flow should not exceed 1 litre/min if the lowest dew points are to be reached. The detector is not suitable for use with halogens or other corrosive gases. The meter will operate from a 240 or 115 V 50 Hz supply and the maximum ambient temperature of the control unit is 40°C and of the thermo-electric optical unit 50°C.

3.2   WET- AND DRY-BULB HYGROMETERS

This type of hygrometer is based upon the fact that water will evaporate more readily in a dry atmosphere than in a wet one. In fact, if the atmosphere is saturated with water vapour then vapour will condense at the same rate as the water vaporises, and no net evaporation takes place.

Two thermometers are placed side by side. The bulb of one is surrounded by a muslin bag which is kept wet by means of a wick which dips into a reservoir of water. If the air surrounding the wet bulb is not saturated, water will evaporate from the muslin bag. In order to change water to water vapour, heat must be supplied. This heat is partly absorbed from the thermometer bulb which will indicate a lower temperature than that of the dry bulb, although the temperature of the surrounding air is the same for both bulbs. The rate of evaporation from the wet bulb, and hence the difference between the temperatures of the wet and dry bulbs, will depend upon the relative humidity of the air or gas surrounding the thermometers. The value of the relative humidity may be found from tables or graphs relating it to the dry-bulb temperature and the 'depression' of the wet-bulb temperature. Tables of this nature are given in the Appendix, page 276.

The relationship between the vapour pressure of the air surrounding the bulb p and its saturation vapour pressure P_w at the same temperature may be obtained from the formula

$$p = p_w - AP(t - t_w) \tag{3.1}$$

where P = Atmospheric pressure
$\quad\quad t$ = Dry-bulb temperature
$\quad\quad t_w$ = Wet-bulb temperature
$\quad\quad A$ is a numerical factor.

The value of A increases with the increase in the velocity of air over the wet bulb. It has been discovered that, provided the velocity of the air exceeds about 3 m/s the factor A assumes a constant value for a particular instrument, and this value may be found by taking simultaneous readings with the wet- and dry-bulb hygrometer and a Regnault's hygrometer.

Unless arrangements are made to ensure a sufficiently rapid flow over the wet bulb, the instrument will be very unreliable. This rapid flow may be conveniently obtained in portable instruments by mounting the thermometers on a frame which is pivoted about a handle so that the instrument may be whirled in the hand. After the muslin covering the wet bulb has been moistened, the hygrometer should be whirled rapidly in the air for about half a minute, stopped, and quickly read, the wet bulb first. This should be repeated three or four times, and the mean of the readings taken. The number of revolutions per second made by the instrument should be sufficient to ensure that the speed of the wet bulb relative to the air is at least 5 m/s.

Alternatively, when a wet and dry bulb are located where the air circulation is poor, a fan driven by an electric or clockwork motor is used to draw air past the thermometers. Where forced ventilation is resorted to, the instrument is often called a 'psychrometer', and the value of A in equation 3.1 becomes 0.000 666 per °C.

3.2.1 Industrial psychrometers

Many forms of the wet- and dry-bulb psychrometer have been developed for industrial use. In all forms two identical thermometer bulbs are mounted close together, one being dry and the other covered by a muslin bag with a wick, or by a ceramic sleeve. The bag or sleeve is maintained at the correct state of wetness by water contained in a conveniently placed reservoir and maintained at a constant level as shown in *Figure 3.2*.

When the hygrometer is mounted in an air duct, the natural speed of the gas is often sufficient, but where this is not so, a fan is used to maintain an air velocity of about 5 m/s past the bulbs. The bulbs are arranged so that the gas passes over the dry bulb first and then over the wet one. In this way the true dry-bulb temperature may be measured. The instruments used may be mercury-in-glass, gas or liquid expansion, vapour pressure, bimetallic-spiral, or electrical resistance thermometers, or thermocouples. When the thermometers are mounted in ducts having walls at a different temperature from the temperature of the air, transfer of heat by radiation from the thermometers to the walls, or from the walls to the thermometers, should be reduced by the use of radiation shields around the bulbs. Whatever form the bulbs take, the thermometers must be capable of measuring the wet- and dry-bulb temperatures accurately, as small errors in the measurement of the wet-bulb depression represent large errors in the measurement of the relative humidity. For example: for a dry-bulb temperature of 18.0°C and a wet-bulb temperature of 16.0°C the relative humidity is 82%, but for the same dry-bulb temperature and a wet-bulb temperature of 15.5°C the relative humidity is only 77%, a difference of 5%. Thus, if the dry-bulb temperature reading is ½°C high, and the wet-bulb temperature is ½°C low, an error of about 5% is introduced into the relative humidity reading. When the dry-bulb temperature is 10°C this error is increased to 12% r.h.

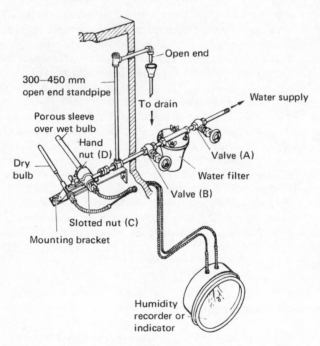

Figure 3.2   Wet- and dry-bulb installation (Courtesy Foxboro-Yoxall Ltd.)

In many hygrometers the wet- and dry-bulb temperatures are recorded simultaneously on a chart, and the relative humidity obtained from hygrometer tables. Where electrical resistance thermometers are used, it is possible to design an instrument which indicates or records the relative humidity directly.

In air conditioning plants it is usual to control the air temperature from the dry-bulb reading and the state of humidity from the wet-bulb depression.

3.2.2 Electrical direct reading humidity meters

Many attempts have been made to establish an exact relationship between the relative humidity and the temperatures of the wet- and dry-bulb thermometers. Many tables, curves and formulae based on experimental data have been published. These express the relationship with a reasonable degree of accuracy.

The direct reading air temperature and humidity instrument is based upon the fact that if the difference between the wet- and dry-bulb temperatures for various values of the relative humidity are plotted against the dry-bulb temperature, a series of straight lines is obtained having a common origin, and the slope of each line is characteristic of the relative humidity which it represents. When resistance thermometers are used, this fact may be represented by the equation

$$R_d = M_x D_x - K \tag{3.2}$$

where R_d = Dry-bulb equivalent resistance

M_x = Slope for a given value, x percentage of relative humidity

D_x = Change in resistance equivalent to the difference in temperature between the wet and dry bulbs for the given value, x percentage of relative humidity

K is a constant.

The value of M_x may be regarded as the product of two separate factors, (a) a function of the dry-bulb temperature, and (b) a function of the difference between the wet- and dry-bulb temperatures. The relative humidity portion of the instrument is designed to measure this product.

The instrument consists of two resistance temperature bulbs, one wet and one dry, and two recorders, one for air temperature and one for relative humidity. The temperature of the dry bulb is first measured in the usual way by balancing the Wheatstone bridge network, a galvanometer being used to detect out-of-balance. The temperature recorder is of the standard pattern except for the fact that it has an additional resistance network which applies to the second recorder an e.m.f. which is the required function (a) of the dry-bulb temperature. When the 'range switch' is now turned to relative humidity the relative humidity network produces an output which is the function (b) of the wet-bulb depression. When the relative humidity scale is now adjusted for galvanometer balance, the position of the scale is a measure of the relative humidity.

The instrument is suitable for multi-way recording, a dry-bulb temperature range of −7 to +43°C, a relative humidity range of from 50 to 100% relative humidity, and is claimed to have an accuracy of within 1% at temperatures above 0°C.

Figure 3.3 shows the arrangement used in the transmitter, and the path of the gas past the thermometer bulbs. Where there is insufficient natural flow through the transmitter, a motor-driven suction fan, connected to E by a length of rubber tubing, is used to produce the necessary flow.

The Speedomax direct reading relative humidity recorder also employs electrical circuits to convert temperature readings into an indication of relative humidity.

The instrument is based upon the fact that if the wet-bulb temperature is plotted against the dry-bulb temperature for a constant relative humidity, a graph is obtained with a slope characteristic of the relative humidity. The temperatures of the wet and dry electrical resistance bulbs are measured by connecting them in two Wheatstone bridge circuits as shown in *Figure 3.4*. The e.m.f. between d and e in the wet-bulb resistance network is automatically balanced against a portion of the e.m.f. between a and b in the dry-bulb resistance network. The main slidewire is connected between a and b, and the contact C is adjusted by detecting the direction of the out-of-balance voltage and using it to control the movement of C so that the point of balance is attained. (See Volume 1, page 345.)

In the actual instrument, both Wheatstone bridge circuits are supplied by the same source of potential so that the balance point obtained is independent of mains fluctuations. Also, the point E is not fixed, but is a moveable contact on a second slidewire which is mounted on the disc supporting the main slidewire, so that both contacts are adjusted simultaneously. This adjustment

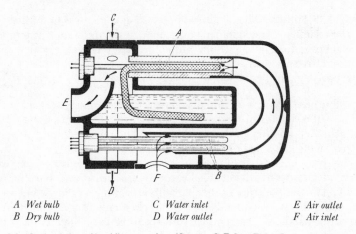

A	Wet bulb	C	Water inlet	E	Air outlet
B	Dry bulb	D	Water outlet	F	Air inlet

Figure 3.3   Sectional view of humidity transmitter (Courtesy G.E.C.—Elliott Process Instruments Ltd.)

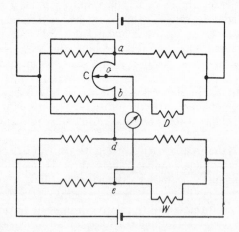

Figure 3.4   Speedomax G. direct reading humidity recorder (Courtesy Leeds and Northrup Ltd.)

compensates for the fact that the relative humidity lines on the wet- and dry-bulb temperature graph do not have a common origin.

The instrument has a range of 10–100% r.h. at a minimum wet-bulb temperature of 0°C and a maximum dry-bulb temperature of 65°C.

In the Gregory balanced-temperature hygrometer, the problem is approached in a completely different way. In this type of instrument, shown diagrammatically in *Figure 3.5*, the wet- and the dry-bulb temperatures are maintained equal. In place of wet and dry bulbs, a differential thermocouple is employed, one junction W forming the wet bulb and the other junction D the dry bulb. Provided the two junctions are at the same temperature, there will be no current through the galvanometer G or other detector.

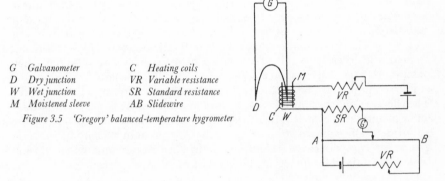

G	Galvanometer	C	Heating coils
D	Dry junction	VR	Variable resistance
W	Wet junction	SR	Standard resistance
M	Moistened sleeve	AB	Slidewire

Figure 3.5 'Gregory' balanced-temperature hygrometer

To make good the loss of heat from the wet bulb owing to evaporation of water from the moistening sleeve, an electric current is passed through a heating coil C consisting of fine wire wound around the wet bulb. The size of the current is adjusted by means of the rheostat VR, so that the galvanometer G remains in the zero position. The amount of heat required to maintain the wet bulb at the same temperature as the dry bulb will be directly proportional to the mass of moisture evaporated, and the mass evaporated will depend upon the relative humidity of the surrounding atmosphere. The amount of heat produced in the heater will depend upon the square of the current flowing through it. The size of the current flowing may be measured directly by an ammeter included in the heater circuit, and if the ammeter is of a type which depends upon the heating effect of a current, it may have a scale which bears a linear relationship to the mass of water evaporated from the wet bulb. For more accurate measurement of the current, a standard resistance is put in series with the heating coil and the fall of potential across this standard resistance measured by means of a potentiometer which may be calibrated in terms of the relative humidity of the atmosphere surrounding the bulb.

By the use of sensitive detectors in the thermocouple and potentiometer circuits, this method may be made very accurate and may provide a useful laboratory standard of reference for checking other types of hygrometers. The instrument has a range of 0–100% r.h.

In the atmosphere of the average factory, however, this instrument has been found to be unsatisfactory owing to the fact that it is extremely sensitive to dust. A very small deposit of dust is sufficient to upset its calibration completely.

3.3 HAIR HYGROMETERS

Certain materials such as hair, wood fibre, paper, silk and goldbeaters' skin change in length when the humidity of the surrounding air changes. Human hair becomes longer as the humidity of the surrounding air increases, and shortens as the air becomes drier. This property of hair may be utilised to operate a pointer, as in the 'hair hygrometer'.

A typical movement of a pocket type instrument is illustrated in *Figure 3.6*. The operating mechanism consists of approximately twelve strands of natural hair, each about 180 mm long, secured at one end by passing through a hole in a pin A and driving in a wooden peg. The position of the secured end of the hair may be varied by operating the adjustment screw B. Screwing B in or out rotates the pin carrying the hair and so moves the point at which the hair is secured and, therefore, the zero reading of the instrument. The hair then passes across the case, around a pulley C, which is free to rotate, back along the diameter of the case and is secured to a lever attached to the pointer spindle. The effective length of the lever is adjustable so that the rotation of the pointer for a given change of length of the hair can be varied. Operation of the adjustment alters the magnification so that the instrument may be made to give a correct reading at the scale maximum. The hair is maintained in tension by means of the hair-spring D and great care is taken to ensure that load is carried equally by each hair.

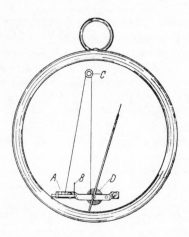

Figure 3.6   Pocket hair hygrometer (Courtesy Negretti and Zambra Ltd.)

The hair hygrometer is not a precision instrument but is largely used for industrial purposes where readings of high precision are not required. When used under normal variations of humidity (40–95%) and temperature (5–27°C) a well made instrument will give readings which are accurate to within 3 or 4%. They should be checked periodically (say every three months) and adjusted if necessary. An instrument may be checked by wetting the hairs with a small camel-hair brush, when the instrument should read 95%. It is a peculiar characteristic of hairs that when 'wetted' with water, as distinct from the effect of a 100% humid atmosphere, the extension ceases at a value equivalent to a relative humidity of 95%.

Another and better method of checking an instrument is to compare the readings with those obtained with a precision wet- and dry-bulb hygrometer of the ventilated or whirling type.

The instrument should not be subjected to rapid changes of humidity or temperature as this will cause it to give incorrect readings, and it will not regain its normal condition for several hours.

Hair decreases in length with increase in temperature, the reduction in length being about 0.4% of the original for each degree Celsius rise in temperature. The instrument will, therefore, read high at low temperatures and low at high temperatures. Instruments are adjusted to read accurately at a temperature of 15–18°C but the error in reading will not be more than 3 or 4% provided the air temperature is within the range 5–27°C. If used at temperatures outside this range the instrument should be checked and reset at the working temperature. If not reset, the instrument will read approximately 10% low at 38°C and 10% high at −6°C.

It is not advisable to use hair hygrometers in extremes of either humidity or temperature, as permanent damage to the hairs may result. Temperatures about 65°C cause the hairs to become brittle, and exposure to very low humidities (5% or below) or low temperatures (below −9°C) causes a semi-permanent contraction to take place.

3.3.1 Recording hair hygrometers

The actuating element in the wall mounting or recording type of hygrometer consists of specially treated human hairs contained in a ventilated brass tube, mounted vertically. The upper ends of the hairs are secured to an adjustable screw while the lower ends operate the pen arm spindle by means of a connecting arm and crank. Adjustment of the zero end of the scale span is made in a similar manner to that used in the pocket type instrument.

A similar actuating element may be used to operate a controller.

3.4   ELECTRICAL METHODS

A wide range of instruments for measuring moisture, based on electrical measurements, are available.

3.4.1   For solids

Moisture in solids may be measured by measuring the change in electrical resistance which will be decreased as the moisture content increases. These methods are not capable of high accuracy as the electrical resistance will change with the packing density as well as with change of moisture content.

For measurement of the moisture content of wood or bales of fibres or textiles
an approximate value of the moisture content may be obtained by measuring
the resistance between two electrodes in the form of spikes or discs at a fixed
distance apart pressed into or on to the surface, but it will be necessary to have
the instrument calibrated for the particular substance and the result of the
surface measurement may not be representative of the rest. Where an accurate
measurement is required it may be obtained by nuclear techniques, where the
density and the moisture content may be measured individually and a more
reliable value obtained. This method will be described in Section 4.2.
Microwave absorption may also be used or absorption of infra-red radiation of
a selected wavelength.

However, an indication of the moisture in a solid can be obtained if it is in
equilibrium with a gas, the moisture content of which is known.

3.4.2   For gases or liquids

Certain substances have the property of absorbing or giving off moisture very
rapidly in such a way that the quantity of moisture they contain depends upon
the partial pressure of the water vapour in the atmosphere surrounding the
substance. Such substances are known as hygroscopic substances. When the
moisture content of a hygroscopic substance changes, its electrical properties,
such as electrical resistance or specific inductive capacity, also change.
Measurement of the electrical properties of the substance may, therefore, be
used to measure the moisture content of the substance, and if the moisture
content of the substance is in equilibrium with the moisture content of the gas,
or of a material which is being dried, then the moisture content of the gas or
material may also be measured.

Moisture probes may reach moisture content equilibrium with the gas by
being placed in the gas, or the probe may be designed so that the gas flows
through the detector. The moisture content of the probe may be measured by
measuring its electrical resistance, its electrical capacitance or by evaporating
or electrolysing the moisture from the probe and measuring the current
required to restore equilibrium.

Another method involves measuring the change in frequency of an
oscillating crystal when moisture is deposited upon it. Certain probes designed
for measuring moisture in gas can be designed to measure the moisture in
liquids, an application which is very important where it is essential that the
level of moisture in a hydrocarbon feed stock or similar product is controlled to
close limits. Instruments will be described under the electrical measurement
involved.

3.4.2.1   METHODS EMPLOYING CAPACITANCE MEASUREMENT

The Shaw meter functions by measuring the change in capacitance of the
sensor owing to changes in moisture content of a hygroscopic dielectric layer.
The resultant change in capacitance is measured by means of an oscillator, a
capacitance sensing sub circuit, and a detector. The dielectric layer is only
10 μm thick, giving a quick response to moisture change in the surrounding

gas. The pore size is very small so that the water vapour condenses rapidly. The sensor is covered by a fine layer of deposited gold which acts as a filter and forms one electrode of the capacitor, which has a capacitance of about 0.5 μF. The industrial sensor is protected by a sintered bronze cover. If required, the sensor may be up to 300 m from the rest of the electronics, to which it is connected by a coaxial cable. Three sensors are available, one having a dew-point range of −80 to −20°C, the second having a dew-point range of −30 to +20°C. The normal element covers a range of 0–99% r.h. The sensor has no significant temperature coefficient and an accuracy of ±1 p.p.m. or 3°C dew point over 90% of the range, whichever is the greater. A sensor for measuring the concentration of moisture in a wide range of hydrocarbons is also available.

Another capacitance-type sensor is made by M.C.M. It consists of an aluminium rod anodised to produce a porous aluminium oxide surface a few micrometres thick. Very fine insulated wire is wound helically round the rod and secured firmly in position at each end. The aluminium rod and the fine wire act as the electrodes of the capacitor, and the aluminium oxide as the dielectric. As the vapour pressure of water changes around the sensor, whether it be in a gas or liquid, the number of water molecules held in the pores of the oxide surfaces changes, producing a corresponding change in the capacitance of the sensor with a very high speed of response, as the thickness of the responsive layer is only a few micrometres.

The insulated wire electrode virtually cuts out the conductivity change of the layer, so rendering the capacitance a relatively linear relationship to the moisture content, as shown in the calibration curves for three ranges shown in *Figure 3.7.*

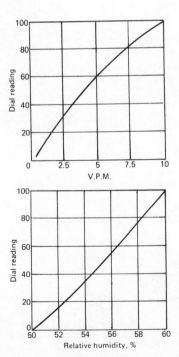

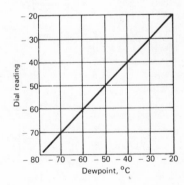

Figure 3.7 Calibration curves of M.C.M. Moisture Meter (Courtesy Moisture Control and Measurement Ltd.) Zero and span controls are incorporated in the circuit so that it is possible to set instruments to read zero for the lowest humidity to be measured, and full scale deflection for the highest humidity to be measured.

The detection circuit consists of a solid state capacitance bridge operating in the MHz region. A single sensor will cover the full 0–100% r.h. range or the −80 to +100°C dew-point range. With high gain ten complete scale lengths are available or a reduced gain may be used to cover the full humidity range.

The sensor can be used at pressures near absolute zero to 140 bar, and the reading is unaffected by the rate of flow of surrounding gas. The accuracy is ±3% of the full scale, and the resolution 0.1% r.h., or 0.2°C dew point. The sensor will operate at temperatures from 0 to 120°C but the sample temperature must be controlled when absolute humidity readings are required.

3.4.2.2 METHODS EMPLOYING MEASUREMENT OF RESISTANCE OR CONDUCTIVITY

In the 'Gregory' electrolytic type of hygrometer the moisture content of the

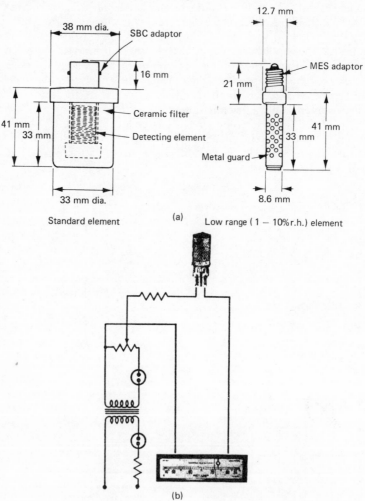

Figure 3.8   The 'Gregory' electrolytic hygrometer (Courtesy Negretti and Zambra Ltd.)

hygroscopic substance is ascertained by measuring its electrical conductivity. The element shown in *Figure 3.8(a)* consists of a plastics frame carrying platinum-clad electrodes. Around these electrodes is wound a skein of very fine glass fibres impregnated with a hygroscopic salt such as lithium or calcium chloride. The electrical conductivity of the element is measured by applying to it a constant a.c. voltage, obtained from a transformer and a voltage stabilising unit, as shown in *Figure 3.8(b)*, and measuring the current which flows by means of an a.c. measuring instrument calibrated to indicate percentage of relative humidity at 20°C. A temperature correction chart is provided to enable true readings to be obtained at other temperatures. A portable indicator working from a 12 V battery supply is also available, and in both types of instrument the voltage applied to the instrument is adjusted to a standardising point before a reading is taken.

The instrument is made in a variety of ranges between 10% and 100% r.h., and may be employed to operate a humidity controller. The instrument responds rapidly to changes in humidity, and it is claimed that a final reading can be obtained in about 30 s. The effective life of the sensitive element varies with the conditions under which it is used from 4 to 12 months, and impending failure is usually indicated by discolouration of the electrodes or fibres.

The Amnico-Dunmore hygroscopic element, employed in conjunction with the Honeywell self-balancing a.c. bridge circuit, consists of a double winding of precious metal wire wound on a polystyrene cylinder. The windings end in plug-in contact pins at the base. The surface of the cylinder and windings is coated with a film of partially hydrolysed polyvinyl acetate containing a small quantity of lithium chloride. A change in the amount of moisture held in the coating causes a change in the electrical resistance between the windings, and this resistance is measured by an a.c. bridge circuit. The instrument is calibrated to read relative humidity directly on a linear scale. Where necessary, a temperature-sensitive resistor may be mounted inside the humidity winding and will give temperature compensation between 10 and 49°C, and may be used to record temperature, in addition to humidity, on a multipoint recorder.

Elements of this type are made in a variety of ranges between 1.2 and 99% r.h., suited to a variety of uses. The full range sensing unit covers a range of 9–95% r.h. and the accuracy claimed for this type of instrument is ±1% r.h.

Another sensor for moisture measurement manufactured by the Phys-Chemical Research Corp. is produced by depositing electrically conducting grids on the surfaces of a chemically treated wafer of styrene copolymer. The absence of a surface coating or emulsion and the high temperature characteristics of the special styrene result in a rugged sensor which is unaffected by water immersion. Moisture is absorbed into the surfaces of the sensor, changing the resistance between the conducting grids. The resistance of the sensor is measured by an a.c. bridge and the out-of-balance rectified and indicated as relative humidity indication. The sensor can be incorporated in a humidity recorder or controller. One sensor can be arranged to cover a relative humidity range of 0–100%. As the sensor is temperature dependent and reads correctly at 25°C, a correction of about 0.4 r.h. per °C must be applied manually, or automatically, if accurate readings are required at other temperatures. The sensor will operate at temperatures between −15 and +90°C and has a response time of 30 s for a 63% change of relative humidity.

3.4.2.3 ALUMINIUM OXIDE SENSORS

A sensor which was developed for measuring moisture under difficult conditions in the space programme, and is now successfully solving problems in industry, is based on the use of porous aluminium oxide. The sensor consists of an aluminium strip which is anodised by a special process to provide a porous oxide layer. A very thin coating of gold is evaporated over this structure. The aluminium base and the gold layer form the two electrodes of what is essentially an aluminium oxide capacitor.

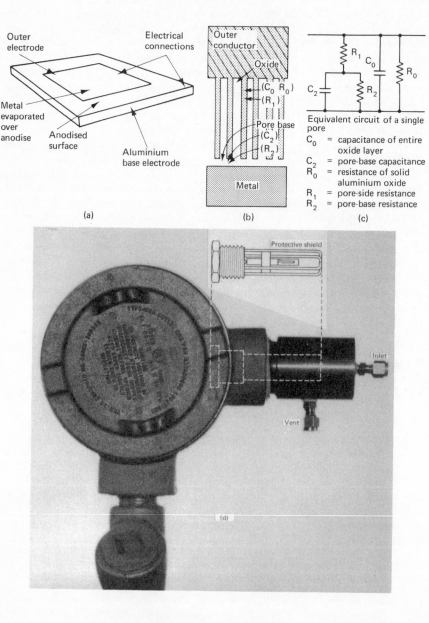

Outer electrode
Electrical connections
Metal evaporated over anodise
Anodised surface
Aluminium base electrode

Outer conductor
Oxide
$(C_0 R_0)$
(R_1)
Pore base
(C_2)
(R_2)
Metal

Equivalent circuit of a single pore
C_0 = capacitance of entire oxide layer
C_2 = pore-base capacitance
R_0 = resistance of solid aluminium oxide
R_1 = pore-side resistance
R_2 = pore-base resistance

(a)   (b)   (c)

Protective shield
Inlet
Vent

(d)

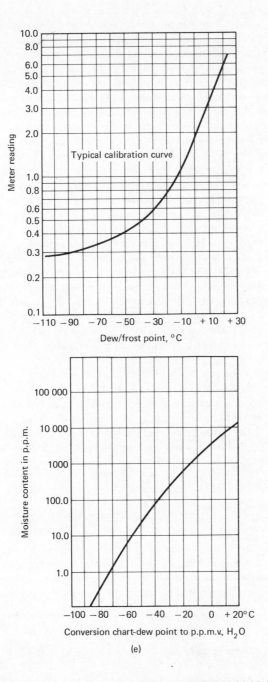

Figure 3.9   Aluminium oxide sensor (Courtesy Endress and Hauser (UK) Ltd.) (a) Mechanical construction (b) Pore structure (c) Electrical equivalent (d) Weather-proof sample cell (e) Calibration curves

Water vapour is rapidly transported through the gold layer and adsorbed on the pore walls in a manner functionally related to the vapour pressure of water in the atmosphere surrounding the sensor. The number of water molecules adsorbed on the oxide structure determines the conductivity of the pore wall. Each value of pore wall resistance provides a distinct value of electrical impedance which in turn is a direct measure of the water vapour pressure.

The construction of the sensor and its electrical equivalent and calibration are shown in *Figure 3.9*. The actual sensor is usually in the form of a small rectangular plate suitably protected, but a version in the form of an aluminium rod on to which the oxide and metal films are deposited is also available.

The impedance of the sensor is a measure of the water vapour pressure of moisture in the surrounding gas, or in liquid hydrocarbons into which the sensor may be inserted. Water molecules are transported from the hydrocarbon through the gold layer and adsorbed on the pore walls of the sensors. The number of water molecules so adsorbed determines the pore wall conductivity, which then provides a value of electrical impedance that can be functionally related to the water vapour pressure. Since the pore wall openings are small in relation to the size of hydrocarbon molecules, admission into the pore cavity is limited to small molecules such as water. The surface of the aluminium oxide sensor can then be viewed as a semi-permeable structure allowing the measurement of the water pressure in liquid hydrocarbons in the same manner as is accomplished in a gaseous medium. For the same composition of water in hydrocarbon fluid, the same value of electrical output of the sensor will be registered whether directly immersed in the liquid or placed in the gas space above it.

To determine the mass of water within a hydrocarbon fluid, Henry's law must be applied. Henry's law states that the mass of gas dissolved by a given volume of solvent at constant temperature is proportional to the pressure of gas with which it is in equilibrium, i.e. the ratio of the mass of water to the mass of parent liquid is equal to the partial pressure of the water vapour times a constant. This constant must be computed for each parent fluid. Henry's law for a given liquid could be expressed as

$$C = KP \ ....$$

where C = Concentration of water in the fluid expressed as mass per cent (or p.p.m. mass)

P = Vapour pressure of water measured by the probe

K = Henry's constant for the particular fluid and equals C_s/P_s where C_s is the concentration of water in the fluid at saturation, and P_s the saturation vapour pressure of water at the temperature of the measurement. Thus

$$C = (C_s/P_s) \, P \text{ or } C = C_s \, (P/P_s) \ ....$$

Thus the percentage saturation of water in solvent = $(C/C_s) \times 100 = (P/P_s) \times 100$.

The standard probe will measure dew points between -110 and $+20°C$, representing a moisture content in air of from $10^{-3} \mu g \ dm^{-3}$ to $2 \times 10^4 \ \mu g \ dm^{-3}$. For measurement of moisture in liquids at 20°C it is possible to measure percentage saturation levels as low as $5 \times 10^{-6}\%$. The moisture in a straight chain hydrocarbon can be determined to as little as 5×10^{-6} p.p.m. by mass.

Special high humidity probes are available for dew points between 20 and 60°C.

The dew point may be measured in gases at pressures between a few micrometres mercury absolute and 3.30 bar. The speed of the response of the probe is high. It responds to a 63% change of relative humidity in a few seconds and it does not have a significant temperature coefficient over a very large temperature range (-110 to $+70$°C).

The impedance of the probe is measured by a highly stable all solid state electronic circuit. An explosion proof version for use in the presence of hydrocarbons is available.

3.4.2.4 FOXBORO DEWCEL SYSTEM

Moisture determination by the use of the Dewcel is based upon the fact that for every partial pressure of water vapour in an atmosphere in contact with a saturated salt solution, there is an equilibrium temperature at which the solution neither absorbs nor gives up moisture to the surrounding atmosphere. Below this equilibrium temperature, the salt solution absorbs moisture. Above this temperature, the saturated salt solution dries out until only dry crystals are left.

The Dewcel is a thin-walled metal socket (to fit a Foxboro thermometer bulb) covered with a woven glass tape impregnated with lithium chloride. A 25 V a.c. power supply is connected to a heating unit consisting of two gold plated silver wires wound parallel to each other over the tape. Current can flow from one wire to the other only through the solution on the tape. If the temperature of the Dewcel is below the equilibrium temperature, the salt absorbs moisture from the atmosphere, the conductivity of the solution on the tape between the wires increases, and the flow of current increases, raising the Dewcel temperature and driving off moisture, thus reducing the electrical conductivity and consequently the heating current until an equilibrium is attained. The temperature at which this equilibrium is attained is the Dewcel equilibrium temperature, measured by the thermometer bulb which may be of the liquid expansion or resistance thermometer type. This temperature is used as a measure of the dew-point temperature, absolute humidity or vapour pressure by the use of the appropriate chart.

The Dewcel should be protected from air velocities above 15 m/min and should not be exposed to ambient temperatures above 105°C. The dew point of air at higher temperatures may be measured by cooling a sample of air to a temperature within operating range before passing it over the Dewcel.

When used to measure relative humidity two thermometer bulbs are used; one bulb measures the ambient temperature and the second bulb measures the dew-point temperature, and both temperatures are recorded on the same chart. A table or a chart is then used to convert these readings to relative humidity.

3.4.2.5 ELECTROLYTIC METHOD OF MEASURING MOISTURE CONTENT

In the trace moisture analyser illustrated in *Figure 3.10* the principle of the

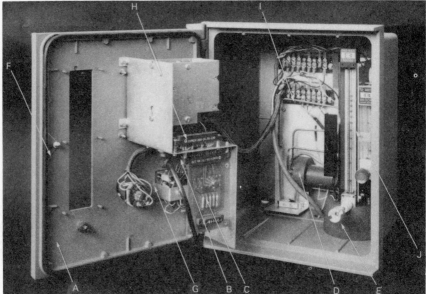

A *Aluminium case designed for industrial environment, door secured by captive screw F*
B *Plug in circuit boards*
C *Solid state electronics*
D *Potted electrolytic cell made of corrosion resisting material, plug-in type*
E *Temperature controlled flow control system controlled to ±0.5°C*
G *High alarm module*
H *Current output board*
I *By-pass flow system for fast response, diverting a portion of the sample so that the sampling rate is greater than 100cm³/min*
J *Integral flow meters for adjusting sample and by-pass flow rates*
L *Meter sensitivity and stand-by selection switch*

Figure 3.10   Electrolytic moisture meter (Courtesy Beckman Instruments RIIC Ltd.)

method is that sample is passed at a constant rate through the sample tube in the detector cell. Water vapour in the sample is absorbed by a thin layer of phosphorus pentoxide (P_2O_5) coating the inside of the tube and covering and connecting two rhodium electrodes wound in parallel helices on the inner wall of the tube.

The moist phosphorus pentoxide is an electrical conductor and a d.c. current flows between the electrodes electrolysing the moisture into hydrogen and oxygen, thus drying the phosphorus pentoxide and reducing its conductivity. Thus, equilibrium will be established when the rate of removal of moisture balances the rate of absorption. By Faraday's law, the current flowing between the electrodes must be a measure of the quantity of moisture electrolysed. As the flow rate of the sample is constant, the current must be a measure of the concentration of moisture in the incoming gas. Rhodium was chosen as the electrode material after considerable research showed that it had a longer life and produced less recombination of the oxygen and hydrogen than with a similar platinum electrode system, and permitted effective moisture measurement over a wide variety of ranges and applications. The system is accurate to ±5% of full scale on any range and measures 90% of a moisture step change in 1 min or less.

3.4.2.6 MEASUREMENT OF HUMIDITY BY QUARTZ CRYSTAL OSCILLATORS

A meter which has a wide range of application in the petroleum, chemical and other fields compares the changes in frequency of two hygroscopically coated quartz crystal oscillators which vibrate at 9×10^6 Hz. Water vapour is alternately sorbed and desorbed rapidly and reversibly on each crystal, resulting in a mass difference with a corresponding change in frequency. These frequency changes are compared electronically, and the moisture content of the gas indicated as p.p.m. water vapour by volume. The meter employs two crystals with a system of flow switching so that each crystal is exposed alternately to the moist sample gas, and to a dry reference gas for 30 s. While one crystal is adsorbing moisture, the other is drying, and vice versa.

Since adsorption of moisture by a coated crystal lowers its frequency the frequency of one crystal will be lowered while the frequency of the other will be raised. The resulting audio frequency difference signal is amplified, clipped and passed through an RC circuit to the meter whose indication swings slowly between zero and some maximum value.

This maximum value is proportional to the maximum frequency difference, and is a measure of the moisture content of the gas sample. The time between successive maximum readings is 30 s and the record of the output on a potentiometric recorder would have a saw tooth appearance. If a continuous record of moisture is required the recorder balancing motor circuit can be interrupted in synchronisation with the flow switching circuit so that a continuous record is obtained without affecting the calibration or speed of response.

The principle of the measurement is illustrated in *Figure 3.11(a)* and the flow diagram shown in *Figure 3.11(b)*. The solenoid valves are switched by a timer in the control unit every 30 s. The heatless dryer has two sections. While one section is drying the reference gas the other is being regenerated. The same

78

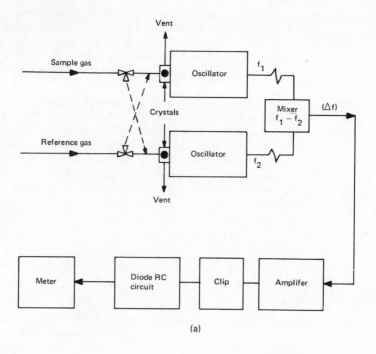

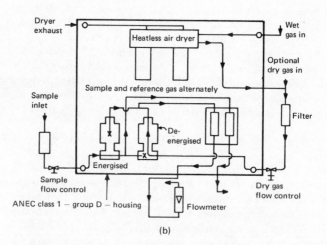

Figure 3.11   Quartz oscillator moisture meter (Courtesy Du Pont Instruments (UK) Ltd.)
(a) Principle (b) Flow diagram (c) Sample module (d) Control module

(c)

(d)

timer operates the solenoid valves and the dryer regeneration cycle. *Figure 3.11(c)* shows the sample module, which is explosion proof for use in ANEC Class 1 Group D Division 1 locations. It contains a stainless steel sample cell, heatless dryer to produce ultra-dry reference gas, and associated electronic circuits. Parts in contact with the sample gas are stainless steel and other suitable materials. A rotameter and flow control valve are mounted externally.

The control module shown in *Figure 3.11(d)* is non-explosion-proof but it can be air purged for Division 2 locations. The meter in the control module reads directly in p.p.m. water vapour by volume, and an output of 0–10 mV is available for external recording. In most applications, the sample module and control module can be separated by as much as 300 m and connected by shielded cable.

4

MEASUREMENTS EMPLOYING NUCLEAR TECHNIQUES

4.1   RADIOACTIVITY

The nature of the structure of the atom has been discussed in Section 4.5.1 of Volume 1. Up to the time of the discovery of radioactivity, the atoms of an element were regarded as the smallest indivisible parts of the element and the mass of an atom as a permanent feature peculiar to the atom. At the end of the last century workers such as Rutherford discovered that the atoms of substances such as radium and uranium known as radioactive substances were continuously disintegrating and emitting penetrating radiations. These were given the names alpha, beta and gamma radiations. Alpha particles were discovered to be helium ions having a positive charge moving with a velocity about one tenth of the velocity of light and with little penetrating power, and could be stopped by thin aluminium foil.

Beta particles are negative electrons moving with speeds approaching the velocity of light and have considerably greater penetrating power than alpha particles but a much smaller mass. Gamma radiation consists of electromagnetic waves of a very short wavelength similar to X rays. Their energy and hence their penetrating power is determined by their frequency, and they have considerable penetrating power.

As the radiation from radioactive substances is due to disintegration of the substance, the quantity of substance and hence rate of production of radiation will decay with time. The rate of decay of a substance is expressed in terms of its half-life. The half-life of a radioactive substance is the time taken for its rate of radiation to decay to half its former value and this time may be anything from a millionth of a second to thousands of years.

4.1.1   Artificial radioactivity

It has been discovered that by subjecting non-radioactive elements to radiation, particularly from charged-particle accelerators or nuclear reactors producing particles of high energy, a very large number of radioactive substances can be produced. In fact by the controlled exposure of samples it is possible to produce at least one radioactive isotope for every element in the periodic table. Isotopes are species of an element having the same atomic number but different mass numbers. By subjecting an element to particle bombardment atoms of the substance can be produced which have too many or too few neutrons for its normal quota of protons and planetary electrons. As

81

its chemical properties are determined by its planetary electrons it will behave in the same manner as the normal element but owing to the abnormal state of its nucleus it will tend to revert to normal, at the same time producing radioactivity.

The atomic weight or mass number of an element is determined by the combined mass of the protons and neutrons in the nucleus, while its position in the periodic table, or atomic number, is determined by the electron charge on the protons in the nucleus. In order to define the isotope the chemical symbol is often written in the form $_ZX^A$ where Z is the atomic number and A is the mass number. For example the radioactive form of iodine of atomic number 53 and mass number 131 is written as $_{53}I^{131}$, although it would be referred to as Iodine 131, as the name iodine implies the atomic number.

The nature of the radiations and half-life of an isotope may be obtained from tables.

4.2   APPLICATION OF RADIO-ISOTOPES

A wide range of instrumentation has been developed using radio-isotopes. The isotope may form the source of alpha, beta or gamma radiation or the radiation may fall on a target, thus producing a source of X rays. The measurements are based on the measurement of the radiation which is scattered or absorbed in the material under test or upon the measurement of the characteristic X rays of a given wavelength which are generated by fluorescence in the substance.

The type of radiation used will be dependent upon the parameter to be measured, and the measuring device used to measure the radiation will be dependent upon the type, wavelength and intensity of radiation to be measured. By selection of a suitable source, technique and measuring device a wide range of parameters may be detected and measured on-line. Among these parameters are thickness of paper or metal sheet, mass per unit area, basis weight, coating thickness, density, moisture content, elemental composition, conveyor belt load, clay content of paper, sulphur or metal content of hydrocarbons, or ash content of coal or coke, and others.

The detector will in general be some form of gas-filled detector or scintillation counter with the appropriate electronics to operate a meter or recorder calibrated in suitable units of measurement.

4.2.1   The gas-filled detector

In its simplest form this type of detection system, shown in *Figure 4.1*, consists of a wire anode surrounded by a cylindrical metal cathode but insulated from it. The system may be housed in a glass tube, although in some forms the metal housing forms the cathode. The tube contains a gas such as argon to which other gases or vapours are added at a reduced pressure, usually of the order of 5–70 cm Hg. A potential is applied between the anode and cathode, and the magnitude of this potential determines the behaviour of the detector so that the detector may be an ionisation chamber, a proportional counter or a Geiger-Muller counter.

If the voltage applied to the detector is progressively increased from zero the

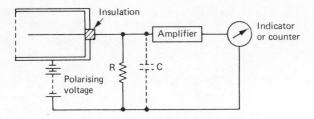

Figure 4.1   Simplified gas-filled detector circuit

ionisation current increases in the manner shown in *Figure 4.2.* At point B the current reaches a constant value and the chamber is said to be saturated, and further increase in the voltage will not affect the ionisation current until point C is reached, where there is a sharp increase in current produced by the moving electrons having sufficient energy to produce further ionisation by colliding with other gas molecules. These secondary ions in turn produce further ions by collision, which is referred to as an avalanche process.

Detectors operated with voltages between B and C are called 'ionisation chambers'. They are designed to collect the ions produced by the incident radiation with the minimum loss due to recombination and as little multiplication of ions by secondary emission as possible. Dependent upon whether the capacitance of the detector and the time constants of the associated electronic circuits are small or large the ionisation chamber may be used to count or integrate. In the counting method the pulse size is proportional to the number of ion-pairs produced by each ionising event, while when operated in the integrating mode the chamber current will merely indicate the total radiation falling over the integrating period.

The pulse counting method is suitable for detecting and analysing alpha particles but beta particles and gamma radiation seldom produce sufficient ionisation to be detectable above the background noise.

4.2.1.1   PROPORTIONAL COUNTERS

When the applied potential is increased beyond C *(Figure 4.2)* the gas amplification due to secondary ionisation becomes constant and independent of the size of the ionising event initiating the effect, while the height of the pulse on the anode increases in proportion to the electrode voltage. This is known as the proportional region and counters operating in this region are called 'proportional counters'. Although the pulses obtained when operating at the lower voltages in this region require electronic amplification, such counters are stable and give reproducible results. The proportional response of the counter means that the pulse height is a measure of the radiation energy so that the counter can be used to identify the radiation producing the count.

By increasing the applied voltage a stable gas amplification of the order of 1000 may be obtained so that the electronic amplification may be reduced and the effect of noise becomes less important.

For detecting fast neutrons methane or other hydrogenous gas or vapour is added to the argon so that the fast neutrons collide with the hydrogen nuclei in the methane gas and give up their energy to the latter. The recoil protons thus produced ionise the argon producing a pulse.

To detect slow neutrons a gas such as boron trifluoride is added which produces alpha particles through the reaction

$$n + {}_6B^{10} \rightarrow {}_2He^4 + {}_3Li^7 + Q$$

The alpha particles are then detected in the usual way.

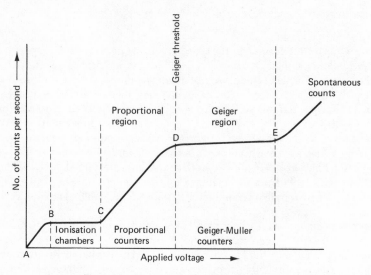

Figure 4.2   Characteristic curve of gas-filled detectors

4.2.1.2   THE GEIGER COUNTER

If the voltage applied to the tube is further increased saturation effects due to the space charge of positive ions appear. The final number of electrons collected then becomes independent of the initial ionisation. The lowest voltage at which this occurs is known as the Geiger threshold voltage, D. If now an ion pair is produced inside the counter, the electron moves towards the anode. When it reaches the strong field near the central wire, multiplication occurs and an 'electron avalanche' occurs. The limit is reached when the positive ion space charge reduces the electric field near the wire to a level below that required for multiplication.

Unless the tube is self-quenching recovery after the electron avalanche has occurred will not take place until the applied voltage is removed and the ions and electrons have recombined. This is a slow process and devices have been developed to speed up the process. A more satisfactory solution is to make the tube self-quenching and modern tubes are of this type. To achieve this either an organic vapour such as ethyl alcohol or ethyl formate, or a halogen gas such as bromine, chlorine or iodine is added to the tube filling. These quenching agents are dissociated by the positive ions causing de-excitation, and no electrons are produced. The tubes may then be used with a low external resistance ensuring rapid recovery, and the discharge terminates after one clear pulse as before.

A good counter has a region of two or three hundred volts above the Geiger threshold before spontaneous discharge occurs. Thus, by a suitable choice of filling gases and applied voltage with a suitable window to admit the radiation, tubes suitable for detecting and measuring a wide range of nuclear particles and radiation may be developed.

A wide range of commercial Geiger-Muller tubes are available and details of their construction and characteristics may be obtained from manufacturers' literature.

4.2.2   The scintillation counter

The scintillation counter consists of a transparent phosphor scintillator producing a fleeting pulse of light which falls on the photocathode of a photomultiplier. This produces a pulse of current which is amplified by a linear amplifier before being applied to the counting unit.

The essential properties of the phosphor are that the maximum fraction of the incident radiation should be absorbed in its mass and that it is transparent to light but strongly luminescent under electron bombardment. The build time of the light should be short and the decay time due to afterglow negligible. The phosphor used is dependent upon the nature of the radiation to be detected. For gamma ray detection, sodium iodine activated with 1% of thallium is often used. For use with beta emission, anthracene or stilbene are used. Liquid scintillation media are also used, the excitation occurring in the solvent and the fluorescent solute producing the light.

The light from the phosphor falls on the photocathode of the photomultiplier shown in principle in *Figure 4.3*. Many forms of photomultiplier exist but the principle is the same. The electrons emitted from the photocathode are accelerated through a curved path under the influence of the electric field and a magnetic field at right-angles to the electric field, so that they fall on the next electrode known as a dynode which is so sensitised that each electron falling on it produces several secondary electrons. These are focused and deflected by the electric and magnetic fields so that they fall on the next dynode where each

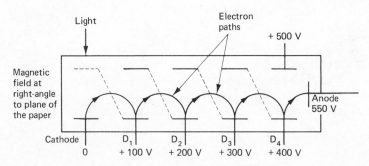

Figure 4.3   Principle of photomultiplier

incident electron again produces several secondary electrons. These electrons then fall on D_3 and so on, being finally collected on the anode.

Thus if each incident electron produces n secondary electrons and there are eleven focusing and deflecting stages the original photoelectrons will be multiplied n^{11} times. Thus the overall amplification of a typical photomultiplier can be made over one million and a pulse as large as 100 V can be obtained. This can be further amplified and applied to the discriminator and counting unit.

A wide range of both scintillators and photomultipliers are available and details of their construction and characteristics can be obtained from manufacturers' literature.

4.2.3   Measurement of mass, mass per unit area and thickness

The techniques employed in these measurements are basically the same. The radiation from a gamma ray source falls on the material and the transmitted radiation is measured by a suitable detector. In the nucleonic belt weigher shown in *Figure 4.4*, designed to measure the mass flow rate of granular material such as iron ore, limestone, coke, cement, fertilisers, etc., the absorption across the total width of the belt is measured. The signal

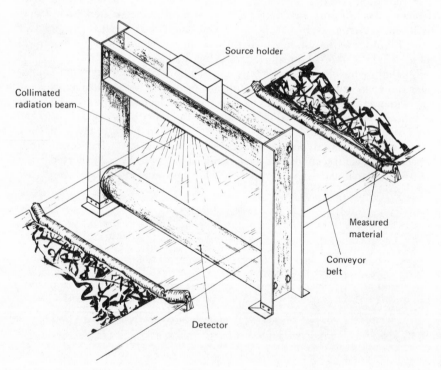

Figure 4.4   Nucleonic belt weigher (Courtesy Nuclear Enterprises Ltd.)

representing the total radiation falling on the detector is processed with a signal representing the belt speed by a solid state electronic module and displayed as a mass flow rate and a total mass. The complete equipment comprises a C-frame assembly housing the source, consisting of Caesium 137 enclosed in a welded steel capsule mounted in a shielding container with a radiation shutter, and the detector, a scintillation counter whose sensitive length matches the belt width, housed in a cylindrical flameproof enclosure suitable for Groups 11 A and B gases, with the preamplifier. A calibration plate is incorporated with the source to permit a spot check at a suitable point within the span. In addition, there is a dust and moisture proof housing for the electronics which may be mounted locally or up to 300 m from the detector.

The precision of the measurement is better than ±1%, the operating temperature of the detector and electronics is −10 to +40°C. The detector and preamplifier may be serviced by unclassified staff as the maximum dose rate is less than 0.75 mrad/h.

Similar equipment may be used to measure mass per unit area by restricting the area over which the radiation falls to a finite area, and if the thickness is constant and known the reading will be a measure of the density.

Similarly if the mass per unit area is constant and known, the reading can be made a measure of the thickness. *Figure 4.5* shows a nucleonic gauge in use measuring the thickness of steel strip.

Figure 4.5   Nucleonic gauge in use measuring thickness of steel strip (Courtesy Nuclear Enterprises Ltd.)

4.2.4 Measurement of coating thickness

In industry a wide variety of processes occur where it is necessary to measure
and sometimes automatically control the thickness of a coating applied to a
base material produced in strip form. Examples of such processes are the
deposition of tin, zinc or lacquers on steel, or adhesives, wax, clay bitumen or
plastics to paper, and many other processes.

By nucleonic methods measurement to an accuracy of ±1% of coating
thickness can be made in a wide variety of circumstances by rugged equipment
capable of a high reliability. Nucleonic coating-thickness gauges are based on
the interaction of the radiation emitted from a radio-isotope source with the
material to be measured. They consist basically of the radio-isotope source in a
radiation shield and a radiation detector contained in a measuring head, and
an electric console.

When the radiation emitted from the source is incident on the subject
material, part of this radiation is scattered, part is absorbed and the rest passes
through the material. A part of the absorbed radiation excites characteristic
fluorescent X rays in the coating and/or backing.

Depending on the measurement required, a system is used in which the
detector measures the intensity of scattered, transmitted or fluorescent
radiation. The intensity of radiation monitored by the detector is a measure of
the thickness (mass per unit area) of the coating. The electric console contains
units which process the detector signal and indicate total coating thickness
and/or deviation from the target thickness. The measuring head may be
stationary or programmed to scan across the material. Depending on the type
and thickness of coating and base materials, and machine details, one of four
gauge types is selected: differential beta transmission, beta backscatter, X ray
fluorescence and preferential absorption.

4.2.4.1 DIFFERENTIAL BETA-TRANSMISSION GAUGE *(Figure 4.6)*

The differential beta-transmission gauge is used to measure coatings applied

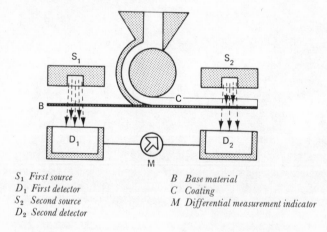

S_1 First source
D_1 First detector
S_2 Second source
D_2 Second detector

B Base material
C Coating
M Differential measurement indicator

Figure 4.6   Differential beta-transmission gauge (Courtesy Nuclear Enterprises Ltd.)

to base materials in sheet form when the coating has a total weight of not less than about one-tenth of the weight of the base material, when both sides of the base and coated material are accessible and when the composition of coating and base is fairly similar. Here the thickness (mass per unit area) of the coating is monitored by measuring first the thickness of the base material before the coating is applied, followed by the total thickness of the material with its coating, and then subtracting the former from the latter. The difference provides the coating thickness. The readings are obtained by passing the uncoated material through one measuring head and the coated material through the other, the coating being applied between the two positions. The intensity of radiation transmitted through the material is a measure of total thickness. Separate meters record the measurement determined by each head, and a third meter displays the difference between the two readings, which corresponds to the coating thickness.

Typical applications of this gauge are the measurement of wax and plastics coatings applied to paper and aluminium sheet or foil, or abrasives to paper or cloth.

4.2.4.2 BETA-BACKSCATTER GAUGE *(Figure 4.7)*

The beta-backscatter gauge is used to measure coating thickness when the process is such that the material is only accessible from one side and when the coating and backing material are of substantially different atomic number,

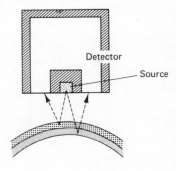

Figure 4.7 Beta-backscatter gauge (Courtesy Nuclear Enterprises Ltd.)

such as plastics or rubber on a steel calender roll, or a lacquer coat on a metal strip. The radio-isotope source and the detector are housed in the same enclosure. Where radiation is directed for example on to an uncoated calender roll it will be backscattered and measurable by the detector. Once a coating has been applied to the roll the intensity of the backscattered radiation returning to the detector will change. This change is a measure of the thickness of the coating. Typical applications of this gauge are the measurement of rubber and adhesives on calenders, paper on rollers, or lacquer, paint or plastics coatings applied to sheet steel.

4.2.4.3 MEASUREMENT OF COATING AND BACKING BY X RAY FLUORESCENCE

X ray fluorescent techniques, employing radio-isotope sources to excite the characteristic fluorescent radiation, are normally used to measure exceptionally thin coatings. The coating-fluorescence gauge monitors the increase in intensity of an X ray excited in the coating as the coating thickness is increased. The backing-fluorescence gauge excites an X ray in the backing or base material and measures the decrease in intensity due to attenuation in the coating as the coating thickness is increased. The intensity of fluorescent radiation is normally measured with an ionisation chamber, but a proportional or scintillation counter may sometimes be used.

By the use of compact geometry, high efficiency detectors and a fail-safe radiation shutter, the dose rates in the vicinity of the measuring head are kept well below the maximum permitted levels, ensuring absolute safety for operators and maintenance staff.

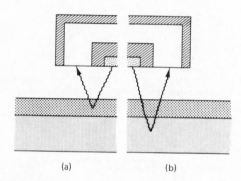

Figure 4.8   X ray fluorescence gauge (Courtesy Nuclear Enterprises Ltd.) (a) Coating-fluorescence gauge which monitors the increase in intensity of X rays excited in coating as its thickness increases (b) Backing-fluorescence gauge monitors the decrease in intensity of radiation excited in the backing material as the coating thickness increases

(a)   (b)

Figure 4.8(a) illustrates the principle of the coating-fluorescence gauge, which monitors the increase in intensity of an X ray excited in the coating as the coating thickness is increased. *Figure 4.8(b)* illustrates the principle of the backing-fluorescence gauge which monitors the decrease in intensity of an X ray excited in the backing material as the coating thickness increases.

The instrument is used to measure tin, zinc, aluminium and chromium coatings applied to sheet steel, or titanium coatings to paper or plastics sheet.

4.2.4.4 THE PREFERENTIAL ABSORPTION GAUGE *(Figure 4.9)*

This gauge is used when the coating material has a higher mean atomic number than the base material. The gauge employs low energy X rays from a sealed radio-isotope source which are absorbed to a much greater extent by materials with a high atomic number such as chlorine, than by materials such as paper or textiles which have a low atomic number. It is thus possible to monitor variations in coating thickness by measuring the degree of preferential X ray absorption by the coating, using a single measuring head. The instrument is used to measure coatings which contain clay, titanium, halogens, iron or other substance with a high atomic number which have been applied to plastics, paper or textiles.

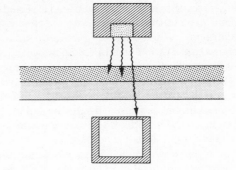

Figure 4.9 Preferential absorption gauge (Courtesy Nuclear Enterprises Ltd.)

4.2.5 Nuclear method of on-line measurement of moisture

This type of equipment can be used to measure continuously the moisture content of granular materials in hoppers, bins and similar vessels. The measuring head is mounted external to the vessel and the radiation enters by a replaceable ceramic window *(Figure 4.10)*.

The transducer comprises a radio-isotope source of fast neutrons and a slow neutron detector assembly, mounted within a shielding measuring head. The source is mounted on a rotatable disc. It may thus be positioned by an electro-pneumatic actuator either in the centre of the shield, or adjacent to the slow neutron detector and ceramic radiation 'window' at one end of the

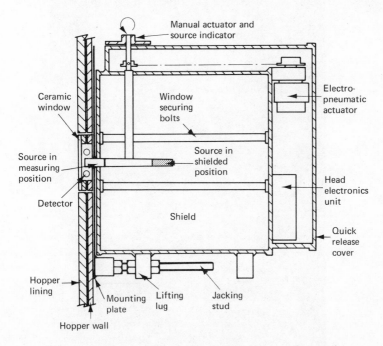

Figure 4.10 Moisture meter for granular material in hoppers, surface mounting (Courtesy Nuclear Enterprises Ltd.)

measuring head, which is mounted externally on the vessel wall. Fast neutrons emitted from the source are slowed down, mainly by collisions with atoms of hydrogen in the moisture of material situated near the measuring head. The count rate in the detector increases with increasing hydrogen content and is used as an indication of moisture content.

The slow neutron detector is a standard, commercially available detector and is accessible without dismantling the measuring head. The electronics, housed in a sealed case with the measuring head, consist of an amplifier, pulse height analyser and a line driver module which feed pre-shaped 5 V pulses to the operator's unit.

The pulses from the head electronic unit are processed digitally in the operator's unit to give an analogue indication of moisture content on a 100 mm meter mounted on the front panel, or an analogue or digital signal to other equipment. The instrument has a range of 0–20% moisture and a precision of ±0.5% moisture, with a response time of 5–25 s. The sample volume is between 100 and 300 litre and the operating temperature of the detector is 5–70°C and of the electronics 5–30°C. *Figure 4.11* shows the coke moisture gauge in use on a coke hopper.

Figure 4.11   Coke moisture gauge in use on hoppers (Courtesy Nuclear Enterprises Ltd.)

4.2.6   Measurement of sulphur contents of liquid hydrocarbons

Sulphur occurs in many crude oils at a concentration of up to 5% by weight and persists to a lesser extent in the refined product. As legislation in many countries prohibits the burning of fuels with a high sulphur content to minimise pollution, and sulphur compounds corrode engines and boilers and inhibit catalysts, it is essential to reduce the concentration to tolerable levels. Thus rapid measurement of sulphur content is essential and the measurement of the absorption of appropriate X rays provides a suitable on-line method. In general, the mass absorption coefficient of an element increases with increase of atomic number *(Figure 4.12(a))* and decreases with shortening the wavelength of the X rays. In order to make accurate measurement the wavelength chosen should be such that the absorption will be independent of changes in the carbon–hydrogen ratio of the hydrocarbon. When the X rays used have an energy of 22 keV the mass attenuation for carbon and hydrogen are equal. Thus by using X rays produced by allowing the radiation from the radio-element Americium 241 to produce fluorescent excitation in a silver target which gives X rays having an energy of 23 keV, the absorption is made independent of the carbon–hydrogen ratio. As this source has a half-life of 450 years, no drift occurs owing to decay of the source. The X rays are passed through a measuring cell through which the hydrocarbon flows and as the absorption per unit weight of sulphur is many times greater than the absorption of carbon and hydrogen, the fraction of the X rays absorbed is a measure of the concentration of the sulphur present. Unfortunately the degree of absorption of X rays is also affected by the density of the sample and by the concentration of trace elements of high atomic weight and of water.

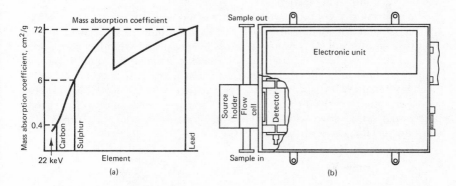

Figure 4.12   On-line sulphur analyser (Courtesy Nuclear Enterprises Ltd.)
(a) Mass absorption coefficient (b) Arrangement of instrument

The concentration of X rays is measured by a high resolution proportional counter so the accuracy will be a function of the statistical variation in the count rate and the stability of the detector and associated electronics, which can introduce an error of ±0.01% sulphur. A water content of 650 p.p.m. will also introduce an error of 0.01% sulphur. Compensation for density variations may be achieved by measuring the density with a non-nucleonic meter and electronically correcting the sulphur signal.

Errors caused by impurities are not serious since the water content can be reduced to below 500 p.p.m. and the only serious contaminant, vanadium, seldom exceeds 50 p.p.m.

The stainless steel flow cell has standard flanges and is provided with high pressure radiation windows and designed so that there are no stagnant volumes. The flow cell may be removed for cleaning without disturbing the source. Steam tracing or electrical heating can be arranged for samples likely to freeze. The output of the high resolution proportional counter, capable of high count rates for statistical accuracy, is amplified and applied to a counter and digital-to-analogue convertor when required. Thus both digital and analogue outputs are available for display and control purposes.

The meter has a range of up to 0–6% sulphur by weight and indicates with a precision of ±0.01% sulphur by weight or ±1% of the indicated weight, whichever is the larger. It is independent of carbon–hydrogen ratio from 6:1 to 10:1 and the integrating times are from 10 to 200 s. The flow cell is suitable for pressures up to 15 bar and temperatures up to 150°C, the temperature range for the electronics being −10 to +45°C.

The arrangement of the instrument is as shown in *Figure 4.12(b)*.

4.2.7   Measurements on fluids in pipes or tanks

Nuclear methods may be used to make certain measurements on fluids flowing in pipes from 12.7 mm to 1 m in diameter. For plastics or thin-walled pipes up to 76 mm in diameter the combined unit of source and detector shown in *Figure 4.13(a)* is used, while for larger pipes the system consisting of a separate holder and detector shown in *Figure 4.13(b)* is used.

The gamma-ray source is housed in a shielded container with a safety shutter so that the maximum dose rate is less than 0.75 mrad/h, and is mounted on one side of the pipe or tank. A measuring chamber containing argon at 20 atmospheres is fitted on the other side of the pipe or tank. It is fitted with a standardising holder and has a detection sensitivity of ±0.1%.

The system may be used to measure density over a range of 500–4000 kg/m³ with a sensitivity of 0.5 kg/m³, specific gravity with an accuracy of ±0.0005, percentage solids down to ±0.05%, and moisture content of slurries of a constant specific gravity to within ±0.25%.

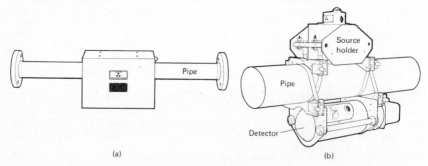

(a)   (b)

Figure 4.13   Fluid density measuring systems (Courtesy Nuclear Enterprises Ltd.) (a) Combined detector/source holder (b) Separate units for larger pipes

The principle of the measurement is that the degree of absorption of the gamma rays in the flowing fluid is measured by the ionisation chamber, where output is balanced against an adjustable voltage source which is set by means of the calibrated control to the desired value of the material being measured. Deviations from this standard value are then shown on the calibrated meter mounted on the indicator front panel. Standardisation of the system for the larger pipes is performed manually and a subsidiary source is provided for this purpose. The selection of the type of source depends on (a) the application, (b) the wall thickness and diameter of the pipe, and (c) the sensitivity required. Sources in normal use are Caesium 137 (source life 30 years), Americium 241 (460 years), and Cobalt 60 (5 years).

The measuring head has a temperature range of -10 to $+55°C$ and the indicator 5–40°C, and the response time minimum is 0.1 s, adjustable to 25 s.

4.2.8 The radio-isotope calcium monitor

The calcium content of raw material used in cement manufacture may be measured on-line in both dry powder or slurry form. The basis of the method is to measure the intensity of the characteristic K X rays emitted by the flowing sample using a small Fe^{55} radio-isotope source as the means of excitation. This source is chosen because of its efficient excitation of Ca X rays in the region which is free from interference by iron.

In the form of instrument shown in *Figure 4.14(a)*, used for dry solids, a sample of material in powder form is extracted from the main stream by a screw conveyor and fed into a hopper. In the powder presentation unit the powder is extracted from the hopper and fed on to a continuously weighed sample presenter at a rate which is controlled so as to maintain a constant mass of sample per unit area on the latter within very close limits. After measurement, the sample is returned to the process. A system is fitted to

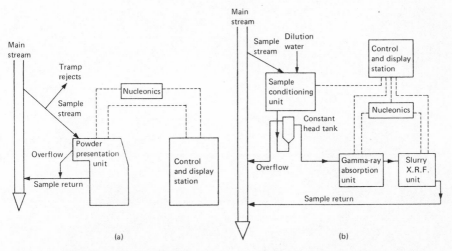

Figure 4.14   Block diagrams of calcium in cement raw material measuring instrument (Courtesy Nuclear Enterprises Ltd.) (a) Dry powder form of instrument (b) Slurry form of instrument

provide an alarm if the mass per unit area of sample wanders outside preset limits, and aspiration is provided to eliminate air-borne dust in the vicinity of the sample presenter and measuring head.

Under these conditions it is possible to make precise reproducible X ray fluorescence measurements of elements from atomic number 19 upwards without pelletising.

The signal from the X ray detector in the powder presentation unit is transmitted via a head amplifier and a standard nucleonic counting chain to a remote display and control station. Analogue outputs can be provided for control purposes.

In the form used for slurries shown in *Figure 4.14(b)*, an additional measurement is made of the density and hence the solids content of the slurry. The density of the slurry is measured by measuring the absorption of a highly collimated 660 keV gamma-ray beam. At this energy the measurement is independent of changes in solids composition.

The dry powder instrument is calibrated by comparing the instrument readings with chemical analysis carried out under closely controlled conditions with the maximum care taken to reduce sampling errors. This is best achieved by calibrating while the instrument is operating in closed loop with a series of homogeneous samples recirculated in turn. This gives a straight line relating percentage of calcium carbonate to the total X ray count.

With slurry a line relating percentage calcium carbonate to X ray count at each dilution is obtained producing a nomogram which enables a simple special purpose computer to be used to obtain the measured value indication or signal.

In normal operation the sample flows continuously through the instrument and the integrated reading obtained at the end of 2–5 min, representing about 2 kg of dry sample or 30 litre of slurry, is a measure of the composition of the sample.

An indication of CaO to within ±0.15% for the dry method and ±0.20% for slurries should be attainable by this method.

5

ON-LINE ANALYSIS INSTRUMENTS FOR CONTINUOUS ASTM HYDROCARBON PROCESSING PROCEDURES

The quality of process streams and finished products in the hydrocarbon process industry is usually controlled by laboratory techniques laid down by the American Society for Testing and Materials (ASTM) and the American Petroleum Institute. These procedures have been used in refineries all over the world. Over the past 20 years, considerable research has been carried out by refiners and instrument manufacturers to produce instruments which carry out analyses which give the same results as the standard procedures, but in an automatic and where possible a continuous on-line manner. This removes the necessity of removing samples from time to time from the process stream and carrying out laboratory tests in order to control the quality of the process stream. It also has the added advantage that the results are continuously available (although the tests may be carried out discontinuously on a time cycle) and may be used to control the plant, usually by altering the desired value on controllers of the more conventional parameters such as temperature, pressure, flow, etc. In this section the instruments used to measure the following parameters will be described:

1. Reid vapour pressure
2. Distillation characteristics
3. Pour point
4. Flash point
5. Cloud point
6. Octane number.

Other analyses carried out in hydrocarbon processing are described in other chapters where instruments are classified under the physical method involved.

5.1   VAPOUR PRESSURE ANALYSER

Vapour pressure of volatile oil and petroleum products is measured by the Reid method described in the ASTM standard D323/72. In this method the external atmospheric pressure is counterbalanced by the atmospheric pressure initially present in the air chamber so that the Reid vapour pressure is the absolute vapour pressure at 37.8°C.

An instrument whose output has excellent correlation with the Reid vapour pressure is the Hallikainen kinetic vapour pressure analyser shown in

97

principle in *Figure 5.1*. This instrument has a low maintenance requirement, is reliable, and suitable for use as a continuous measurement of the vapour pressure of a finished petrol stream.

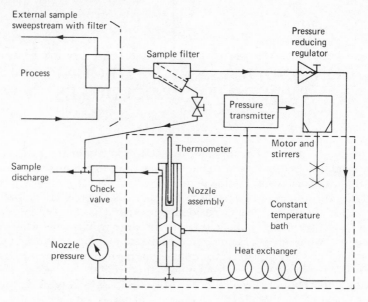

Figure 5.1   Vapour pressure analyser (Courtesy Hallikainen Instruments Ltd.)

The analyser consists of a constant temperature bath in which the heat exchanger and nozzle assembly are immersed. The temperature of the sample is regulated at 37.8 ±0.05°C by means of a two-term temperature controller, using a resistance thermometer as the primary sensing element, located in the bath, and a 1500 W immersion heater as the heat source. A stainless steel cooling coil through which cooling water may be circulated is also provided.

The sample first passes through a Y strainer with a screen of 150 μm aperture size to filter out particles, and hence to a conventional regulator which maintains a constant pressure upstream of the vapour pressure sensing nozzle. The nozzle increases the velocity head in the mixing section so that the pressure head at the downstream side of the nozzle approaches zero (application of Bernoulli's theorem). The minimum pressure in this chamber is limited to the vapour pressure of the sample material. This vapour pressure is sensed by an absolute pressure transmitter and measured as the kinetic vapour pressure. Precise sample temperature indication is provided by an etched stem thermometer located in a well downstream of the nozzle assembly. The sample upon leaving the nozzle passes through a check valve which provides about 0.25 bar back pressure on the system to prevent flow reversal in the event of instrument malfunction. Where the sample is to discharge to a line under pressure, the inlet pressure being sufficient for the requirements, the check valve is replaced by a back-pressure valve and a pressure gauge to indicate the back pressure. The transmitter output may be a pneumatic signal or an electric output signal.

Housing. The oil bath and electronic controls are each contained in a light-weight aluminium explosion proof housing designed to the American National Electrical Code for Class 1 Group D Division 1 hazardous areas, i.e. equivalent approximately to BS 4683:71 Gp 11A. The oil bath cover and box are insulated with Maranite and fibre glass and enclosed in a 16-gauge steel housing.

Range. Vapour pressure range 0–1.4 bar absolute (standard model for petrols, etc). Other ranges for higher vapour pressure products are also available.

Repeatability. ±0.003 bar on the 0–1.4 bar absolute range.

Response time. 30 s.

Inlet pressure limitation. 35 bar g maximum. A minimum of 3.5 bar g at the nozzle is required for analysers discharging to atmosphere. For analysers discharging into lines under pressure it is necessary to consult the manufacturer for inlet pressure requirement. The flow rate into the apparatus is 1.1–3.8 litre/min, depending on the nozzle back pressure.

Inlet temperature limitation. 21–66°C.

Materials of construction. All metal parts in contact with the samples are stainless steel.

An instrument which duplicates the major features of the ASTM method in that it saturates the vapour with air and produces four volumes of vapour per volume of liquid at the required temperature of 37.8 ±0.1°C is manufactured by Precision Scientific Development. It is widely used to control the addition of butane to petrol blends, because butane is most valuable when used in petrols, but the extent to which butane may be added is limited by the Reid vapour pressure (R.v.p.) specification.

The instrument reads directly in R.v.p. units and enables blends to be controlled to within less than 0.07 bar R.v.p. of specification. The method of operation is illustrated in *Figure 5.2.*

A positive displacement sampling pump continuously withdraws 100 ml/min from the stream to be analysed. Sample is preheated to 37.8°C in a coil immersed in the constant temperature bath, and then sprayed into an air saturation chamber, also at 37.8°C. (Petrol streams contain varying amounts of dissolved air; this affects the vapour pressure. In the ASTM D323 test for R.v.p., the sample is air saturated at 0–4.4°C before testing.) The partial pressure of air in the saturator, automatically controlled, is equivalent to the saturation conditions of ASTM D323.

The liquid level in the saturator is controlled by a float-operated needle valve. Air-saturated liquid is pumped from the saturator through a vaporising chamber also immersed in the 37.8°C bath. Control of vapour–liquid ratio is achieved by using a volumetric displacement pump of patented construction to withdraw liquid, vapour, and air from the vaporising coil at the rate of 500 ml/min. The exhaust pump is jacketed by the 37.8°C bath liquid to ensure constant temperature.

A pressure sensor is located at the outlet of the vaporising chamber and actuates an indicating transmitter that is calibrated directly in R.v.p. units. A 0.2–1 bar g pneumatic signal may be transmitted to conventional recording or controlling elements. The sample is returned by the pump back to the process, or to a sump if desired.

The instrument is suitable for use in a ANEC Class 1 Group D location (i.e. approximating to B.A.S.E.E.F.A. Zone 0 Group 11A). It has a range of 0.14–1.3 bar R.v.p. with an accuracy of ±0.07 bar and a repeatability of 0.07 bar with a response time of 50–60 s to reach 63% of the input step change including the 25–30 s dead time.

A sample rate of 100 ml/min is required, free of water and suspended matter, at a pressure of 0.7 bar g and a temperature between 10 and 43°C.

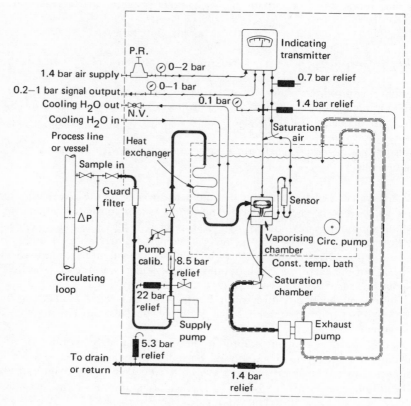

Figure 5.2   Reid vapour pressure monitor (Courtesy Precision Scientific Development)

5.2   DISTILLATION ANALYSIS

An important parameter in a fuel quality is its distillation characteristic. The important points on its distillation characteristic usually include (a) the initial boiling point (i.b.p.), (b) various per cent recovered points, i.e. the 20% point is the temperature of the vapour when 20 cm³ of the original 100 cm³ sample has been collected in the receiver, and (c) the final boiling point (f.b.p.) or end point, which is the maximum thermometer reading attained during the test, which occurs after the evaporation of the liquid from the bottom of the flask.

A suitable instrument for obtaining this characteristic is the Hone Spidar distillation analyser which carries out the same function as the ASTM standard 86/72 and IP 123/68 laboratory tests, but in an on-line automatic manner on a continuously repeating cycle giving up-dated information on sample distillation.

The analyser is air purged and is suitable for use in an American National Electrical Code Class 1 Group B Division 1 location, i.e. equivalent approximately to the British Ex(p) Gp 11c Zone 0 classification. Versions for PTB and other classifications are also available.

5.2.1 Principle

The analyser is shown schematically in *Figure 5.3* and includes all the basic elements of the standard apparatus, flask, heater, condenser, calibrated receiver and temperature sensing element. In addition there is a burette to charge 100 cm^3 of sample to the flask and the electrical and pneumatic components necessary for the complete automatic operation of the analyser.

The burette, flask, condenser and receiver are stainless steel, heating is electrical and the temperature is measured by thermocouples. The detector is a fluidic device, filling, flushing and draining are done by air-operated valves and the whole sequence of operation is controlled electrically.

The sequence flow diagram shows the analyser layout and inter-connections. A similar diagram is provided on the control unit cover together with indicator lamps to show the operational state. Each valve has a position indicator and a programming card is permanently fixed to the main frame to enable the complete cycle of events to be followed.

5.2.2 Sequence of operation

1. The sample flow through the burette B is stopped, leaving in it 100 cm^3 of up-to-date sample. This level can be checked visually.

2. This 100 cm^3 is fed into the flask D which has already been flushed and cooled after the previous distillation.

3. The heater is switched on and the sample distilled through the condenser into the receiver K. Vapour temperature throughout the test is indicated locally (M) and can be recorded remotely if required. The liquid level in the receiver can be seen throughout the test except on the initial boiling point and end point versions.

4. When the distillate level in the receiver K reaches the pre-set value (e.g. 20 cm^3 = 20% point) the detector is operated and initiates several operations. The heater is switched off and the programmer started to carry out the next cycle of operations. The new distillation point temperature is also recorded on a remote recorder via a peak-picking device fitted to the integral thermocouple current transmitter.

5. The electrical programmer operates the pneumatic valves in the correct sequence to flush and drain the flask and receiver, ready for the next analysis. All operations are shown by red and green lamps on the mimic diagram on the control unit box lid. Each complete test takes between 5 and 30 min, depending upon the boiling point temperature and selected distillation point.

102

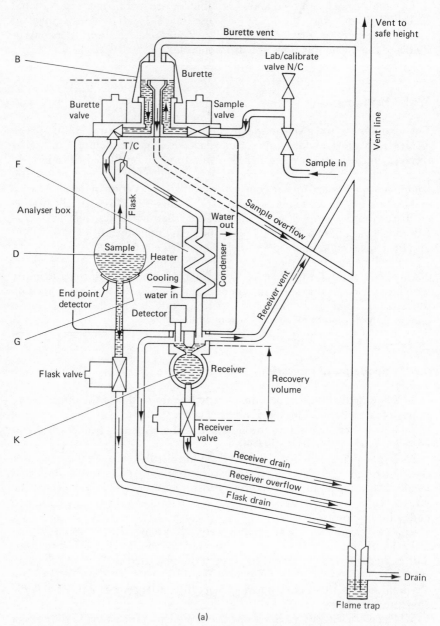

Figure 5.3   Continuous distillation analyser (Courtesy Hone Instruments Ltd.) (a) Diagrammatic arrangement

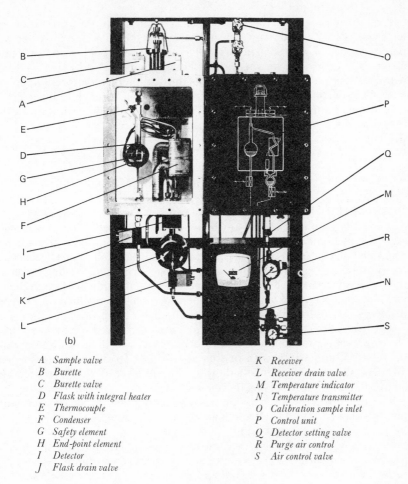

(b)

A	Sample valve
B	Burette
C	Burette valve
D	Flask with integral heater
E	Thermocouple
F	Condenser
G	Safety element
H	End-point element
I	Detector
J	Flask drain valve
K	Receiver
L	Receiver drain valve
M	Temperature indicator
N	Temperature transmitter
O	Calibration sample inlet
P	Control unit
Q	Detector setting valve
R	Purge air control
S	Air control valve

Figure 5.3(b)   Physical arrangement

5.2.3   Specification

Sample conditions required

Flow: 26 dm³/h

Temperature: as cool as possible and at least 30°C below the initial boiling point.

Input pressure: 0.14–1.4 bar g

Output signal: 4–20 or 0–20 mA or 0–10 mA d.c. two-wire system can be provided corresponding to a pre-selected temperature range. The range depends upon the requirements, with a maximum span of 100°C.

Repeatability: 1°C

Typical cycle times up to the 90% recovery point, including 3 min refilling time: petrol 15 min, kerosene 18 min, gas oil 30 min.

Several models are available which vary in detail to suit the application, e.g. for crude distillation units it is usual to record the 10% and 90% recovery points, or the 5% and 95% points. Solvents or special boiling point products are usually controlled on the initial boiling point and end point, and light petrols on the end point only. The use of the distillation monitor in the control loop of the particular unit can result in considerable economies by achieving on-specification products in a shorter time and reduction in downgraded or re-run products, or poisoning of expensive catalyst.

5.3 POUR POINT OF PETROLEUM OILS (ASTM D97)

In ASTM D97, the pour point of an oil is defined as the lowest temperature, expressed as a multiple of 3°C, at which the oil is observed to flow when cooled and examined under prescribed conditions. In the laboratory method the oil, contained in a closed test jar, is cooled in steps in suitable cooling jackets. At the appropriate temperature the test jar is removed from the cooling jacket and tilted just enough to determine whether there is a movement of oil in the test jar. The process is repeated until a temperature is found at which the oil ceases to flow. 3°C is added to this temperature and the result is the pour point.

The automated on-line instrument produced by Precision Scientific Development is used to monitor any distillate fuel stream having a pour point between −58 and +10°C with an accuracy of ±1°C. In this instrument about 2 ml of sample are retained in a shallow layer in the test cell which is refrigerated by use of the Peltier effect in a thermo-electric cooler.

The test cell assembly is continuously tilted slowly from the horizontal through about 10° to the left and back again. A beam of light is reflected from the sample surface to a photocell which is in one leg of a bridge circuit. As long as the sample is liquid, its surface remains horizontal despite the tilting of the test assembly. However, when the sample begins to solidify, the sample surface moves from the horizontal and the light beam is reflected away from the photocell, changing its resistance, thereby unbalancing the bridge circuit and signalling that a pour point has been reached. The d.c. power input to the thermo-electric device is shut off when the pour point is reached and the sample solenoid is energised, allowing a fresh sample to purge the cell of the previous sample and also warm the cell. At the end of a preset time the sample solenoid valve is closed. After another short time delay, to allow the surface of the new sample to come to equilibrium, the d.c. power unit to the thermo-electric device is again turned on, starting a new cooling cycle. The temperature of the test sample is continuously measured by an Iron-Constantan thermocouple and recorded, producing an inverted 'spike' or peak. The lowest temperature corresponds to the pour point.

The cycle time is from 5 to 20 min, depending upon the pour point of the sample, which must have a viscosity less than 20 cSt at the maximum temperature of 38°C and a pressure less than 2.2 bar g. The instrument requires at least 2 litre/min of cooling water to remove the heat from the heated junction of the thermo-electric cooler. The instrument is suitable for use in a ANEC Class 1 Group D location (i.e. approximating to B.A.S.E.E.F.A. Zone 0 Group 11A) and requires an electrical supply of 200 W at 115 V 50 or 60 Hz.

5.4   FLASH POINT MEASUREMENT

For safety and legislative reasons it is essential to know the flash point of volatile inflammable products. The standard laboratory test method for checking flash point temperatures, approved by the ASTM and IP, consists of heating a known quantity of product in a cup at a low constant rate with continual stirring of the sample. At regular intervals the stirring is stopped and a small flame directed into the cup. The flash point is the lowest temperature at which application of the test flame causes the vapour over the sample to ignite.

The on-line flash point analyser carries out the test continuously and automatically and eliminates the need for laboratory testing. The continuous flash point instrument is shown in *Figure 5.4(a)* and *(b)*. *Figure 5.4 (a)* shows the principle and *Figure 5.4(b)* the actual instrument.

In this instrument a test flame is not used to detect the flash point. Instead a platinum/palladium catalyst is used as the detector for the critical hydrocarbons vapour concentration that corresponds with the flash point. This particular vapour/air mixture reacts on the catalyst surface to produce a known reproducible catalyst temperature. It is the differences between this temperature and the temperatures caused by concentrations other than the critical (flash point) concentration that are used to control the heat applied to the fresh sample feed before it is mixed with air. If the vapour-air mixture flowing over the catalytic detector is below flash point concentration, then the detector temperature falls. This is sensed, compared with the 'set-point' temperature for the flash point concentration, and the error used to increase the heat to the liquid feed. As the sample becomes hotter, more vaporisation occurs, until the flash point concentration is reached and the detector is again at the 'set-point' temperature. The reverse occurs when the vapour/air mixture is above flash point concentration, and the heating of the liquid is reduced.

The 'set-point' temperature has been established by extensive research and is factory set for the chosen range of operation of the analyser. A catalytic detector was chosen to determine the flash point since the catalyst lowers the temperature at which the oxidation of the hydrocarbon vapours occurs. By reacting at a lower temperature than with a test flame or sparking electrical contacts, the carbonisation of product is virtually eliminated and 'coking' problems are vastly reduced.

The oxidation temperature is reduced by the catalyst due to absorption of the hydrocarbon molecules on the catalyst surface. Their chemical bonds are weakened and they become more reactive to oxygen.

5.4.1   Operation

The analyser is shown schematically in *Figure 5.4(a)*. A similar diagram is provided on the control unit cover, together with indicator lamps and meters to show the operational state. A controlled flow of clean sample enters the main tube heater O via a tube-in-tube heat exchanger R, in which the hot outgoing sample preheats the cool incoming sample. After the heater the sample enters the mixing chamber P where it is mixed with preheated air. Excess sample passes to the overflow chamber Q and then to drain via the heat exchanger and flame trap. The vapour/air mixture produced passes through

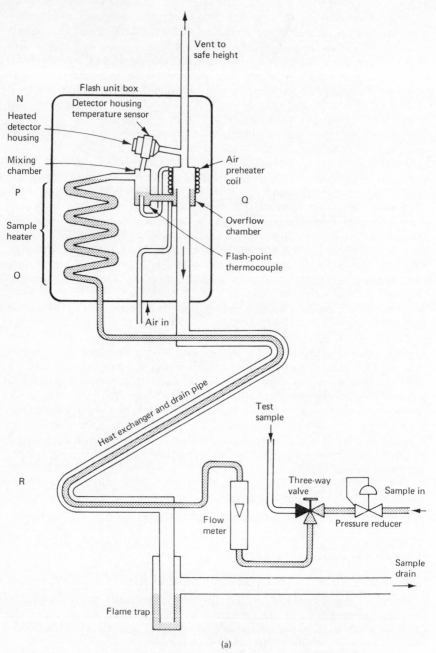

Figure 5.4   The 'Flasher' continuous flash point analyser (Courtesy Hone Instruments Ltd.)
(a) Schematic arrangement

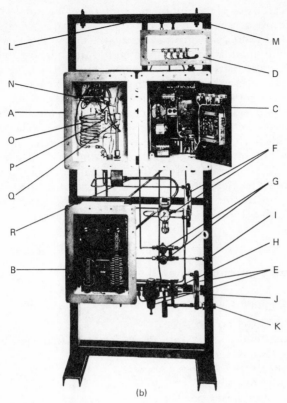

(b)

A   Flash unit
B   Power pack unit
C   Control unit (including temperature transmitter)
D   Terminals box
E   Sample pressure reducer and flow indicator
F   Flash unit air supply pressure regulator and flow indicator
G   Air purge pressure regulators
H   Run/test sample three-way valve
I   Air inlet
J   Sample inlet
K   Sample drain
L   Vent
M   Test sample inlet
N   Heated detector housing with detector
O   Main sample tube heater
P   Mixing chamber
Q   Overflow chamber with air preheater coil
R   Heat exchanger and drain pipe

Figure 5.4(b)   Physical arrangement

the heated detector housing N where the vapour concentration is detected by means of the catalytic oxidation of the vapour, and is then vented.

The detector which is in the vapour/air stream above the mixing chamber produces a variable voltage output which is dependent upon the catalyst temperature (and hence the vapour concentration). This voltage signal is the input to the main amplifier and is compared with the 'set-point' temperature value. A voltage is produced at the output which is proportional to the input error.

The amplifier output is fed into a modulator that has a saw-tooth waveform of approximately 1 s period as its other input. When the voltage of the saw-tooth exceeds that of the amplifier output, the modulator switches on and remains so until the saw-tooth returns to zero. Thus, a series of pulses are produced whose widths vary in direct relation to the amplifier output voltage. This pulse width modulated output is used to gate an integrated circuit that produces the required firing voltage of the main tube heater controller.

Thus, the main heater which heats the sample feed is switched on and off in a ratio that is determined by the detector output. If the detector output is low with respect to the 'set-point' then the heater will be on more than it is off, and with the detector output high the reverse will be true. When the detector output is identical with the 'set-point' value, then the heater will be on and off at exactly the right ratio to heat the incoming sample sufficiently to produce a vapour concentration corresponding to the critical flash point concentration.

The flash point temperature is measured by a thermocouple attached to the liquid section of the mixing chamber. A built-in transducer converts this thermocouple signal into a standard 4–20 mA d.c. output for transmission purposes.

5.4.2   Sample conditions required

The following sample conditions are required:

Flow: 2 dm³/h of clean sample.
Temperature: inlet temperature should be at least 10°C below the flash point.
Inlet pressure: 0.35–7.0 bar g
Drain: to atmosphere.
Vent: to atmosphere at a safe height.

The output signal is 4–20 mA, corresponding to the selected temperature range chosen, which should have a minimum span of 50°C. Single-pole changeover contacts rated at 5 A 125 V a.c. are provided to give a signal on air purge failure, which cuts off the electrical supply to the equipment. The equipment is air purged and is suitable for use in an American National Electrical Code Class 1 Group D Division 1 location, i.e. approximately equivalent to BS 4683:71 Gp 11A. PTB versions are also available.

5.5   CLOUD POINT MONITOR

In the standard ASTM test method, the sample from which all water has been removed is heated to at least 14°C above the cloud point and placed in a test jar. This is placed in a vessel in a suitable cooling medium for the range required, and at every 1°C the test jar is removed, inspected for clouding and replaced in the cooling jacket. The cloud point is the temperature at which a cloud or haze of wax crystals appears in the test jar.

The Hone cloud point monitor carries out this process in an automatic and continuous on-line manner and is designed to monitor one stream only, so that its output may be used in a control system. It will determine the cloud point of samples within the range −35 to +10°C with a repeatability of ±0.25°C on a time cycle dependent upon the initial sample temperature, but normally about

3 min. The equipment is suitable for use in a BS 4683 Group 11A and 11B hazardous location.

The sample must be available at 20 dm³/h but will be used at approximately 5 dm³/h. The temperature must not exceed 25°C or the pressure 7 bar g. The sample is fed into the monitor via an in-line filter, and a pressure reducing valve, relief valve, two-stage water separator and flowmeter are provided.

The instrument consists of a container of sample, a method of temperature cycling the sample, a method of detecting the sample's temperature, and a method of detecting the crystallisation of the wax content of the sample.

Sample is flushed through the test cell via a pneumatic valve, and a small quantity is retained in the cell when the valve closes. The cell is vented to atmosphere, thus relieving the pressure on the sample. The sample is cooled by a thermo-electric cooling unit which utilises the Peltier effect, and water is circulated through a small heat exchanger to the hot side of the thermo-electric unit to remove the extracted heat. The cooler unit has a maximum heat removal capacity of 54 W.

Light from a small lamp is directed through the cell and on to a phototransistor. When a cloud or haze appears in the sample, the resulting change in the output from the phototransistor switches off the cooling unit. The cell is at the same time flushed with new sample in preparation for the next test. The temperature at which the sample clouds is recorded as a peak on a continuous line strip chart recorder, or alternatively—by means of the switch and relay mounted in the recorder—an output pulse from the monitor converts the recorder to a peak picker. In the latter case the recorder can give a continuous output for a computer or other control device. The input to the recorder is from a thermocouple located within the test cell. The temperature so recorded is the same as that generally obtained by Method IP 15 or ASTM D97.

The sample flow is controlled by a pneumatic valve which gets its air from a solenoid valve in the control unit. Instrument air at about 1 bar pressure is fed to the unit, and about 14 dm³/h of this air is bled off into the unit at 125 mm water gauge to provide the air purge.

A pressure switch isolates the electrical supply should the purge pressure fail. The instrument also has built-in safety devices to guard against air failure, water failure or sample failure, and will fail safe on partial power failure. The instrument also detects and rejects samples which are not transparent in layers 40 mm in thickness or do not produce a cloud within the temperature range of the instrument.

In the Hone instrument illustrated in *Figure 5.5* a differential temperature technique is used to give a reading which correlates with the ASTM D97-1P15 results and is not affected by the water content or colour of the sample.

The principle of the method is based on the fact that, upon cooling the sample a crystal lattice is formed, and that the forming of this lattice impedes convection currents. The temperature at which the lattice structure develops coincides with the temperature at which a visible cloud appears. A thermo-electric cooling unit surrounds the sample container, the bottom of which protrudes from the cooling unit. Two thermistors, protruding into the sample at either end of the sample container, are connected into the opposite arms of a Wheatstone bridge circuit for differential temperature measurement, while a thermocouple located approximately in the centre of the sample container measures the sample temperature. When the power to the cooling unit is switched on the sample cools and convection currents fall down the walls of the sample container and rise along the axis. The lower thermistor becomes colder than the upper thermistor and the bridge becomes unbalanced. At the cloud point temperature, or wax precipitation temperature, convection ceases; the lower thermistor no longer receives the cold stream

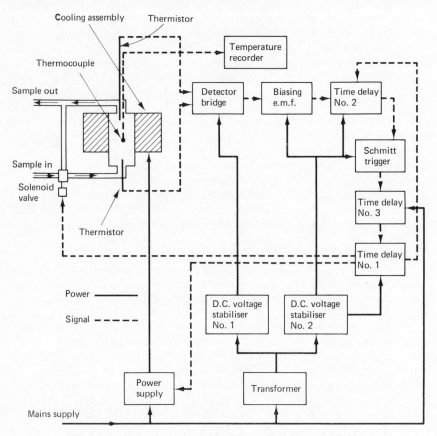

Figure 5.5   Process cloud point analyser (Courtesy Hone Instruments Ltd.)

falling from the walls and the upper thermistor no longer receives the relative warmth of the ascending convection stream. On the contrary the upper thermistor is cooled by heat conduction to the cooling unit. The differential temperature between the two thermistors is suddenly reduced and, when zero, the detector bridge balances and a transistorised Schmitt trigger operates. The sample temperature, as detected by the thermocouple, is then at the cloud point temperature and the measurement of this indicated on a recording potentiometric millivoltmeter or similar instrument.

   The sequence of events during a cycle may be summarised with reference to *Figure 5.5* as follows:

   1. The 3 min time delay No. 1 is initiated. The two-way solenoid valve is

energised so that the sample container is purged by the sample. Power to the cooling unit is isolated during this period.

2. At the end of the delay period the solenoid valve is de-energised, thus trapping a sample in the container and allowing the sample stream to by-pass the sample container. Power is supplied to the cooling unit, the trapped sample begins to cool and time delay No. 2 is initiated. This delay is included to mute the Schmitt trigger for approximately 90 s in order that the trigger does not operate at the beginning of the test.

3. At the cloud point temperature the Schmitt trigger operates and time delay No. 3 is initiated.

4. After approximately 5 s time delays Nos. 1 and 2 reset, then time delay No. 3 resets, time delay No. 1 is initiated and the cycle is repeated.

The time required for a complete cycle is about 10 min but this period depends on the sample inlet temperature and also on the cloud point temperature.

A cloud point trough picker is built into the analyser. This enables the instrument to be used for the automatic control of a process.

The analyser has a cloud point temperature range from -35 to $+15°C$ and a repeatability of $\pm\frac{1}{2}°C$ and is housed in two explosion proof boxes suitable for ANEC Class 1 Group D locations (approximating to B.A.S.E.E.F.A. Zone 0 Group 11A). One box houses the sample container and cooling unit while the other contains the electronics. Components with a significant temperature effect are mounted in a heated enclosure maintained at 55°C.

The inlet sample pressure may be between 1.4 and 6.5 bar g and the temperature at least 10°C above the expected cloud point with a maximum of 60°C. A sample flow rate of 200–250 cm^3/min is required. The analysis time is about 10 min and the sample is filtered through a 22 μm filter. A cooling water flow of 2 dm^3/h at a temperature below 25°C is required, and an electrical supply at 220 or 115 V a.c. 50 Hz, of 0.6 kVA.

5.6   ON-LINE OCTANE MEASUREMENT

5.6.1   Octane number

A vital quality of a finished petrol is the measure of its resistance to detonation as indicated by its octane rating. Several octane numbers are defined, but the most commonly measured value is the ASTM-IP Research Octane Number which forms the basis of the British Star system.

The ASTM-IP Research Octane Number of a fuel of 100 and below is the percentage by volume, to the nearest tenth, of iso-octane (equals 100.0) in a blend with n-heptane (=0.0) that exactly matches the knock intensity of the unknown sample when compared by the standard test method in the standard CFR (Cooperative Fuel Research) engine.

For fuels above 100 the octane number is defined by the following equation, which expresses octane number on the basis of millilitres of tetraethyl lead required in iso-octane to match exactly the knock intensity of the unknown sample when compared by this method.

$$\text{Octane number (above 100)} = 100 + \frac{28.28T}{1.0 + 0.736T + \sqrt{(1.0 + 1.472T - 0.035\,216T^2)}}$$

where $T = $ cm^3 tetraethyl lead per US gallon of iso-octane, and only positive roots are used in the equation.

The octane number of the fuel is determined by comparing its knock tendency with those for blends of ASTM reference fuels of known octane number under standard operating conditions. This is done by varying the compression ratio of the standard single-cylinder engine for the sample to obtain standard knock intensity as measured by an electronically controlled knock-meter. When the knock-meter reading for the sample is then bracketed between those for two reference blends, approximately one number above and one number below the sample, the rating of .the sample is calculated by interpolation. The knock testing unit, which is obtainable only from Waukesha Motor Co. Fuel Research Division, consists of a single-cylinder engine of continuously variable compression ratio with suitable loading and accessory equipment mounted on a stationary base. The engine equipment specified must be used without modification, and installed and used in accordance with the standard ASTM Designation D2699-70, IP Designation 237/69.

5.6.2   The Octel comparator

The Octel comparator is shown with the CFR engine in *Figure 5.6*. One of the standard fuel bowls of the CFR engine is replaced by a special fuel bowl *(Figure 5.7)* consisting of a bi-conical cavity of 100 ml capacity. The petrol level in the

Figure 5.6   Octel Comparator Mark 3 with CFR engine (Courtesy Associated Octel Co. Ltd.)

Figure 5.7   Fuel bowl and valve assembly (Courtesy Associated Octel Co. Ltd.)

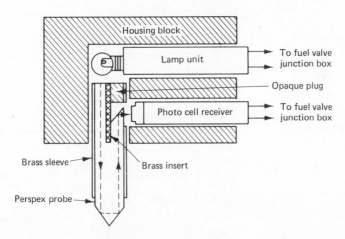

Figure 5.8   Photo head detector unit (Courtesy Associated Octel Co. Ltd.)

filled fuel bowl is controlled by an optical dipstick shown in section in *Figure 5.8*. While the level of the fuel is below the dipstick tip, light travelling down the dipstick from the lamp is totally internally reflected on to the photocell at the top. When the tip of the dipstick is immersed, the light is refracted into the fuel and no longer reflected back to the photocell, so that a signal is obtained which cuts off the flow of petrol to the fuel bowl.

The internal geometry of the fuel bowl is chosen to control the rate of change of air–fuel mixture strength so that when the level of fuel in the bowl is optimum, producing the maximum knock, the change of petrol level is minimum. The engine is also fitted with a modified fuel level sight glass which reduces the sample dead volume in the system to a minimum to speed up the engine response when the petrols are changed, while still retaining enough fuel to keep the engine running during change-over period.

The principle of operation of the comparator is that it alternately takes a sample of line petrol and a sample of reference petrol of accurately known octane number, and by comparing the maximum knock intensity which each sample produces in a CFR engine, gives an output signal which is proportional to the difference in octane number of the two samples. This output may be fed to a recorder and a blend controller so that a product of constant octane number may be obtained. The method of controlling the octane number is to make a blend of petrol components which has the correct characteristics such as vapour pressure, boiling range, density, etc., but an octane number less than the final requirement. This deficiency in octane number is then remedied by adding lead-alkyl anti-knock compound under the control of one or two component controllers of the blending control system. The set point of one or both of these component controllers can then be changed by the output signal from the on-line octane analyser to keep the octane number on specification to close limits. The advantage of changing the concentration of lead-alkyl as opposed to any other component is that the octane number may be changed without affecting any other property of the petrol so that a petrol fulfilling its complete specification may be obtained.

The console houses the programmer, the relays and the amplifiers, and on the front panel is fitted a knock intensity recorder, an octane difference indicator, an off-set control and a row of annunciators indicating the state of sequence.

A flow switch is fitted in the cooling water supply to the engine to provide an alarm and engine shut-down if the cooling water flow to the engine falls below a safe minimum. Fuel bowl flooding will also cause the engine to be shut down. High and low knock limits can be set and when the high knock limit is exceeded the engine is automatically switched to reference fuel. Any of the disturbances initiates the alarm, the particular fault being shown by the indicator lamps.

5.6.2.1 OPERATION

The line or reference petrol sample is introduced into the fuel bowl by the appropriate solenoid valve under control of the programmer. The output from the standard transistorised detonation meter, which is a measure of the knock intensity, is amplified and is sampled by a capacitor and diode system which retains the peak value. The values of maximum knock intensities for line and reference petrols are compared and if any difference exists, it is detected by a differential amplifier and produces an error signal which is indicated on the comparator and may be displayed on a recorder in the blending control room. An off-set control is included which allows the reference fuel to differ in octane number by a pre-set small amount from the desired octane number of the finished petrol. Ideally, the reference and the blended petrols will have identical knock characteristics; under these conditions the output amplifier is arranged to produce 30 mA d.c. Deviations of 2 octane number from the reference set point will cause the comparator output to swing between 10 and 50 mA d.c. Standard deviation of output signal has been found to be less than 0.15 Research octane number when comparing petrols of similar compositions.

Each time the fuel bowl is refilled an erase relay is operated to discharge the sampling capacitor in readiness for the next cycle. The complete system is contained in a console sited in the CFR engine room and connected to a standard CFR engine by one multi-core cable and a junction box. Three carburetter bowls are left unaltered, so that the engine can be used for standard ASTM ratings by operation of the change-over switch.

The operating sequence and function of the electrical circuits is explained below. The operating steps are designated (a), (b), (c), etc., and refer to *Figure 5.9*, where two complete cycles are covered, and the electrical components are designated C, D, etc., and are shown diagrammatically in *Figure 5.10*. Just prior to point (a) in the cycle the fuel bowl is filling with line petrol. When the petrol touches the tip of the optical dipstick in the fuel bowl, the light beam directed on to the photocell is interrupted (a). This de-energises a relay which closes the line petrol solenoid valve, energises the reset solenoid, which allows the programmer to return to zero, and also operates the erase relay. After two or three seconds, a clutch releases and the programmer starts. The petrol level in the fuel bowl now falls as the engine runs. When the petrol leaves the tip of the optical dipstick, the erase relay resets and the BOWL FULL light goes out. A voltage proportional to the knock intensity signal now builds up on capacitor C, and a peak picking diode D ensures that the maximum signal is retained. At point (b) the read-in switch closes, energising the line relay, thus transferring the peak signal to the correct storage capacitor C_2. During the read-in interval a chart driver switch closes and advances the knock intensity recorder chart a short distance. With the reading complete, the programmer resets the line relay (c). At point (d) in the cycle the drain-start switch closes, energising the drain valve V, and a bistable relay RLA/2 is changed over. The bistable relay will now route signals to the reference petrol solenoid valve and the reference storage amplifier. The drain-stop switch operates at (e), closing the drain valve and opening the selected petrol solenoid valve. The fuel bowl now fills with reference petrol and the cycle is repeated.

The row of annunciators on the front panel centre chassis indicates the control actions as the cycle proceeds. With the aid of the built-in test signal and meter, the operation of all circuits and amplifiers in the comparator may be checked.

With the push button switch in the test unit (top chassis) in the test position, the switches associated with the annunciators are made operative. Any of the control actions may now be performed manually. The store line and store

116

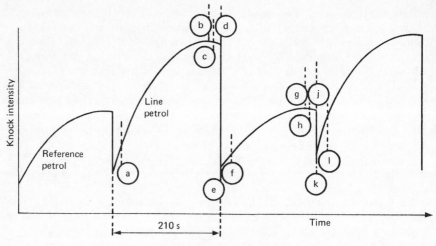

Figure 5.9   Operating sequence table (Courtesy Associated Octel Co. Ltd.)

Idealised knock-meter record
(read in conjunction with *Figure 5.9*)

Stage of cycle	Time after start of cycle, s	State of programmer outputs 1 2 3 4 5 6	Action
a	0	0 0 0 0 0 1	Bowl full. Storage capacitor C1 discharged. Timer reset. Engine running on blender sample
b	183	0 0 0 1 0 0	Voltage on C1 transferred to line storage amplifier ('Read in')
c	192	0 0 0 0 0 0	'Read in' completed
d	195	0 0 1 0 0 0	Fuel bowl draining
e	198	1 0 0 0 0 0	Bowl filling with reference petrol
f	210	0 0 0 0 0 1	Bowl full. Storage capacitor C1 discharged. Timer reset. Engine running on reference petrol
g	183	0 0 0 0 1 0	Voltage on C1 transferred to reference storage amplifier
h	192	0 0 0 0 0 0	Voltage transfer complete
j	195	0 0 1 0 0 0	Fuel bowl draining
k	198	0 1 0 0 0 0	Bowl filling with sample from blender
l	210	0 0 0 0 0 1	Bowl full

0 = Valve or relay de-energised.   1 = Valve or relay energised.

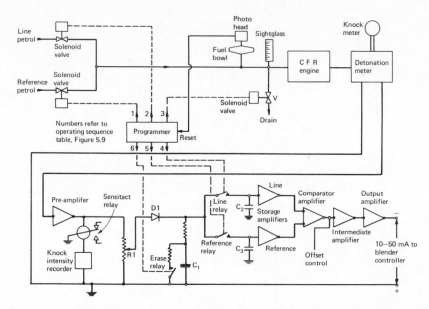

Figure 5.10   Octel Comparator Mark 3—schematic operation (Courtesy Associated Octel Co. Ltd.)

reference switches are push on/push off type. The run/warm-up switch is also a push on/push off type but its operation is not affected by the switch in the test panel. All other switches have momentary action.

When the push button switch is in the normal position, the switches cannot be operated from the front panel; operation is now automatic by the programmer.

The amplifier system consists of the following sections:

Line petrol signal storage amplifier.
Reference petrol signal storage amplifier.
Comparator amplifier incorporating a differential amplifier for the error signal and an output amplifier for the control signal.

The line and reference storage amplifiers will indicate the voltage across the input capacitor with negligible loading.

The output of the differential amplifier can swing ±10 V depending on the degree of unbalance which exists at its input.

The output booster amplifier converts the signal of the differential amplifier to a d.c. control signal. For a zero signal at its input, the amplifier causes 30 mA to flow in the output circuit. A −10 V signal changes the output to 50 mA and a +10 V signal changes the output current to 10 mA. An adjustable resistance in the output circuit permits change of load resistance to compensate for loop resistance, additional recorders, etc.

The engine and comparator are housed in a suitably ventilated engine cell which is fitted with alarms to indicate ventilation failure or the presence of fire, hydrocarbon gas or carbon monoxide in the engine cell. The installation has to be in accordance with the ASTM requirements, and in accordance with the Institute of Petroleum and local authorities codes of practice for electrical safety.

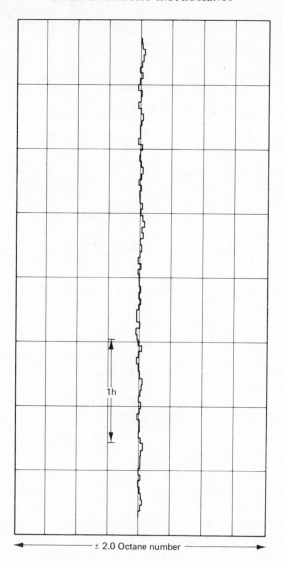

± 2.0 Octane number

Figure 5.11   Typical output records (Courtesy Associated Octel Co. Ltd.)

A suitable sampling system must be provided and water cooled jacketed tanks at a suitable level for storing reference petrol. These tanks may also be pressurised with nitrogen to prevent evaporation.

The line petrol sample is filtered by an in-line filter and collected in a sample pot, which holds about 120 cm³, over the period of the whole cycle so that it represents average composition during the 7 min collection period. The rate of filling is adjusted so that the pot is just beginning to overflow when the sample is transferred to the special carburetter bowl. The overflow from the sample pot and the fuel bowl is collected and passes through a flame trap to a storage tank outside the engine room, from which it is pumped back into the blend header when a pre-set level is reached. A typical recorder trace is shown in *Figure 5.11.*

5.6.2.2 FLOW RATE OCTANE ERROR INTEGRATOR

This instrument may be used with an Octel comparator to totalise the octane error of a blend. As shown in *Figure 5.12,* two signals are fed to the instrument: the octane error signal from the Octel comparator and a signal which is a measure of the total flow rate of the blend. The product of these two signals is integrated and continuously displayed on an 'up-down' counter with 'Nixie' tube readout showing the magnitude and direction of the total error in units as desired (e.g. Δ octane barrels, Δ octane cubic metres, etc.).

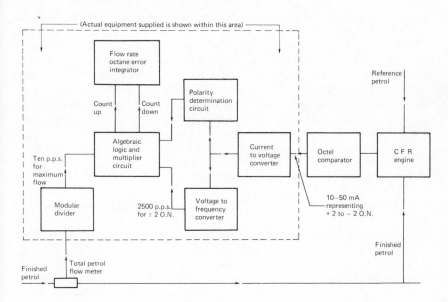

Figure 5.12   Flow rate octane error indicator (Courtesy Associated Octel Co. Ltd.)

The integrator is of use to (a) determine precisely the octane number of the completed blend, and (b) enable an operator to correct the blend quality manually to compensate accurately for changes in component composition and blending errors.

6

MEASUREMENT OF CHEMICAL COMPOSITION

6.1 SPECTROCHEMICAL ANALYSIS

The general analysis of substances is a rather specialised field which cannot be covered adequately in a book such as this. A student wishing to study this technique is therefore recommended to study the principles in a good physics text book and follow this by a study of the literature provided by the specialist manufacturers, such as Hilger and Watts, Rank Precision Industries, Unicam Instruments, or to read *Spectrochemical Methods of Analysis,* Editor J. D. Winefordner, published by Wiley Interscience, or some similar work.

The only instruments described in this section will be instruments used in-line in chemical plants such as non-dispersive infra-red analysers.

6.1.1   Non-dispersive infra-red analysers

Measurement of the absorption of infra-red radiation enables the quantity of many gases in a complex gas mixture to be measured in an industrial environment. Carbon monoxide, carbon dioxide, nitrous oxide, sulphur dioxide, methane and other hydrocarbons and vapours of water, acetone, ethyl, alcohol, benzene and others may be measured in this way. Oxygen, hydrogen, nitrogen, chlorine, argon and helium do not absorb infra-red radiation and are therefore ignored by the instrument. The instrument is illustrated in *Figure 6.1(a).* Two beams of infra-red radiation of equal energy are interrupted by a rotating shutter which allows the beams to pass intermittently but simultaneously through an analysis cell assembly and a parallel reference cell, and hence into a Luft-pattern detector.

The detector consists of two sealed absorption chambers separated by a thin metal diaphragm. This diaphragm, with an adjacent perforated metal plate, forms an electrical capacitor. The two chambers are filled with the gas to be detected so that the energy characteristic of the gas to be measured is selectively absorbed.

The reference cell is filled with a non-absorbing gas. If the analysis cell is also filled with a non-absorbing gas equal energy enters both sides of the detector. When the sample is passed through the analysis cell, the measured gas present absorbs some of the energy to which the detector is sensitised, resulting in an imbalance of energy causing the detector diaphragm to be deflected and thus changing the capacitance. This change is measured electrically and a corresponding reading is obtained on the meter.

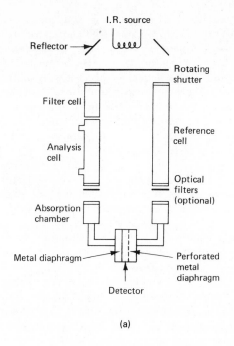

(a)

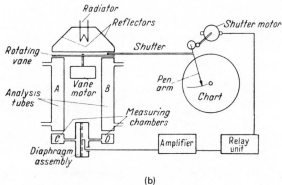

(b)

Figure 6.1 (a) Luft-type infra-red gas analyser (Courtesy Grubb Parsons) (b) Infra-red gas analyser of the concentration recorder

Any other gas also present in the sample will not affect the result unless it has absorption bands which overlap those of the gas being determined. In this event, filter tubes containing the interfering gas or gases can be included in one or both optical paths, so that the radiations emerging from these tubes will contain wavelengths which can be absorbed by the gas to be detected but will contain very little radiation capable of being absorbed by the interfering gases in the sample, since such radiations have already been removed.

The length of absorption tube to be used depends upon the gas being estimated and the concentration range to be covered. The energy absorbed by a column of gas l cm long and containing a concentration c of absorbing component is approximately $E\,l\,k\,c$, where E is the incident energy and k is an absorption constant, provided that kcl is small compared with unity. Thus at low concentrations it is advantageous to use long absorption paths provided kcl remains small and the relationship between energy absorbed and the measured concentration remains reasonably linear. At higher concentrations the energy absorbed is $E[1 - \exp(-kcl)]$, and the relationship between energy absorbed and concentration departs greatly from linearity when absorption exceeds 25%. When the absorption reaches this value it is, therefore, necessary to reduce the length of the absorption cell, and the product $c \times l$ should be kept approximately constant.

The most convenient method of calibrating the instrument is to pass mixtures of the pure gas and air of known composition through the measuring cell and note the output for each concentration of measured gas. For day to day checking a simple internal calibrating device is fitted, and it is only necessary to adjust the sensitivity control until a standard deflection is obtained.

The instrument is usually run from a.c. mains through a constant voltage transformer. Where utmost stability is required an a.c. voltage stabiliser may be used, as the constant voltage transformer converts frequency variations to voltage changes. Generally, the instrument is insensitive to temperature changes, although the gas sensitivity depends on the temperature and pressure of the sample gas in the absorption tube, since it is the number of absorbing molecules in the optical path which determines the meter deflection. For instruments sensitive to water vapour the detecting condenser has a temperature coefficient of sensitivity of 3% per 1°C and it is therefore necessary to maintain the detector at a constant temperature.

The approximate maximum sensitivity to certain gases is given in *Table 6.1*.

Table 6.1.

Gas	Minimum concentration for full scale deflection, Vol. %	Gas	Minimum concentration for full scale deflection, Vol. %
CO	0.05	NO_2	0.1
CO_2	0.01	SO_2	0.02
H_2O	0.1	HCN	0.1
CH_4	0.05	Acetone	0.25
C_2H_4	0.1	Benzene	0.25
N_2O	0.01		

Errors due to zero changes may be avoided by the use of a null method of measurement illustrated in *Figure 6.1(b)*. The out-of-balance signal from the detector is amplified, rectified by a phase sensitive rectifier, and applied to a servo system which moves a shutter which cuts off as much energy from the radiation on the reference side as has been absorbed from the analysis side, and so restores balance. The shutter is linked to the pen arm which indicates the gas concentration.

On-line infra-red absorption meter using two wavelengths

In order to overcome the limitations of other infra-red analysers and provide a rugged reliable drift-free analyser for continuous operation on a chemical plant, ICI Mond Division developed an analyser based on the comparison of the radiation absorbed at an absorption band with that at a nearby wavelength. By use of this comparison method many of the sources of error such as the effect of variation in the source intensity, change in the detector sensitivity or fouling of the measurement cell windows are greatly minimised.

The absorption at the measurement wavelength (λ_m) is compared with the nearby reference wavelength (λ_r) at which the measured component does not absorb. The two measurements are made alternately in time using a single absorption path and the same source and detecting system.

The principle of the system is illustrated in *Figure 6.2*. The equipment consists of two units, the optical unit and the electronics unit, which are connected by a multicore cable. The source unit contains a sealed infra-red source which consists of a coated platinum coil at the focus of a calcium fluoride collimating lens. A chopper motor with sealed bearings rotates a

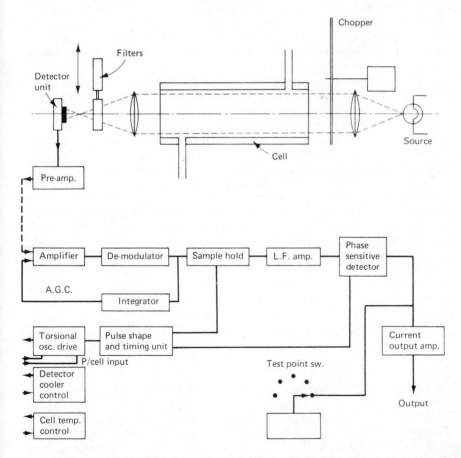

Figure 6.2   Dual wavelength comparison method (Courtesy Feedback Instruments Ltd.)

chopper disc which modulates the energy beam at 600 Hz. The source operates at low voltage, and at a temperature well below the melting point of platinum. It is sealed in a nitrogen atmosphere. Energy from the source passes through the absorption cell to the detector unit. A calcium fluoride lens focuses the energy on to an indium antimonide detector. This is mounted on a Peltier cooler in a sealed unit. The temperature is detected by a thermistor inside the sealed module. A preamplifier mounted in the detector unit amplifies the signal to a suitable level for transmission to the electronics unit. Between the lens and the detector module two interference filters, selected for the measurement and reference wavelengths, are interposed alternately in the beam, at about 6 Hz, so that the detector receives chopped energy at a level corresponding alternately to the measurement and reference transmission levels. Its output is a 600 Hz carrier modulated at 6 Hz.

The two filters are mounted on a counterbalanced arm, attached to a stainless steel torsion band. An iron shoe at the opposite end of the arm moves in and out of the gap in an electromagnet. It also cuts two light beams which illuminate two silicon phototransistors. The light is provided by two aircraft type signal lamps which are under-run to ensure very long life. A drive circuit in the electronics unit causes the system to oscillate at its own natural frequency. One of the photocells provides positive feedback to maintain the oscillation, and the other provides negative feedback to control the amplitude. There are no lubricated parts in the detector unit, and the whole can be hermetically sealed if desired.

The absorption cell is a thick-walled tube with heavy flanges. Standard construction is in mild steel, nickel plated, but type 316 stainless steel construction is available where required. The windows are of calcium fluoride, sealed with Viton O-rings and retaining rings. A heater wire is wound on the cell, and the sample gas passes through a tube in thermal contact along the length of the cell before entering it at the end. Provision is made for rodding out tubes and entries in case of blockage. A thermistor embedded in the cell wall detects the cell temperature which is controlled by a circuit in the electronics unit. The cell is thermally insulated and sealed inside a plastics bellows. The enclosed space is coupled to the purge system. The two end units each have a sealing window so there is a double seal between the cell and the interior of the detector and source units. Since the source is inside a further sealed module, there is minimal danger of the hot source being exposed to leakage from the sample cell. The gaps between the three units are normally sealed with neoprene gaskets and the whole device is sufficiently well sealed to maintain a positive purge pressure of at least 2 cm water gauge with a purge gas consumption of 8.3 cm^3/s. For use with highly flammable sample gases, the sealing gaskets at either end of the absorption cell may be replaced by vented gaskets. In this case a relatively large purge flow may be maintained around the cell, escaping to atmosphere across the windows. Thus, any leak at the windows can be flushed out.

To facilitate servicing on site the source, detector, torsional vibrator, lamps, preamplifier and source voltage control are all removable without the use of a soldering iron. Since the single-beam system is tolerant to window obscuration and the internal walls of the absorption cell are not polished, cell cleaning will not be required frequently, and in many cases adequate cleaning may be achieved *in situ* by passing solvent or detergent through the measuring cell.

There is no need to switch the instrument off while doing this. If it becomes necessary the cell can be very quickly removed and disassembled.

The electronics unit contains the power supplies together with signal processing circuits, temperature control circuits, output and function check meter operating controls and signal lamps. The housing is of cast-aluminium alloy, designed for flush panel mounting. The circuitry is mostly on five plug-in printed circuit boards. The indicating meter, controls and signal lamps are accessible through a window in the door. The unit is semi-sealed, and a purge flow may be connected if sealed glands are used at the cable entry. The signal processing circuits are contained on two printed circuit boards. Output from the preamplifier is applied to a gain-controlled amplifier which produces an output signal of 3 V peak-to-peak mean. Thus the mean value of I_r + I_m is maintained constant. The signal is demodulated and smoothed to obtain the 6 Hz envelope waveform. A sample-and-hold circuit samples the signal level near the end of each half-cycle of the envelope, and this produces a square wave whose amplitude is related to $I_r - I_m$. Since $I_r + I_m$ is held constant, the amplitude is actually proportional to $(I_r - I_m)/(I_r + I_m)$ which is the required function to give a linearised output in terms of sample concentration. This signal is amplified and passed to a phase-sensitive detector, consisting of a pair of gating transistors which select the positive and negative half-cycles and route them to the inverting and non-inverting inputs of a differential amplifier. The output of this amplifier provides the 0–5 V output signal.

The synchronising signals for the sample/hold and phase-sensitive detector circuits are derived from the torsional oscillator drive circuit via appropriate time delays. The instrument span is governed by selection of feedback resistors in the low frequency amplifier, and a fine trim is achieved by adjusting the signal level at the gain-controlled amplifier. This is a pre-set adjustment—no operator adjustment of span is considered necessary or desirable. A front panel zero adjustment is provided. This adds an electrical offset signal at the phase-sensitive detector. The system is normally optically balanced (i.e. $I_r = I_m$) at some specified concentration of the measured variable (usually zero).

The current output and alarm circuits are located on a separate printed circuit board. The voltage output is applied to an operational amplifier with selected feedback and offset signals to produce 0–10 mA, 5–20 mA or 10–50 mA output. The required output is obtained by soldered selector links. The output current is unaffected by load resistances up to 1 kΩ at 50 mA, or 5kΩ at 10 mA.

A front panel alarm-setting potentiometer provides a pre-set signal which is compared with the analyser output voltage in a differential amplifier. The output of this opens a relay if the analyser output exceeds a pre-set value, which may be either a low or high analyser output as required. The alarm condition is indicated by two signal lamps on the panel and the system can be arranged to operate external alarms, or shut-down circuits.

The power to the cell heater and the detector cooler is controlled from a bridge circuit containing thermistors which detect the temperatures of the absorption cell and detector.

The indicating meter on the front panel has a calibrated output scale, and is used in conjunction with a selector switch to monitor key points in the circuit, in particular the degree of obscuration in the measuring cell. By choosing the appropriate absorption bands the analyser may be made suitable for a wide range of gases or liquids. For gases, it may be used for CO_2, CO, SO_2, CH_4, C_2H_6, C_2H_4, C_6H_6, C_2H_2, NH_3, N_2O, NO, NO_2, $COCl_2$, H_2O, with ranges of 0–300 p.p.m. or 0–100%.

It may also be used for measuring water in ketones, hydrocarbons, organic acids, alcohols, glycols and oils. The accuracy is ±1% and the response time for 90% change is 3 s.

Measurements based on reflected radiation

Just as measurements of moisture, or other components, may be made by comparison at two wavelengths of transmitted infra-red radiation, the method will work equally well by measuring the attenuation when infra-red is reflected or back-scattered. The principle is illustrated in *Figure 6.3*.

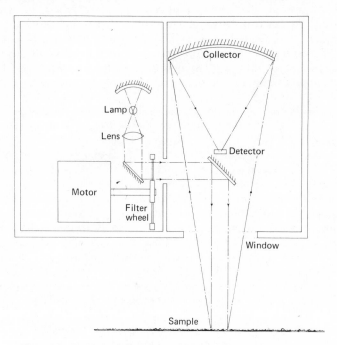

Figure 6.3   Backscatter infra-red gauge (Courtesy Infra-red Engineering Ltd.)

For water measurement of paper or granulated material on a conveyor belt, the intensity of the reflected beam at the moisture absorption wavelength of 1.93 μm may be compared with the intensity at a reference wavelength of 1.7 μm. The beams are produced by interposing appropriate filters contained in a rotating disc in front of a lamp producing appropriate radiation. The radiation is then focused on to the measured material, and the reflected beam focused on to a lead sulphide photoelectric cell. By measuring the ratio of the intensity of radiation at two wavelengths, the effects of source variation, detector sensitivity and drift in the electronic circuitry are minimised. Furthermore, calibration has shown that for a number of materials the results are substantially independent of the packing density.

However, if the measured material is a strong absorber of radiation a powerful source of radiation such as a water-cooled quartz halogen lamp may be necessary.

With this type of instrument on-line measurement of the moisture content of sands, clay, dust or flake, refractor mixtures, paper, textiles, feeding stuffs and a wide range of other materials may be undertaken with an accuracy of $\pm 1\%$ of instrument full scale.

Chemiluminescence

When certain chemical reactions take place, energy may be released in the infra-red band. Measurement of the intensity of this radiation may be used to measure the concentration of reactants present. For example in the Grubb Parsons Chemitox instrument this principle is used to measure the concentration of oxides of nitrogen. The reaction, at low pressure, of ozone with nitric oxide produces nitrogen dioxide which subsequently emits radiation in the $0.6–3.0 \mu m$ band. The intensity of the emission is in direct proportion to the concentration of nitric oxide if an excess of ozone is used, so that the measurement of the energy of the emission by a photomultiplier provides a sensitive and accurate method of measuring the nitric oxide content. By heating the sample prior to the reaction stage any nitrogen dioxide present is converted to nitric oxide and is thus included in the measurement. A wide range of measuring ranges from 0–1 to 0–5000 p.p.m. is possible, with a repeatability and linearity of $\pm 1\%$ of full scale. The reading will be affected by the presence of certain gases, the most significant being $15\% CO_2$, -3% on the 0–100 p.p.m. range, $1\% SO_2$, -12% on the 0–100 p.p.m. range.

6.2 MASS SPECTROMETERS

The mass spectrometer is capable of carrying out quick and accurate analysis of a wide variety of solids, liquids and gases and has a wide range of application in process monitoring and laboratory research. When combined with the gas chromatograph it provides an extremely powerful tool for identifying and quantifying substances which may be present in extremely small quantities.

While the optical spectrometer resolves a beam of light into components according to their wavelengths, a mass spectrometer resolves a beam of positive ions into components according to the ratio of their mass/charge, or if all carry single elementary charges, according to their masses. As with the optical spectrometer the mass spectrometer may be used to identify substances and to measure the quantity present.

The original mass spectrometer was devised by F. W. Aston about 1919 to measure the mass of individual positive ions. The accuracy of the instrument enabled the different masses of what appeared to be chemically identical atoms to be measured, resulting in the discovery of isotopes. Considerable development has taken place over the years, resulting in very versatile instruments having very high resolving power and sensitivity.

The resolving power of a mass spectrometer is a measure of its ability to separate ions having a very small difference in mass. If two ions of masses M_1 and M_2 differing in mass by ΔM give adjacent peaks in their spectrum as shown in *Figure 6.4* and the height of peak is H above the base line, then on the 10% valley definition the peaks are said to be resolved if the height of the valley h is less than or equal to 10% of the peak H, i.e.

$$(h/H) \leqslant 10$$

The resolution is then $M_1/\Delta M$, e.g. if the peaks representing two masses 100.000 and 100.005 are separated by a 10% valley, the resolution of the instrument is 100.000/0.005, i.e. 20 000. Instruments with a resolution of 150000 are readily available. The sensitivity on the other hand is a measure of the smallest detectable quantity of the substance being identified. An example of the extreme sensitivity of modern instruments is:

At a resolution of 1000, 3 ng/s of a compound, relative molecular mass 300, will give a spectrum with a signal-to-noise ratio of 10:1 for a peak having an intensity of 5% of the base peak when a mass range of 10:1 is scanned in 3 s.

The mass spectrometer has a very wide range of use in process monitoring and laboratory research. It is used in refineries for trace element survey, analysis of lubricating oils and identifying and quantifying the substances in mixtures of organic compounds. Its use in detecting and measuring the concentration of pollutants in air, water and solids is rapidly increasing, also its use in biochemical analysis in medicine and other fields, particularly the analysis of drugs in biological extracts.

By means of a double-beam instrument an unknown sample may be compared with a standard so that the unknown components are readily

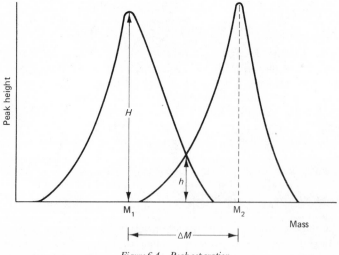

Figure 6.4   Peak separation

identified and the concentration measured. By suitable modifications an instrument can be made to provide an energy analysis of electrons released from the surface of a sample by X-radiation, or ultra-violet light.

6.2.1   Principle of the instrument

There are many different types of mass spectrometers but the ones described here are the most commonly used.

In all types the pressure is reduced to about 10^{-5} N/m² in order to reduce collisions between particles in the system. The spectrometer consists of an inlet system by which the sample is introduced into the region in which ions of the sample are produced. The separation of ions according to their mass-to-charge ratio may be achieved by magnetic or electric fields or by a combination of both. The differences between the various types of mass spectrometer lie in the manner in which the separation is achieved. In the instrument illustrated in *Figure 6.5* the ions are accelerated by an electrical potential through accelerating and defining slits into the electrostatic analyser, where ions having energies within a restricted band are brought to a focus at the monitor slit which intercepts a portion of the ion beam. They then enter the electromagnetic analyser which gives direction and mass focusing. This double focusing results in ions of all masses being focused simultaneously along a given plane. The ions can be recorded photographically on a plate over a period of time to give a very high sensitivity and reduction of the effects of ion-beam fluctuation.

Alternatively, the accelerating or deflecting field may be arranged so that ions of a given mass are focused on a detector which may consist of a plate or, if initial amplification of the charge is required, on to an electron multiplier or scintillation detector. By arranging the deflecting field to change in a predetermined manner, the instrument may be arranged to scan a range of masses and so record the abundance of ions of each particular mass. Such a record is known as a mass spectrum and mathematical analysis of this mass spectrum enables the composition of the sample to be determined. Mass spectra obtained under constant conditions of ionisation depend upon the structure of the molecules from which the ions originate. Each substance has its own characteristic mass spectrum, and the mass spectrum of a mixture may therefore be analysed in terms of the spectra of the pure components, and the percentage of the different substances in the mixture calculated.

Analysis of the mass spectrum of a mixture may involve the solution of a large number of simultaneous equations, but the work involved in computation may be reduced by fractionation of the mixture before analysis and by working out the portion of the peaks due to heavier isotopes first.

6.2.1.1   INLET SYSTEMS

The mode of introduction of the sample into the ion source is dependent upon the nature of the sample and in particular its volatility.

The simplest system designed to introduce reference compounds into the ion source includes a 35 cm³ reservoir into which the compound is injected

130

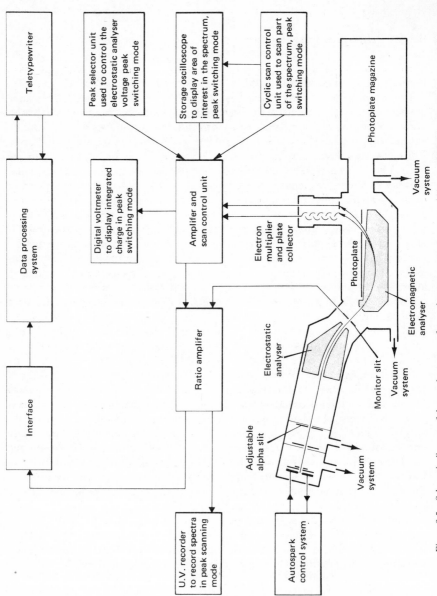

Figure 6.5   Schematic diagram of the complete system of a spark source mass spectrometer (Courtesy AEI Scientific Apparatus Ltd.)

through a septum. Flow into the ion source is through a molecular leak and a shut-off valve is provided. Facilities for pumping out the system and obtaining temperatures up to 100°C are provided.

Relatively volatile gases and liquids may be introduced by a probe attached to a small reservoir into which the sample is injected and from which it flows to the ion source at a controlled rate. The temperature of the system may be controlled between ambient and 150°C.

For less volatile substances an all-glass heated system may be used. Glass is used for the system so that catalytic decomposition of the sample is reduced to a minimum. The system can be operated at temperatures up to 350°C and incorporates its own controlled heating and temperature monitoring facilities. It includes both large and small reservoirs to enable a wide range of quantities of liquid or solid samples to be introduced.

To introduce less volatile and solid samples into the ion chamber a probe may be used. The sample is loaded on to the tip of the probe, which is inserted into the ion source through a two-stage vacuum lock.

The probe may be heated or cooled independently of the ion chamber as required from −50 to +350°C. The temperature is measured by a platinum resistance thermometer, forming part of the temperature control system, which enables the temperature to be set from the instrument control panel.

Effluents from a gas chromatograph column usually flow at about 50 cm^3/min and consist mainly of carrier gas. In order to reduce the flow, the gas is passed through a molecular separator designed to remove as much as possible of the carrier gas but permitting the significant components to pass into the mass spectrometer.

6.2.1.2   ION SOURCES

In the system shown the ions are produced by a spark passed between electrodes formed from the sample by applying a controlled pulsed r.f. voltage. Positive ions representative of the sample are produced in the discharge and are accelerated through a simple ion gun. This beam is defined by resolving slits before it passes into the analyser section.

Other methods may be employed in order to produce ions of the sample which are impelled towards the exit slit by a small positive potential in the ion chamber. These methods involve increasing the energy of the sample by some form of radiation. Organic compounds require photons of energy up to 13 eV to produce ionisation so that a high energy beam of short wavelength radiation is sufficient. Where energies greater than 11 eV are required window materials become a problem so that the photon source has to emit radiation directly into the ion source. A helium discharge at 21.21 eV provides a convenient source of photons capable of ionising all organic compounds.

Electrons emitted by a heated filament and accelerated by about 70 eV and directed across the ion chamber may also be used to ionise many substances. While 70 eV produces the maximum ion yield, any voltage down to the ionisation voltage of the compound studied may be used.

The electric field production near a sharp point or edge at a high potential will have a high potential gradient and may be used to produce ions. Ions can also be formed by the collision of an ion and a molecule. This method can produce stable but unusual ions, e.g.

$$CH_4^+ + CH_4 \rightarrow CH_5^+ + CH_3$$

and is most efficient at pressures of about 10^{-2} N/m^2.

It is most important to realise that the process of producing ions from molecules will in many cases split up the original molecule into a whole range of ions of simpler structure and the peak of maximum height in the spectrum does not necessarily represent the ion of the original molecule. For example the mass spectrum of m-xylene $C_6H_4(CH_3)_2$ may contain 22 peaks of different m/e values, and the peak of maximum height represents a m/e ratio of 91 while the ions having the next highest peak have a m/e ratio of 106.

6.2.1.3 SEPARATION OF THE IONS

The mass spectrometer shown in *Figure 6.5* employs the Mattauch-Herzog geometry but other forms of geometry achieve a similar result.

The positive ions representative of the sample produced in the ion source are accelerated by a controlled electrostatic field of V volts in a simple gun, the spread of the ions being controlled by the resolving slits. If an ion of mass m and charge e can be regarded as starting from rest, then its velocity v after falling through a potential V volts will be represented by the equation

$$\tfrac{1}{2} mv^2 = eV \tag{6.1}$$

The ion beam then passes through the electrostatic analyser where it passes between two smooth curved plates which are at different potentials, such that an electrostatic field of B exists between them which is at right-angles to the path of the ions. The centrifugal force on the ions will therefore be given by

$$mv^2/r = eB \tag{6.2}$$

Combining the equations we see that the radius of curvature r of the path will be given by

$$r = mv^2/eB = 2eV/eB = 2V/B \tag{6.3}$$

Thus, the curvature of the path of all ions will be dependent upon the accelerating and deflecting fields only and independent of the mass/charge ratio. Therefore, if the field B is kept constant the electrostatic analyser focuses the ions at the monitor slit in accordance with their translational energies. The monitor slit can be arranged to intercept a given portion of the beam. The energy-focused ion beam is then passed through the electromagnetic analyser where a magnetic field at right-angles to the electrostatic field is applied (i.e. at right-angles to the plane of the diagram). Moving electric charges constitute an electric current so that if each carries a charge e, and moves with a velocity v, at right-angles to a uniform magnetic field H, each particle will be subject to a force F where $F = Hev$ in a direction given by Fleming's left-hand rule, i.e. in a direction mutually at right-angles to the magnetic field and the direction of the stream. Thus the ions will move in a curved path radius r such that

$$mv^2/r = Hev \qquad (6.4)$$

or
$$r = mv^2/Hev = mv/He \qquad (6.5)$$

but
$$mv^2 = 2eV \text{ or } v = \sqrt{(2eV/m)} \qquad (6.6)$$

$$\therefore r = (m/eH)\sqrt{(2eV/m)} \text{ or } r^2 = (m^2/e^2H^2)\,(2eV/m) = (2V/H^2)\,(e/m) \quad (6.7)$$

or
$$m/e = (H^2r^2)/2V \qquad (6.8)$$

At constant values of the electrostatic and electromagnetic fields all ions of the same m/e ratio will have the same radius of curvature. Thus, after separation in the electromagnetic analyser, ions having a single charge will be brought to a focus along definite lines on the photographic plate according to their mass, starting with the lower mass on the left-hand edge of the plate and increasing to the higher mass on the right.

The ions will therefore give rise to narrow bands on the photographic plate and the density of these bands will be a measure of the number of ions falling on the band. The sensitivity range of the plate is limited, and it is necessary to make several exposures for increasing periods of time to record ions which have a large ratio of abundance. By using long exposure, ions which are present in very low abundances may be accurately measured. The intensity of the photographic lines after development of the plate may be compared with a microphotometer similar to that used with optical spectrometers.

As all ions are recorded simultaneously, ion beam fluctuations affect all lines equally and the photographic plate also integrates the ions over the whole of the exposure.

The instantaneous monitor current may be measured and used to control the sparking at the electrodes at optimum by adjusting the gap between the electrodes.

The integrated monitor current is a guide to the exposure, and the range of masses falling on the photographic plate may be controlled by adjustment of the value of the electrostatic and magnetic fields.

The plate collector and the electron multiplier detection systems enable quantitative analysis to be carried out with greater speed and precision than with the photographic plate detector. For high sensitivity the ions may be caused to fall on the first dynode of the electron multiplier and the final current further amplified, and recorded on the ultra-violet sensitive strip recorder. The logarithmic ratio of the monitor and collector signals is used in recording spectra in order to minimise the errors due to variations in the ion beam.

In the peak switching mode the operator can select the peaks of interest and display them on an oscilloscope and examine them with greater precision. Increasing the resolving power of the instrument will enable what may initially appear to be a single peak to be split up into its components representing ions differing in mass by a small amount.

Provision is made for changing the amplification in logarithmic steps so that a wide range of abundances may be measured. Where a rapid qualitative and semi-qualitative analysis is required for a very wide range of masses, consecutive masses are swept across the multiplier collector by allowing the magnet current to decay from a pre-set value at a pre-set rate while the accelerating voltage is kept constant. Values of ion current from the individual ion species received at the detector are amplified and instantaneously compared with a fraction of the total ion current at the monitor by means of two logarithmic amplifiers which feed into a summing amplifier. This gives a signal proportional to the relative ion concentrations, which is recorded on the ultra-violet sensitive strip recorder and has the form shown in *Figure 6.6*.

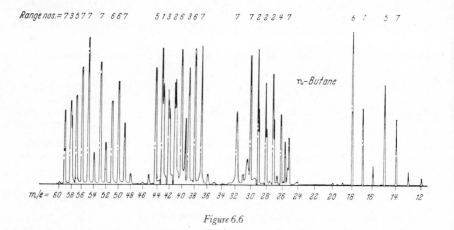

Figure 6.6

Where large amounts of data are generated the output from the ratio detector of the electrical detection system can be fed through a suitable interface into a data acquisition and processing system. If necessary this system can be programmed to print out details of the elements present in the sample and an indication of their concentration.

6.2.1.4   OTHER METHODS OF SEPARATION OF IONS

Two methods of separation of ions are available using only electrostatic fields. These are found in the 'time of flight' type instrument and the quadrupole mass spectrometer.

Time of flight type mass instrument

This type of instrument usually has a relatively low resolution but a very fast response time so that it is used largely for investigating fast reactions.

In this instrument the ions are accelerated through a potential V, thus acquiring a velocity v given by

$$\tfrac{1}{2}mv^2 = eV \text{ or } v = \sqrt{[(e/m)\, 2V]} \tag{6.9}$$

If the ions then pass through a field-free region, length d, to the detector, the time of transit t will be d/v, i.e.

$$t = d\,[(e/m)\, 2V]^{-1/2} = [(e/m)\, 2d^2V]^{-1/2} \tag{6.10}$$

Thus, the ions will arrive at the detector after times proportional to $(m/e)^{1/2}$. The time intervals between the arrival of ions of different mass at the detector are usually very short and the mass spectrum is most conveniently displayed on a cathode ray tube.

Quadrupole mass spectrometer

This type of instrument is particularly suited to vacuum system monitoring and to a wide range of gas analysis. Although it has a relatively modest resolving power it has the advantages of small analyser size, robustness, and relatively low cost.

The ions are produced in the ion source by bombarding the sample with electrons from a filament assembly with a rhenium or tungsten filament. The ions are extracted electrostatically from the ioniser, and focused by electrostatic lenses into the quadrupole mass filter. The mass filter consists of two pairs of metal rods which are precisely aligned, housed in a chamber at a pressure of $2.6 \times 10^{-4} N/m^2$. One pair is connected to a d.c. voltage source, while the other pair is supplied by a radio frequency voltage. The combination of the d.c. and r.f. voltages creates a hyperbolic potential distribution. The applied voltages increase uniformly from zero to a given maximum and then suddenly fall to zero again, and this voltage sweep is then repeated.

Most ions entering the quadrupole field are deflected by the changing electric fields and strike the rods, where they are neutralised. However, at any given time, ions of one specific mass/charge ratio are deflected about as much toward one rod as toward another. Thus, ions of this mass/charge ratio are passed by the filter, and ions with any other mass/charge ratio are excluded.

As the voltages are swept from zero to their maximum values, the entire mass range is scanned. After passing through the mass filter the ions impinge on an electron multiplier, and a signal proportional to the collected ion current can be displayed on an oscilloscope or a potentiometric strip chart recorder. As the voltages increase uniformly the position of the mass peaks is linearly related to the mass, so the spectrum is extremely easy to interpret. The instrument may have two switched mass ranges such as 2–100 or 12–200 atomic mass units. The analyser is manufactured from stainless steel, ceramic and tungsten or rhenium so that it can operate at up to 200°C with a cooled r.f. unit, and with the r.f. unit removed may be baked at temperatures up to 400°C to remove traces of previously tested samples.

6.3   ELECTROCHEMICAL MEASUREMENTS

Although it is by no means necessary to understand fully the complex theories behind electrochemical measurements in order to maintain industrial instruments for the measurement of electrolytic conductivity, pH, and oxidation–reduction potential, a fundamental knowledge of certain basic principles is essential.

6.3.1   Fundamental chemistry

The base structure of matter has been described to a limited extent in Volume

1. This discussion will be extended here only as far as is necessary to understand electrochemical measurements.

6.3.1.1   RELATIVE ATOMIC AND MOLECULAR MASSES

The simplest substance is an element in which all atoms have the same nuclear charge. An atom is the smallest particle of an element which can exhibit the properties of the element and is identified by its proton number, which is defined as the number of protons in the nucleus, or the number of electrons present in the neutral atom of the element.

Originally it was believed that atoms of an element were identical, but it is known that atoms of an element can have identical chemical properties, which are a function of its orbital electrons, but have nuclei which have a different number of neutrons. These atoms of the same element having the same nuclear charge but differing nuclear masses are called 'isotopes'. Isotopes are identified by their nucleon, or mass, number which is the sum of the number of protons and neutrons in the nucleus. The mass number of an isotope is written as a superscript preceding its symbol, while the proton number is written as a subscript preceding the symbol so that the symbol for one atom of carbon, nucleon or mass number 12 and proton number 6, is $^{12}_{6}C$.

Many elements are a mixture of isotopes. Hydrogen, for example, consists of 99.985% of atoms of prontium $^{1}_{1}H$, 0.015% of atoms of deuterium $^{2}_{1}H$, with a trace of tritium $^{3}_{1}H$. Carbon consists of 98.89% atoms of isotope $^{12}_{6}C$, and 1.11% of atoms of the isotope $^{13}_{6}C$. However, since the relative isotopic masses of the constituents and the isotope ratios are constant, the average relative atomic mass A_r (atomic weight) of an element is constant and may be found in any standard chemistry text book.

Originally the relative atomic mass of an atom, or molecule, was expressed as the ratio of its mass to the mass of the lightest atom, hydrogen, which was defined as one. However, in recent years the mass spectrograph has been the most accurate method of measuring relative atomic masses which range from 1 to over 238. It is very difficult to produce an instrument to cover such a wide range but instruments to cover limited ranges are much easier to produce. If accuracy is to be maintained, it is essential to calibrate the instrument at points within its range. Carbon compounds may be formed containing chains of CH_2 groups differing in relative atomic mass by increments of 14. Thus a wide range of ions for calibrating the mass spectrograph may be prepared from the most abundant carbon isotope $^{12}_{6}C$. Hence, the modern definition of relative atomic (or isotopic) mass is the ratio of mass of one atom (or isotope) to one twelfth of the mass of one atom $^{12}_{6}C$ of the carbon isotope, relative isotopic mass 12.

The relative molecular mass of a substance can be found by adding together the relative atomic masses of the constituent atoms. For example, one molecule of sulphuric acid, H_2SO_4, has a relative mass $2 + 32 + 4 (16) = 98$.

6.3.1.2   COMBINING POWER OR VALENCY

For our purposes we may regard the combining power or valency of an element as the number of hydrogen atoms one atom of the element will combine with or displace; or it is twice the number of oxygen atoms that one atom of the element will combine with or displace. For example:

Sodium	+	Hydrochloric acid	=	Sodium chloride	+	Hydrogen
$2Na$	+	$2HCl$	=	$2NaCl$	+	H_2

i.e. each sodium atom displaces a hydrogen atom, therefore valency of sodium equals 1.

Zinc	+	Sulphuric acid	=	Zinc sulphate	+	Hydrogen
Zn	+	H_2SO_4	=	$ZnSO_4$	+	H_2

i.e. one atom of zinc replaces two hydrogen atoms, therefore its valency is 2.

Sulphur	+	Oxygen	=	Sulphur dioxide
S	+	O_2	=	SO_2

i.e. one atom of sulphur combines with two atoms of oxygen, therefore its valency is 4.

6.3.1.3 AMOUNT OF SUBSTANCE

The amount of substance is not the same as its mass. The amount of substance and its mass, unlike volume, are independent of temperature and pressure. It is also true that the amount of a particular substance is proportional to its mass. Any resemblance between amount of substance and mass ends there, however, as in general the amounts of several different substances are not proportional to their masses. We cannot say that because a quantity of two different elements have the same mass they have the same amounts of substance.

The amount of substance is proportional to the number of specified entities of that substance. The proportionality factor is the same for all substances. It is called the Avogadro constant and is denoted by L. It is not a number but is a number divided by an amount of substance, and so has a dimension of (amount of substance)$^{-1}$.

The specified entity may be an atom, a molecule, an ion, a radical, an electron, a photon, etc., or any specified group of such particles. The ratio of two amounts of substance can therefore be measured (L cancelling) by any method which can be used to measure the corresponding numbers of specified entities. The most precise method of measuring the ratio of the amount of substance B in a given sample of B to the amount of substance A in a given sample of A depends upon the use of a balance and of a mass spectrometer. The balance may be used to find the ratio of the masses of the samples, and the mass spectrometer used to obtain the ratio of the atomic masses of the nuclides contained by the substances to the mass of a standard nuclide N^e, thus enabling the ratio of the amounts of substance to be obtained.

The mole

The amount of substance of a system is measured in terms of the mole, which is defined as the amount of substance of a system which contains as many elementary entities as there are atoms in 0.012 kg of carbon–12. In order to avoid ambiguity the precise nature of the elementary entity must be specified.

In the SI system, units such as the gram atom, gram molecule, gram equivalent, gram ion and gram formula are all obsolete, so

1 mole of Ar not 1 'gram atom' of Ar
1 mole of H_2SO_4 not 1 'gram molecule' of H_2SO_4
1 mole of $\frac{1}{2}H_2SO_4$ not 1 'equivalent of H_2SO_4'
1 mole of SO_4^{2-} not 1 'gram ion' of SO_4^{2-}
1 mole of e^- not 1 'faraday'
1 mole of γ not 1 'einstein'.

Solution concentration

The concentration of a substance in a solution should be expressed as amount of solute in a cubic metre, but the amount of solute in a cubic decimetre (litre) is still sometimes used. It is most usefully expressed in moles of solute per cubic metre of solution, i.e. mol/m^3.

However, concentration is sometimes expressed as molality, which is the number of moles of solute in 1 kg of solution, i.e. mol/kg. It is also still expressed as percentage by mass, or in the case of very dilute solutions as parts solute per million of solution.

6.3.1.4   ELECTRICAL CONDUCTION IN LIQUIDS

As early as 1833, Faraday realised that there are two classes of substances which conduct electricity. In the first class are the metals and alloys, and certain non-metals such as graphite, which conduct electricity without undergoing any chemical change. The flow of the current is due to the motion of electrons within the conductor, and the conduction is described as metallic, or electronic*.

In the second class are salts, acids and bases which, when fused or dissolved in water, conduct electricity owing to the fact that particles carrying positive or negative electric charges move in opposite directions through the liquid. It is this motion of electrically charged particles which constitutes the current. The conduction of electricity by these substances, which are known as electrolytes, generally results in the substance being split up into something simpler, and the process is known as electrolysis.

Theory of electrolytic dissociation

When an electrolyte is dissolved in water it immediately splits up, at least

*See Volume 1.

partially, into atoms or groups of atoms which carry an electric charge. These charged atoms or groups are known as 'ions'.

Consider common salt (sodium chloride), which is formed when the metal sodium is combined with chlorine. In combining with a chlorine atom, a sodium atom (symbol Na) loses an electron to the chlorine atom (Cl) so that it is left with a positive charge. The chlorine atom on the other hand will have acquired a negative charge.

$$Na - e = Na^+, Cl + e = Cl^-, \ (e = \text{charge on an electron})$$

When the sodium chloride is dissolved in water some of the molecules will split up into the charged atoms or ions. This process is called dissociation, or ionisation. A state of equilibrium will exist between the ions and the undissociated salt.

Molecules of salt will be dissociating, and at the same time ions will be recombining. The equilibrium is therefore represented by an equation written with a 'reversible' sign:

Sodium chloride	⇌	Sodium ion	+	Chlorine ion
NaCl	⇌	Na^+	+	Cl^-

Ions do not behave in the same way as atoms. A sodium atom (Na) will act immediately upon water but a sodium ion (Na^+) can exist in water without acting upon the water in any way.

The extent to which a substance dissociates depends partly upon the substance and partly upon the dilution of the solution, and the degree of dissociation, represented by the symbol α, is defined as the fraction of the electrolyte dissociated. The greater the dilution of a solution, the larger is the percentage of the molecules of electrolyte which dissociate, until in very dilute solutions almost all the molecules are dissociated.

The solution of the electrolyte will remain electrically neutral because equal quantities of positive and negative charge of electricity are produced. In the case of common salt, equal numbers of equally charged positive and negative particles are present in the solution. When barium chloride is dissolved in water, one barium ion and two chloride ions are produced from one molecule of salt, but the barium ion will carry two positive charges so that the solution is still electrically neutral.

Barium chloride	⇌	Barium ions	+	Chloride ions
$BaCl_2$	⇌	Ba^{++}	+	$2Cl^-$

Theory of electrolysis

Consider a glass vessel containing a solution of hydrochloric acid. The solution will contain chlorine and hydrogen ions due to dissociation of the acid.

$$HCl \rightleftharpoons H^+ + Cl^-$$

The water in which the acid is dissolved will also be ionised to a very slight extent.

Water	$\rightleftharpoons$	Hydrogen ions	+	Hydroxyl ions
H_2O	$\rightleftharpoons$	H^+	+	OH^-

The ions will be in motion in the solution, but the motion will be entirely random so that there is no flow of electricity in any particular direction.

Imagine a pair of electrodes placed in the solution as shown (*Figure 6.7*). The anode is the electrode connected to the positive terminal of the battery so that it will have a positive electric charge. The cathode, connected to the negative terminal of the battery, will have a negative charge. As like charges repel each other, and unlike charges attract, the negatively charged chlorine ions will be repelled by the cathode but attracted by the anode, while positively charged hydrogen will move to the cathode. The ions moving to the anode are called anions, and those moving to the cathode are called cations.

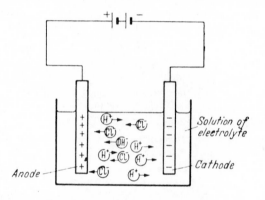

Figure 6.7   *Electrolysis of hydrochloric acid*

When the positively charged hydrogen ions—mainly derived from the acid but a few derived from the water—reach the cathode, they each receive an electron from the cathode and become neutral hydrogen atoms which combine to form molecules of hydrogen gas.

Hydrogen ion	+	Electronic charge	=	Hydrogen atom
H^+	+	e	=	H

and $H + H = H_2$ (hydrogen gas).

Cl^- ions from the acid and a few OH^- ions from the water reach the anode. The chlorine ions are more ready to part with electrons to the anode than are the hydroxyl ions, and are discharged more easily. They are in fact the only ions discharged. They then combine to form molecules of chlorine gas:

$$Cl^- - e = Cl, \text{ and } Cl + Cl = Cl_2$$

When sodium chloride is dissolved in water there will exist in the solution Na^+, Cl^-, H^+ and OH^- ions. Of the Cl^- and OH^- ions, it is the Cl^- ions which are more readily discharged at the anode. Of the Na^+ and H^+ ions, it is H^+ ions which are more readily discharged at the cathode. When a solution of sodium chloride is electrolysed, hydrogen gas is given off at the cathode and chlorine gas at the anode. The removal of hydrogen ions at the cathode results in further dissociation of water molecules so that as fast as hydrogen ions are removed, fresh hydrogen ions are formed. The hydroxyl ions which are formed at the same time as the hydrogen ions will accumulate in the solution and are responsible for its alkaline properties.

Since ions of metals and hydrogen are always positively charged they will always travel to and be discharged at the cathode. Ions of non-metals—except hydrogen—are always discharged at the anode. The actual substance produced at the electrodes in electrolysis depends upon the nature of the solution and upon the nature of the electrodes, for in some cases the primary product of the electrolysis is changed because it reacts with the electrode at which it is released. When solutions of salts of metals such as copper, silver, chromium and nickel are electrolysed, the metal is deposited on the cathode, and this process is the basis of electroplating.

Faraday's laws of electrolysis

1. When an electrolyte is decomposed by an electric current, the mass of substance set free at an electrode is proportional to the quantity of electricity which flows through the solution.

2. When the same quantity of electricity is passed through solutions of different electrolytes, the mass of an ion discharged at an electrode is proportional to its relative molecular mass divided by the number of elementary charges on the ion, i.e. M_r/z. If the same current is passed through solutions of sulphuric acid, silver nitrate and copper sulphate the masses of hydrogen, silver and copper liberated will be in the ratio 1:108:63.6/2. Relative atomic masses of hydrogen, silver and copper are 1:108 and 63.6, but while the hydrogen and silver ions carry one elementary charge, the ion of copper carries two. The quantity of electricity required to discharge one mole of ions each carrying one elementary charge will be $6.022 \times 10^{23} \times 1.602 \times 10^{-19}$ coulombs, as the former is the number of ions in a mole and the latter the charge on each ion, i.e. 9.647×10^4 coulombs (formerly the faraday).

6.3.1.5   CONDUCTIVITY OF SOLUTIONS

Electrolytes conduct electricity with varying ease. The ability of an electrolyte to conduct an electric current is measured in terms of its conductivity, which is the reciprocal of its resistance.

The resistance R of any conductor is given by

$$R = (\rho l/a) \ \Omega, \text{ or } \rho = (Ra/l) \ \Omega \text{ m} \qquad (6.11)$$

where ρ is the resistivity of the substance defined as the resistance between the opposite faces of a cube, each side being one metre, l the length (m) and a the area (m²). Therefore:

$$\text{Conductivity } \kappa \text{ (kappa)} = 1/\rho \ 1/\Omega \text{ m or siemens/m} \qquad (6.12)$$

Molar conductivity (Λ)

The conductivity of electrolytes varies greatly with the concentration, because dilution (a) increases the degree of ionisation, but (b) tends to reduce the number of ions per cubic metre. In order to measure the first effect alone another term is defined. This is the molar conductivity Λ, where

$$\Lambda = \kappa/c \qquad (6.13)$$

where c is the concentration in mol/m³ or mol m⁻³. The basic units of molar conductivity will be (siemens/m) (m³/mol), i.e. siemens m²/mol. For example, the conductivity at 25°C of potassium chloride solution at a concentration of 10^2 mol/m³ is 1.29 1/Ω m, so the molar conductivity

$$\Lambda = (1.29\ S/m)/(10^2\ mol/m^3) = 1.29 \times 10^{-2}\ S\ m^2/mol = 1.29\ S\ dm^2/mol \quad (6.14)$$

The above is calculated in basic SI units but as the cubic metre is rather large and the dm³ is a convenient volume of solution to make up in the laboratory, concentrations are often expressed in mol/dm³, so the molar conductivity may be expressed as S dm²/mol, or S cm²/mol.

When comparing the molar conductivities it is advisable for ease of comparison to specify the mole of substance carrying a mole of elementary charges, e.g. a mole of sodium chloride NaCl, but copper sulphate as one mole of ½CuSO₄.

Molar conductivity at infinite dilution. As the dilution of a solution increases the molar conductivity increases and tends towards a limiting value, denoted by the symbol Λ^{∞}, the molar conductivity at infinite dilution *(Figure 6.8)*. In certain cases, for dilute solutions the empirical relationship

$$\Lambda \doteq \Lambda^{\infty} - k\sqrt{c} \qquad (6.15)$$

exists where k is a constant. The graph of Λ plotted against $\sqrt{c}$ is therefore a line of intercept Λ^{∞} and a slope of $-k$. Thus in cases where the relationship exists the value of Λ^{∞} may be obtained by extrapolation.

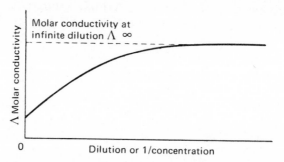

Figure 6.8   Effect of dilution on molar conductivity

Figure 6.9 shows such graphs. Certain substances such as salts of strong acids and alkalis readily ionise in water and give a high molar conductivity over a wide range of concentrations. The solutions of weak electrolytes, such as acetic acid, organic acids or gases, have a low molar conductivity until very high dilutions are reached, when the value of the molar conductivity rises very steeply. Other electrolytes such as zinc sulphate have a behaviour in between these extremes and are sometimes called intermediate electrolytes.

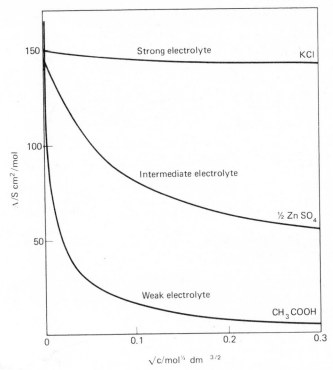

Figure 6.9 Relationship between molar conductivity and $\sqrt{c}$

Conductivity and concentration

Water itself has a very small conductivity. The purest water which has been investigated has a conductivity at 18°C of 4.3×10^{-6} S/m, while ordinary water has a conductivity of between 300 and 600×10^{-6} S/m. The presence of 1 mole of potassium chloride in 50 dm³ of solution at 18°C increases the conductivity to 240×10^{-3} S/m, i.e. increases the conductivity about a thousand-fold.

The measurement of the conductivity of water provides a sensitive and accurate method of determining the quantity of dissolved ionised impurity provided the concentration of impurity is low. The actual concentration for which the relationship between concentration of impurity and conductivity will be linear is shown in *Figure 6.10* and it varies with type of impurity and degree to which it ionises. However, measurement of concentration by conductivity measurement is still possible over a limited range even if the relationship is not linear, provided the conductivity does not reach a maximum or minimum within the range, and the departure of the relationship from linear is not too great. Suppliers of conductivity-measuring equipment have collected considerable data on the conductivity of many electrolytes and mixtures of electrolytes and should be consulted when conductivity measurement is considered for impurity measurement.

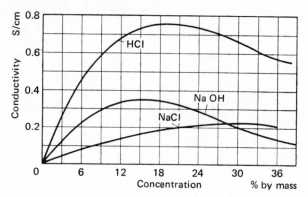

Figure 6.10   Conductivity versus concentration at 18.3°C

6.3.1.6   IONIC CONDUCTIVITY

The molar conductivity of an electrolyte at infinite dilution is the sum of the equivalent conductivities (or 'mobilities') of the anion and cation (Kohlrausch's Law).

$$\Lambda^{\infty} = l_a + l_c \tag{6.16}$$

where l_a = Conductivity due to anions
    l_c = Conductivity due to cations.

The ionic conductivity increases with temperature in accordance with the empirical equation

$$l_t = l_{18}[1 + a(t - 18)] \tag{6.17}$$

Table 6.2 gives the values of the molar conductivities at infinite dilution of some of the more important ions at 18°C, and the values of the temperature coefficient a.

Table 6.2 IONIC CONDUCTIVITIES AT 18°C

Cation	Molar conductivity, S cm²/mol	a	Anion	Molar conductivity, S cm²/mol	a
H^+	315.0	0.01573	Cl^-	65.5	0.0216
Li^+	33.4	0.0265	Br^-	67.6	0.0215
Na^+	43.5	0.0244	I^-	66.5	0.0213
K^+	64.6	0.0217	NO_3^-	61.7	0.0205
NH_4^+	64.3	0.0222	OH^-	174.0	0.018
Ag^+	54.3	0.0229	Ac^-	35.0	0.0238
$\frac{1}{2} Ca^{++}$	51.0	0.0247	$\frac{1}{2} Ox^{--}$	61.0	0.0231
$\frac{1}{2} Mg^{++}$	45.0	0.0256	$\frac{1}{2} SO_4^{--}$	68.3	0.0227

This table makes possible the calculation of the molar conductivity at infinite dilution of many solutions. For example, the molar conductivity of acetic acid is

$$\Lambda^\infty = l_H + l_{Ac} = 315 + 35 = 350 \text{ S cm}^2/\text{mol} \qquad (6.18)$$

It is seen from the table that conductivity varies very considerably from one ion to another. The conductivities of hydrogen ion and hydroxyl ion are very much greater than those of other ions. Since one mole of any ion having a single elementary charge carries the same amount of electricity, the differences in the values of ionic conductivities must be due to different ions having different velocities through the solution when under the influence of the same potential gradient.

The differences in velocity, or mobility, of ions in solution have a very important practical application which will be described later.

Effect of temperature on molar conductivity

Since ionic conductivity increases with increase of temperature, molar conductivity will also increase. In the case of weak electrolytes, however, which undergo ionisation with the release of heat, the degree of ionisation will decrease as the temperature is raised. The effect of this decrease of ionisation may more than counterbalance the increased mobility of the ions so that the conductivity may have a maximum value at some particular temperature and then decrease with increase or decrease of temperature. The variation of conductivity with temperature depends not only upon the influence of temperature upon the electrolyte but also upon the influence of the temperature upon the dielectric constant and viscosity of the solvent. For many solutions at ordinary temperatures the conductivity of the solution increases by about 2% per degree rise in temperature. It is therefore essential to provide some means of temperature compensation on industrial instruments in order to correct for variations in readings on the instrument which are due, not to change in solution concentration, but to deviation of solution temperature from the reference temperature.

6.3.1.7 POLARISATION

When an electric current is passed between platinum electrodes immersed in a solution of an electrolyte, metal or gas is deposited on, or liberated at, the electrodes. The gas or metal is liberated when ions lose their charges by giving up electrons to the anode or by taking electrons from the cathode. The electrodes will therefore acquire a certain surface potential due to the loss or gain of electrons, and the size of this potential will depend upon the nature of the metal or gas liberated. The electrodes are said to be polarised, and their surfaces, along with the electrolyte, form a simple voltaic cell which has a certain e.m.f. known as the polarisation e.m.f. This polarisation e.m.f. acts in the opposite direction to that of the applied e.m.f. This may be shown by disconnecting the source of applied e.m.f., and connecting the electrodes to a voltmeter. An e.m.f. will be indicated by the voltmeter which is in the opposite direction to the applied e.m.f.

Polarisation is also brought about by changes in the concentration of the electrolyte in the neighbourhood of the electrodes owing to the effects of electrolysis. For example, if a solution of copper sulphate is being electrolysed between copper electrodes, copper is dissolved at the anode and is deposited at the cathode; and sulphate ions will be moving from the neighbourhood of the cathode to the neighbourhood of the anode. When a current is passed, therefore, the concentration of copper sulphate at the cathode decreases, owing to the deposition of the copper and the movement of the sulphate ions. At the anode, the concentration of the copper sulphate increases owing to the solution of the copper anode and the movement of the sulphate ions. The concentration of copper sulphate at the two electrodes will, therefore, no longer be the same, and owing to this difference of concentration an e.m.f. is set up which opposes the applied e.m.f. This is known as concentration polarisation.

When electrolysis of a solution of electrolyte commences, the resistance of the solution will be given by applied e.m.f./current, but as soon as the products of electrolysis are formed, the e.m.f. producing the current will be reduced by the amount of the polarisation e.m.f. The relationship of the applied e.m.f. to the current flowing through the solution will not obey Ohm's law.

In order to measure the conductivity of a solution of an electrolyte, an alternating current, such as that produced by an audio-frequency oscillator, must be used. In this way the effects of polarisation are overcome, for the current will flow first in one direction and then in the other, so that the conditions at both electrodes remain the same.

6.3.1.8   ACIDS AND ALKALIS

All acids dissociate when added to water, and produce hydrogen ions in the solution.

$$HNO_3 \leftrightharpoons H^+ + NO_3^-$$
$$H_2SO_4 \leftrightharpoons 2H^+ + SO_4^{--}$$
$$HCl \leftrightharpoons H^+ + Cl^-$$

The extent to which an acid dissociates varies from acid to acid, and increases with increasing dilution until in very dilute solutions almost all the acid is dissociated.

According to the ionic theory, the characteristic properties of acids are attributed to the hydrogen ions (H^+) which they produce in solution. Strong acids (nitric, sulphuric, hydrochloric) are those which produce a large concentration of hydrogen ions when added to water. As a result, they are excellent conductors of electricity. Weak acids like carbonic acid and acetic acid produce only a few hydrogen ions when they dissolve, and their solutions are poor conductors of electricity. The strength of a weak acid is indicated by its dissociation constant K, which is defined by the equation

$$K = ([A^-][H^+])/[HA] \text{ mol/dm}^3 \qquad (6.19)$$

where $[A^-]$ represents the molar concentration of the acidic ions, $[H^+]$

represents the concentration of hydrogen ions, and [HA] the concentration of undissociated acid. As this equation shows, at a given temperature the product of the concentrations of the acidic and hydrogen ions divided by the concentration of undissociated acid is constant. If more acid is added to the solution, a portion of it dissociates immediately to restore the relative amounts of ions and undissociated acid to the former value.

Similarly the typical properties of alkalis in solution are attributed to hydroxyl ions (OH^-). Strong alkalis such as sodium and potassium hydroxides produce a large concentration of hydroxyl ions when added to water. Weak alkalis such as ammonium hydroxide are only slightly ionised in water. The strength of a weak base is also indicated by its dissociation constant K which is defined by the equation

$$K = ([B^+][OH^-])/[BOH] \ mol/dm^3 \qquad (6.20)$$

where [B^+] represents the concentration of basic ions, [OH^-] represents the concentration of hydroxyl ions, and [BOH] the concentration of undissociated base.

Strong electrolytes have no dissociation constant. The expression ([A^-] [H^+])/[HA] (and the corresponding expression for bases) varies considerably with change in concentration. In the case of strong acids (and similarly for bases) the apparent degree of ionisation may be taken as a measure of the 'strength' of the acid.

Ionisation of water

Since even the purest water is slightly conducting, it follows that water itself ionises to a very slight extent into hydroxyl ions and hydrogen ions, so that there exists the equilibrium

$$H_2O \rightleftharpoons H^+ + OH^-$$

At a fixed temperature the degree of dissociation of the water is constant, and

$$([H^+][OH^-])/[H_2O] = K \ mol/dm^3 \qquad (6.21)$$

where K is the dissociation constant for water.

Since the concentration of ions is very small, the concentration of undissociated water molecules may be regarded as constant, therefore [H^+] [OH^-] = Constant = K_w, where K_w is the ionic product for water. That is, in water or any aqueous solution, the product of the concentration of hydrogen ions and hydroxyl ions is a constant provided the temperature is constant.

The concentration of hydrogen ions in water at 25°C as determined from conductivity measurement is very nearly 0.000 000 1 or 1×10^{-7} mol/dm³, and since the concentration of hydroxyl ions must be the same, the product of the concentrations (K_w) is 1×10^{-14}. The variation of K_w with temperature is given by the equation

$$\log_{10} K_w = 14.00 - 0.0331 \ (t\text{-}25) + 0.000 \ 17 \ (t\text{-}25)^2 \qquad (6.22)$$

where t is the temperature in degrees Celcius.

6.3.1.9 HYDROGEN ION EXPONENT OR pH

The range of hydrogen ion concentrations met in practice is very wide. The hydrogen ion concentration in 1 dm^3 of water to which 1 mole of hydrochloric acid has been added is 1 mol/dm^3 if the acid is completely dissociated. It falls to 10^{-14} mol/dm^3 if the mole of hydrochloric acid is replaced by 1 mole of sodium hydroxide, again assumed completely dissociated. A wide range of this nature is best expressed on a logarithmic scale.

A convenient scale of acidity and alkalinity is obtained by defining pH as the common logarithm of the reciprocal of the hydrogen ion concentration:

$$pH = \log_{10}(1/[H^+]) = -\log_{10}[H^+] \qquad (6.23)$$

The pH scale thus provides a system where the acidity of a solution can be expressed in terms of small positive numbers going from 0 for an acid having a hydrogen ion concentration of 1 mol/dm^3 to 14 for an alkaline having a hydroxide ion concentration of 1 or $10°$, or hydrogen ion concentration of 10^{-14}mol/dm^3.

In very strongly acid solutions the pH may be negative and in strongly alkaline solutions it may be greater than 14. A pH value of 7 represents a water neutrality. All solutions with a higher concentration of hydrogen ions than a neutral solution (i.e. an acidic solution) will have a pH value less than 7; while a solution with a lower hydrogen ion concentration than water (i.e. a basic solution) will have a pH value between 7 and 14. The more alkaline the solution, the higher will be its pH value; and conversely, the lower the pH value the more strongly acid is the solution. A change of 1 pH unit represents a ten-fold change in hydrogen ion concentration. A solution of pH value 4 will have 10 times more hydrogen ions per cubic decimetre than a solution of pH value 5. A solution of pH value 10 will have 10 times more hydroxyl, or 10 times fewer hydrogen ions, per cubic decimetre than a solution of pH value 9. Acids which have a greater hydrogen ion concentration than normal acids will have a negative pH value.

It must be realised that pH measuring devices measure the effective concentration, or activity, of the hydrogen ions and not the actual concentration. In very dilute solutions of electrolyte the activity and concentration are identical. As the concentration of electrolyte in solution increases above 0.1 mol/dm^3 however, the measured value of pH becomes a less reliable measure of the concentration of hydrogen ions. In addition, as the concentration of a solution increases the degree of dissociation of the electrolyte decreases.

A dilute solution of sulphuric acid is completely dissociated and the assumption that pH $= -\log 2(H_2SO_4)$* is justified. Anhydrous sulphuric acid is only slightly dissociated, the degree of dissociation rising as the pure acid is diluted.

A maximum hydrogen ion concentration occurs in the neighbourhood of 92% H_2SO_4, but at this concentration the difference between actual hydrogen ion concentration and the activity of the hydrogen ions is large, and the measured pH minimum of about -1.4 occurs at a much lower sulphuric acid content.

---

*The 2 occurs because each molecule of acid provides two hydrogen ions.

A more reliable indication of the ionic behaviour of a solution will be obtained if we define pH in terms of the hydrogen ion activity a_{H^+} so that

$$pH = \log_{10}(1/a_{H^+}) = -\log_{10} a_{H^+} \qquad (6.24)$$

where a_H is related to the hydrogen ion concentration c_{H^+} by the equation

$$a_{H^+} = f_{H^+} c_{H^+} \qquad (6.25)$$

where f_{H^+} is the activity coefficient.

The activity coefficient of an ion is the factor by which the activity differs from the concentration and is a measure of the interaction between ions. It has been shown that ionic interaction varies with concentration, so the activity coefficient also varies with concentration. At infinite dilution, where there is no ionic interaction, the activity coefficient is unity and the relative activity of the ion is equal to its concentration. As the concentration increases the activity coefficient decreases at first, passes through a minimum, and then rises often to a value greater than unity in very concentrated solutions. The initial fall is due to increasing interaction between the ions and the subsequent rise is due to non-ionic effects. This variation of activity coefficient is more marked for polyvalent ions which carry more electric charges and thus are subject to greater electrical forces.

The pH values of common acids and bases are given in the Appendix, page 276.

Whereas pH electrodes were designed specifically to measure the hydrogen ion activity in a solution, electrodes have now been developed to measure the activity of other ions. Such electrodes are known as 'ion-selective electrodes' and will be described in the section on electrodes which follows.

Practical specification of a pH scale

As the value of pH defined as $-\log_{10}$ (hydrogen ion activity) is extremely difficult to measure, in order to ensure that when different workers state a pH value they mean the same thing in all national standards (e.g. BS 1647:1961) an operational definition of pH is adopted.

The e.m.f. E_x of the cell

Pt H_2/Solution X/Concentrated KCl solution/Reference electrode

is measured and likewise the e.m.f. E_s of the cell

Pt H_2/Solution S/Concentrated KCl solution/Reference electrode,

both cells being at the same temperature throughout and the reference electrodes and bridge solutions being identical in the two cells.

The pH of the solution X denoted by pH(X) is then elevated to the pH of the solution S denoted by pH (S) by the definition:

$$pH(X) - pH(S) = (E_x - E_s)/(2.3026\ RT/F) \qquad (6.26)$$

where R = Gas constant
T = Temperature kelvin
F = 1 mole of e^- (Faraday constant)

Thus defined pH is a pure number.

To a good approximation, the hydrogen electrodes in both cells may be replaced by other hydrogen responsive electrodes, e.g. glass or quinhydrone. The two bridge solutions may be of any molality not less than 3.5 mol/kg provided they are the same.

Standards

The difference between the pH of two solutions having been defined as above, the definition of pH can be completed by assigning at each temperature a value of pH to one or more chosen solutions designated as standards. In BS 1647 the chosen primary standard is a solution of pure potassium hydrogen phthalate having a concentration of 0.05 mol/dm^3.

This solution is defined as having a pH value of 4.000 at 15°C and the following values at other temperatures between 0 and 95°C:

Between 0 and 55°C $$pH = 4.000 + \tfrac{1}{2}[(t\text{-}15)^2/100] \qquad (6.27)$$

Between 55 and 95°C $$pH = 4.000 + \tfrac{1}{2}[(t\text{-}15)^2/100] - (t\text{-}55)/500 \quad (6.28)$$

Other reference solutions* are given below which permit an alternative definition of pH which is specifically recommended for use with glass electrodes.

VALUES OF pH (S) FOR FIVE STANDARD AQUEOUS SOLUTIONS

$\theta c/°C$	A	B	C	D	E
0		4.003	6.984	7.534	9.464
5		3.999	6.951	7.500	9.395
10		3.998	6.923	7.472	9.332
15		3.999	6.900	7.448	9.276
20		4.002	6.881	7.429	9.225
25	3.557	4.008	6.865	7.413	9.180
30	3.552	4.015	6.853	7.400	9.139
35	3.549	4.024	6.844	7.389	9.102
38	3.548	4.030	6.840	7.384	9.081
40	3.547	4.035	6.838	7.380	9.068
45	3.547	4.047	6.834	7.373	9.038
50	3.549	4.060	6.833	7.367	9.011
55	3.554	4.075	6.834		8.985
60	3.560	4.091	6.836		8.962
70	3.580	4.126	6.845		8.921
80	3.609	4.164	6.859		8.885
90	3.650	4.205	6.877		8.850
95	3.674	4.227	6.886		8.833

The compositions of the standard solutions are:
A: KH tartrate (saturated at 25°C)
B: KH phthalate, $m = 0.05$ mol/kg
C: KH_2PO_4, $m = 0.025$ mol/kg; Na_2HPO_4, $m = 0.025$ mol/kg
D: KH_2PO_4, $m = 0.008\,695$ mol/kg; Na_2HPO_4, $m = 0.030\,43$ mol/kg
E: $Na_2B_4O_7$, $m = 0.01$ mol/kg
where m denotes molality.

*The values of pH (S) for standard solutions used here are based on McGlashan, M. L., *Physico-chemical Qualities and Units*, Royal Institute of Chemistry, 2nd edition (1971), not BS 1647.

The e.m.f. E_x is measured and likewise the e.m.f. E_1 and E_2 of similar cells with solution X replaced by standard solutions S_1 and S_2, so that E_1 and E_2 are on either side of and as near as possible to E_x. The pH of the solution X is then obtained by assuming linearity between pH and E, i.e.

$$(pH\ (X) - pH\ S_1)/pH\ S_2 - pH\ S_1) = (E_x - E_1/E_2 - E_1) \qquad (6.29)$$

Interpretation of pH. The operational definition of pH has no precise simple fundamental meaning. However, for dilute aqueous solutions having a concentration less than 0.1 mol/dm³ and being neither strongly acid nor alkaline (pH being between 2 and 12) the definition is such that

$$pH = -\log_{10}\{c(H^+)\,y_1/mol/dm^3\} \pm 0.02 \qquad (6.30)$$

where $c(H^+) =$ Concentration of hydrogen ion
$y_1 =$ Activity coefficient of a typical uni-valent electrolyte in the solution.

6.3.1.10   NEUTRALISATION

When acid and base solutions are mixed, they combine to form a salt and water.

Acid	+	Base	=	Salt	+	Water
Hydrochloric acid	+	Sodium hydroxide	=	Sodium chloride	+	Water
H^+Cl^-	+	Na^+OH^-	=	Na^+Cl^-	+	HOH
(dissociated)		(dissociated)		(dissociated)		(largely undissociated)

Thus, if equal volume dilute solutions of strong acid and strong alkali in which the ratio of concentrations to the number of elementary charges on an ion is equal are mixed, they yield neither an excess of H^+ ions nor of OH^- ions and the resultant solution is said to be neutral. The pH value of such a solution will be 7.

Hydrolysis

Equivalent amounts of acid and base will produce a neutral solution only when the acids and bases used are strong electrolytes. When a weak acid or base is used, hydrolysis occurs. When a salt formed by a weak acid and a strong base, such as sodium acetate, is present in water, the solution is slightly alkaline because some of the H^+ ions from the water are combined with acetic radicals in the relatively undissociated acetic acid, leaving an excess of OH^- ions, thus:

Sodium acetate	+	Water	→	Acetic acid	+	Sodium hydroxide
Na^+ Ac^-	+	HOH	→	H Ac	+	Na^+ OH^-
(dissociated)		(largely undissociated)				(dissociated)

The pH value of the solution will therefore be greater than 7. Experiment shows it to be 8.87 in 0.1 mol/dm³ solution at ordinary temperatures.

Similarly, ammonium chloride (NH_4Cl), the salt of a weak base and a strong acid, hydrolyses to form the relatively undissociated ammonium hydroxide (NH_4OH), leaving an excess of H^+ ions. The pH value of the solution will therefore be less than 7. Experiment shows it to be 5.13 at ordinary temperatures in a solution having a concentration of 0.1 mol/dm³.

A neutralisation process therefore does not always produce an exactly neutral solution when one mole of acid reacts with one mole of base.

Conductivity measurement as a guide to neutralisation

When an acid is added to an alkali the concentration of the fast moving hydroxyl ions is reduced, their place being taken by the less mobile acid anions.

$$(Na^+ + OH^-) + (H^+ + Cl^-) = (Na^+ + Cl^-) + H_2O$$

The conductance of the alkali solution, therefore, falls until the neutral point is reached and thereafter the addition of acid causes a marked increase of conductance owing to the presence of the rapidly moving hydrogen ions. The graph showing the relationship between the conductance and the quantity of acid added consists of two straight lines intersecting at A *(Figure 6.11)*, the point of neutralisation. The acid solution must be strong, otherwise the lines will not be straight owing to change in conductance of the solution owing to dilution.

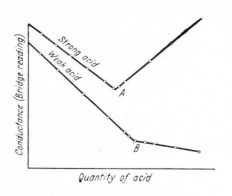

Figure 6.11   Effect of neutralisation on the conductance of a solution

When dealing with a weak acid, it is better to add the acid to the alkali. The conductance of the solution decreases as the acid is added, for the hydroxyl ions are replaced by slower anions of the acid. As the acid is only slightly ionised, and its ionisation is reduced by the presence of the salt of the acid, excess acid does not give an increase of conductance. The neutral point can still be detected by the sharp change in direction of the conductance curve at B *(Figure 6.11)*. Conductivity measurements may also be used as a guide to the progress in many other reactions in which one ion is replaced by another of a different mobility, or where hydrogen or hydroxyl ions are produced or removed by the reaction.

Common ion effect

All organic acids and the majority of inorganic acids are weak electrolytes and are only partially dissociated when dissolved in water. Acetic acid, for example, ionises only slightly in solution, a process represented by the equation

$$HAc \rightleftharpoons H^+ + Ac^-$$

Its dissociation constant at 25°C is only 1.8×10^{-5}, i.e.

$$([H^+][Ac^-])/[HAc] = 1.8 \times 10^{-5} \, mol/dm^3$$
$$or \, [H^+][Ac^-] = 1.8 \times 10^{-5} [H\,Ac] \qquad (6.31)$$

In a solution of acetic acid of moderate concentration, therefore, the bulk of the acid molecules will be undissociated, and the proportion present as acetic ions and hydrogen ions is small. If one of the salts of acetic acid, such as sodium acetate (NaAc) is added to the acetic acid solution, the ionisation of the acetic acid will be diminished. Salts are, with very few exceptions, largely ionised in solution, and consequently when sodium acetate is added to the solution of acetic acid the concentration of acetic ions is increased. If equation 6.31 is to continue to hold, the reaction $H^+ + Ac^- \rightarrow HAc$ must take place, and the concentration of hydrogen ions is reduced and will become extremely small.

Most of the acetic ions from the acid will have recombined; consequently the concentration of un-ionised acid will be practically equal to the total concentration of the acid. In addition, the concentration of acetic ions in the equilibrium mixture due to the acid will be negligibly small, and the concentration of acetic ions will, therefore, be practically equal to that from the salt. The equation

$$([H^+][Ac^-])/[HAc] = K, \, may \, be \, written \, as$$
$$([H^+][salt])/[acid] = K, \, or, \, [H^+] = K\,[acid]/[salt]$$
or taking logarithms $\log_{10}[H^+] = \log_{10} K + \log_{10}[acid]/[salt]$
$$or \, pH = -\log_{10} K - \log_{10}[acid]/[salt]$$
$$= \log_{10}(1/K) + \log_{10}[salt]/[acid] \qquad (6.32)$$

The pH value of the solution may, therefore, be regulated by the strength of the acid and the ratio [salt]/[acid] over a wide range of values.

Just as the ionisation of a weak acid is diminished by the addition of a salt of the acid, so the ionisation of a weak base will be diminished by the addition of a salt of the base, e.g. addition of ammonium chloride to a solution of ammonium hydroxide. The concentration of hydroxyl ions in the mixture will be given by a similar relationship to that obtained for hydrogen ions in the mixture of acid and salt, i.e.

$$[OH^-] = K\,[alkali]/[salt] \qquad (6.33)$$

6.3.1.11 BUFFER SOLUTIONS

In order to standardise pH measuring equipment it is necessary to have standard solutions, the pH values of which are definitely known. The solutions must be such that when they are made up in any laboratory they will have the known pH value. For this purpose, solutions are used which undergo relatively very little change of pH value on the addition of acid or alkali or with considerable change of concentration. Such solutions are called 'buffer' solutions and they usually consist of a mixture of a weak acid and its salt of a strong alkali (acetic acid and sodium acetate), or of a weak base and its salt with a strong acid (ammonia and ammonium chloride). A common buffer solution consists of a mixture of acetic acid and sodium acetate. If a small quantity of hydrochloric acid is added there will be no measurable equivalent change of $[H^+]$ in the solution. The added hydrogen ions will for the most part combine with the acetic ions present to form acetic acid which will be un-ionised.

$$H^+ + Ac^- \rightarrow HAc$$

The increase of H^+, or in other words the decrease of pH value, will be comparatively slight. Similarly, if sodium hydroxide is added to the solution, combination with the reserve acetic acid takes place,

$$OH^- + HAc \rightarrow H_2O + Ac^-$$

and the H^+ and the pH value of the solution remain practically unchanged.

Buffer solutions are, therefore, solutions which contain only a small actual concentration of hydrogen ion (or hydroxyl ion) but a large reserve of potential ions (e.g. acetic and hydrogen ions). When acid or alkali is added, combination with the potential ions takes place and the pH value of the solution undergoes very little change. The tendency of the solution to resist changes in its alkalinity or acidity will of course be limited by the size of the reserve of potential ions. With continued addition of acid, without a corresponding addition of sodium acetate, all acetate ions would be removed from the solution and further addition of acid would greatly increase the hydrogen ion concentration and greatly diminish the pH value of the solution.

By varying the proportions of the constituents in a buffer solution, solutions having known pH values within a wide range may be prepared. The value of the pH of the solution is given by equation 6.32. The weak acids commonly used in buffer solutions include phosphoric, boric, acetic, phthalic, succinic and citric acids. They are used at concentrations of about 0.05N and the acid is partially neutralised by alkali, or the salt introduced directly. Their preparation requires the use of pure reagents and careful measurement and weighing. As equation 6.32 indicates, it is more important to achieve correct proportions of acid to salt than correct concentration. An error of 10% in volume of water present may be ignored in work correct to 0.02 pH units.

The values of the dissociation constants and pK (i.e. $- \log_{10}K$) for a number of acids is given in *Table 6.3*.

A suitable buffer solution is chosen with a value of pK within one unit of the required value and the required pH value obtained by mixing the salt and acid in the correct ratio. By this method, the required value of the $\log_{10}$ [salt]/[acid] term in equation 6.32 will not exceed ± 1, and the ratio of [salt]/[acid] will lie between 10:1 and 1:10, and the solution will retain an appreciable buffer capacity.

Table 6.3.

Acid	Stage	Temperature, °C	Dissociation constant, K mol/dm³	pK (= − log K)
Boric		18	5.5×10^{-10}	9.26
Carbonic	1st	18	3.12×10^{-7}	6.51
Carbonic	1st	25	3.50×10^{-7}	6.46
Carbonic	2nd	25	4.4×10^{-11}	10.36
Phosphoric	1st	25	7.0×10^{-3}	2.16
Phosphoric	2nd	25	7.4×10^{-8}	7.13
Phosphoric	3rd	25	4.8×10^{-13}	12.46
Succinic	1st	25	6.4×10^{-5}	4.19
Succinic	2nd	25	2.7×10^{-6}	5.57
Citric	1st	25	8.7×10^{-4}	3.06
Citric	2nd	25	1.8×10^{-5}	4.74
Citric	3rd	25	4.0×10^{-6}	5.40
Acetic		25	1.75×10^{-5}	4.76

6.3.1.12 ELECTRODE POTENTIALS

When a metallic electrode is placed in a solution, a redistribution of electrical charges tends to take place. Positive ions of the metal enter the solution leaving the electrode negatively charged, and the solution will acquire a positive charge. If the solution already contains ions of the metal, there is a tendency for ions to be deposited on the electrode, giving it a positive charge. The electrode eventually reaches an equilibrium potential with respect to the solution, the magnitude and sign of the potential depending upon the concentration of metallic ions in the solution and the nature of the metal. Zinc has such a strong tendency to form ions that the metal forms ions in all solutions of its salts, so that it is always negatively charged relative to the solution. On the other hand, with copper, the ions have such a tendency to give up their charge that the metal becomes positively charged even when placed in the most dilute solution of copper salt.

This difference between the properties of zinc and copper is largely responsible for the e.m.f. of a Daniell cell. In the Daniell cell shown in *Figure 6.12,* when the poles are connected by a wire, sudden differences of potential

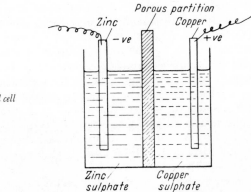

Figure 6.12   Daniell cell

are possible (a) at the junction of the wires with the poles, (b) at the junction of the zinc with the zinc sulphate, (c) at the junction of the zinc sulphate with the copper sulphate, (d) at the junction of the copper with the copper sulphate. The e.m.f. of the cell will be the algebraic sum of these potential differences.

In the measurement of the electrode potential of a metal, a voltaic cell similar in principle to the Daniell cell is used. It can be represented by the scheme

$$\text{Metal 1}\Bigg/\genfrac{}{}{0pt}{}{\text{Solution containing}}{\text{ions of metal 1}}\Bigg/\genfrac{}{}{0pt}{}{\text{Solution containing}}{\text{ions of metal 2}}\Bigg/\text{Metal 2}$$

Under ordinary conditions, when all the cell is at the same temperature, the thermo-electric e.m.f. at the junctions of wires and electrodes will vanish.

The potential difference which arises at the junction of the solutions, known as the liquid/junction potential, or diffusion potential, is due to the difference in rate of diffusion across the junction of the liquids of the cations and anions. If the cations have the greater rate of diffusion than the anions then the solution into which the cations are diffusing will acquire a positive charge, and the solution which the cations are leaving will acquire a negative charge; therefore, there is a potential gradient across the boundary. If the anions have the greater velocity, the direction of the potential gradient will be reversed. The potential difference at the junction of the two liquids may be reduced to a negligible value in two ways:

1. Have present in the two solutions relatively large and equal concentrations of an electrolyte, such as potassium nitrate, which produces ions which diffuse with approximately equal velocities.

2. Insert between the two solutions a 'salt bridge' consisting of a saturated solution of potassium chloride or of ammonium or potassium nitrate. These salts produce ions whose diffusion rates are approximately equal.

When salt bridges are used in pH work, the liquid junction potentials are reduced to less than 1 mV unless strong acids or alkalis are involved. If an excess of neutral salt is added to the acid or alkali, the liquid junction potential will be reduced. Thus the error involved is rarely measurable on industrial instruments.

All measurements of the e.m.f. of cells give the potential of one electrode with respect to another. In the Daniell cell, all that can be said is that the copper electrode is 1V positive with respect to the zinc electrode. It is not possible to measure the potential of a single electrode as it is impossible to make a second contact with the solution without introducing a second metal–solution interface. Practical measurement always yields a difference between two individual electrode potentials.

In order to assign particular values to the various electrode potentials an arbitrary zero is adopted. The potential of a standard hydrogen electrode at all temperatures is taken as zero. In this way all other electrode potentials can be referred to the standard hydrogen electrode. If it is found that the e.m.f. of a cell in which a certain electrode is coupled with a standard hydrogen electrode is x V, with the hydrogen electrode as the negative pole, it may be said that the potential of the electrode in question is x V on the hydrogen scale. If the hydrogen electrode had been the positive pole of the cell the electrode potential would be $-x$ V. The potential of any electrode is thus expressed with respect to the standard hydrogen electrode at the same temperature and the latter is established as a primary reference electrode.

In practice, however, it is not easy or convenient to set up a hydrogen electrode, so subsidiary reference electrodes are used, the potential of which relative to the standard hydrogen electrode has previously been accurately determined. Practical considerations limit the choice to electrodes consisting of a metal in contact with a solution which is saturated with a sparingly soluble salt of the metal and which also contains an additional salt with a common anion. Examples of these are:

The silver/silver chloride electrode $Ag/AgCl_{(s)}$ KCl_{aq}

The mercury/mercurous chloride $Hg/Hg_2Cl_{2(s)}$ KCl_{aq} known as the calomel electrode.

In each case the potential of the reference electrode is governed by the activity of the anion in the solution, which can be shown to be constant at a given temperature.

Variation of electrode potential with ion activity

The most common measurement of electrode potential is in the measurement of pH, i.e. hydrogen ion activity, and selective ion activity, p(ion), and the circuit involved is as shown in *Figure 6.13*.

The measured potential is the algebraic sum of the potentials developed within the system, i.e. the sum of the potentials developed at the reference electrodes, the liquid junction and the selective membrane. The internal

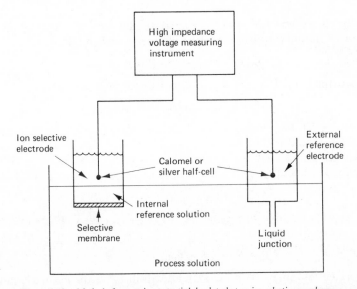

Figure 6.13   Method of measuring potential developed at an ion selective membrane

reference electrode and the selective membrane are regarded as the measuring electrode. The total e.m.f. measured, E, will be

$$E = E_{\text{Int ref}} + E_s + E_j - E_{\text{Ext ref}} \qquad (6.34)$$

where $E_{\text{Int ref}}$ = E.M.F. generated at the internal reference
                  electrode
    E_s = E.M.F. generated at the selective membrane
    E_j = E.M.F. generated at the liquid junction
    $E_{\text{Ext ref}}$ = E.M.F. generated at the external reference
                  electrode.

At a fixed temperature, with the reference electrode potentials constant and the liquid junction potentials zero, the equation reduces to

$$E = E' + E_s$$

where E' is a constant.

The potential developed at the interface of the internal reference solution and the process solution is related to ionic activities of the solution and is given by the Nerst equation

$$E_s = (RT/zF) \log_e (a_1/a_2) \qquad (6.35)$$

where R   = The gas constant $(= 8.31$ J K/mol)
    T = Temperature kelvin
    F   = Faraday constant, i.e. the charge on one mole of
            ions each carrying one elementary charge
            (96 500 coulombs)
    z = Number of elementary charges on each ion including
            the sign $\pm$
    a_1 = Activity of measured ion in the process solution
    a_2 = Activity of measured ion in the internal solution.

Usually the electrodes are constructed so that the ion activity a_2 of the reference solution is constant so equation 6.35 may be written

$$E_s = (RT/zF) \log_e a_1 - (RT/zF) \log_e a_2 \qquad (6.36)$$

which owing to the fact that the ion activity a_2 is constant may be reduced to

$$E_s - (RT/zF) \log_e a_1 - \text{constant} \qquad (6.37)$$

Thus $E = E_o + (RT/zF) \log a_1$ at a constant temperature where E_o includes all the constants and will be the value of the e.m.f. of the electrode system in a solution of unit activity.

Putting in the numerical values

$$E = E_o + 0.1984 \, (T/z) \log_{10} (a_1) \text{ mV} \qquad (6.38)$$

If we consider positive ions each carrying one elementary charge at 25°C this equation becomes

$$E = E_o + 59.16 \log_{10} (a^{+1}) \text{ mV} \qquad (6.39)$$

Thus, a ten-fold increase in ion activity will increase the electrode potential output by 59.16 mV.

If the positive ions each carry two elementary charges this output will be reduced to half, i.e. 29.58 mV per decade change.

The above equations assume that the electrode is sufficiently selective to enable it to respond to one single type of ion. In most cases the electrode will respond to other ions as well, but at a lower sensitivity. Thus the equation becomes

$$E = E_0 + 0.1984\,(T/z)\,\log_{10}\,(a_1 + k_2 a_2 = k_3 a_a + ...)\text{ mV} \qquad (6.40)$$

where k_2, etc., represents the ratio of the sensitivity of the electrode to the ions 2 to that of ion 1. Literature provided by manufacturers with their electrodes usually gives a list of interfering ions and their sensitivity ratios.

Ion selective electrodes

Whereas formerly electrodes were used almost exclusively for measuring hydrogen ion activity (pH), many electrodes have now been developed which respond to a wide range of selected ions. These electrodes are classified into four groups according to the type of membrane used.

1. *Glass electrodes (Figure 6.14(a))*.   Whereas the glass electrode used for pH measurement is designed to pass hydrogen ions preferentially, by suitable choice of materials of production, glass electrodes selective to sodium, potassium, ammonium, silver and other univalent cations may be made.

2. *Solid state electrodes (Figure 6.14(b) and (c))*.   In these electrodes the membrane consists of a single crystal or a compacted disc of the active material. In *Figure 6.14(b)* the membrane isolates the measured from the reference solution. In *Figure 6.14(c)* the membrane is sealed with a metal backing with a solid metal connection. A solid state electrode selective to fluoride ions employs a membrane of lanthanum fluoride ($La\,F_3$). One which is selective to sulphide ions has a membrane of silver sulphide. There are also electrodes available for measurement of Cl^- Br^- I^- Ag^+ Cu^{2+} Pb^{2+} Cd^{2+} and CN^- ions.

3. *Heterogeneous membrane electrodes*.   These are similar to the solid state electrodes but differ in having the active material dispersed in an inert matrix. Electrodes in this class are available for Cl^- Br^- I^- S^{2-} and Ag^+ ions.

4. *Liquid ion exchange electrodes (Figure 6.14(d))*.   In this type of electrode the internal reference solution and the measured solution are separated by a porous layer containing an organic liquid of low water solubility. Dissolved in the organic phase are large molecules in which the ions of interest are incorporated. The most important of these electrodes is the calcium electrode, but other electrodes in this class are available for the determination of Cl^- ClO_4^- NO_3^- Cu^{2+} Pb^{2+} and BF_4^- ions. The liquid ion exchange electrodes have more restricting chemical and physical limitations than the glass or solid state electrodes but they may be used to measure ions which cannot yet be measured with the solid state electrode.

This list is not comprehensive as new ion selective electrodes are constantly being developed.

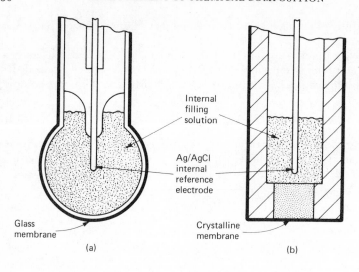

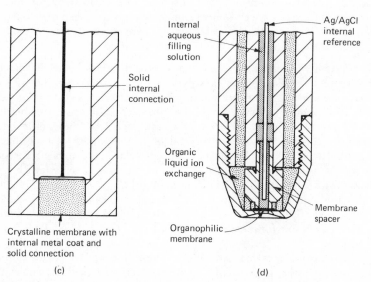

Figure 6.14   *Ion selective membranes (a) Glass (b) Crystalline membrane with internal reference electrode (c) Crystalline membrane with internal metal coat (d) Liquid (Courtesy Orion Research Inc.)*

6.3.1.13   OXIDATION AND REDUCTION POTENTIALS

In elementary chemistry a substance is said to be oxidised when oxygen is combined with it and reduced when oxygen is removed from it. The definition of oxidation and reduction may, however, be extended. Certain elements such as iron and tin can exist in salts in more than one form. Iron, for example, can be combined with sulphuric acid in the form of ferrous iron, valency 2, or ferric iron, valency 3.

    Consider the reaction

Ferrous sulphate	+	Chlorine	=	Ferric chloride	+	Ferric sulphate
$6FeSO_4$	+	$3Cl_2$	=	$2FeCl_3$	+	$2Fe_2(SO_4)_3$

The ferrous sulphate is said to be oxidised to ferric sulphate; the chlorine is the oxidising agent. In terms of the ionic theory, the equation may be written

$$6Fe^{++} + 3Cl_2 = 6Fe^{+++} + 6Cl^-$$

i.e. each ferrous ion loses an electron and so gains one positive charge. When a ferrous salt is oxidised to a ferric salt each mole of ferrous ions gains one mole (1 faraday) of positive charges or loses one mole of negative charges, the negative charge so lost being taken up by the oxidising agent (chlorine). Oxidation, therefore, involves the loss of electrons; reduction, the gain of electrons. Thus the oxidation of a ferrous ion to ferric ion can be represented by the equation

$$Fe^{++} - e = Fe^{+++}$$

When a suitable electrode, such as an inert metal which is not attacked by the solution and which will not catalyse side reactions, is immersed in a solution containing both ferrous and ferric ions, or some other substance in the reduced and oxidised state, the electrode acquires a potential which will depend upon the tendency of the ions in the solution to pass from a higher or lower state of oxidation. If the ions in solution tend to become oxidised (i.e. the solution has reducing properties) the ions tend to give up electrons to the electrode which will become negatively charged relative to the solution. If, on the other hand, the ions in solution tend to become reduced (i.e. the solution has oxidising properties), then the ions will tend to take up electrons from the electrode and the electrode will become positively charged relative to the solution. The sign and magnitude of the electrode potential, therefore, gives a measure of the oxidising or reducing power of the solution, and the potential is called the oxidation–reduction or redox potential of the solution, E_h. E_h may be expressed mathematically by the relationship

$$E_h = E_o + (RT/zF) \log_{10} (a_o/a_r) \tag{6.41}$$

where a_o = Activity of the oxidised ion
a_r = Activity of the reduced ion.

To measure the oxidation potential it is necessary to use a reference electrode to complete the electrical circuit. A calomel electrode is often used (see Section 6.3.3, page 186) as the reference electrode, but other electrodes which produce a potential unaffected by changes in the measured quantity are also employed for specific purposes.

The measuring electrode is usually either platinum or gold but other types are used for special measurements; as, for example, the silver–silver chloride electrode for measurement of the chloride ion content of a solution.

Standard cells

In the actual process of measurement, the unit or standard which is used for comparison must be definite and unchangeable. The need for a standard of e.m.f. was recognised in the early days of the electrical industry, and in 1908 the International Conference on Electrical Standards recommended the use of the Weston standard cell. Owing to its reliability, reproduceability, constancy of e.m.f. and small temperature coefficient, the Weston normal cell is generally used as the standard of e.m.f.

The cell is usually supplied mounted in a circular metal case. The case can be oil filled to reduce temperature gradients, and a thermometer is provided on the top of the case enabling corrections to be made for any variation of the cell temperature from the standard temperature of 20°C. A double cell is also available in which two single cells are mounted together in the same case enabling one to be used as a check on the other.

The cell, shown in *Figure 6.15*, consists of a hermetically sealed, H-shaped glass container. One of the lower limbs of the cell contains a layer of mercury which forms the positive pole. The mercury is covered by a paste of mercurous sulphate and a layer of cadmium sulphate crystals which maintain the cadmium sulphate solution in a saturated state. The opposite limb contains a quantity of cadmium amalgam which forms the negative pole. This amalgam is covered by cadmium sulphate crystals, and the cell is filled above the level of the connecting limb with a saturated solution of cadmium sulphate. A constriction is formed in each of the upright tubes level with the top of the layer of cadmium sulphate crystals. These crystals become loosely cemented together and, owing to the presence of the constriction, form taper plugs which hold the contents of the cell in their proper places so that the cell is unaffected by being moved about or even being sent by post. Platinum wires sealed into the bases of the two limbs make contact with the mercury and the amalgam, and are connected to terminals at the top of the case.

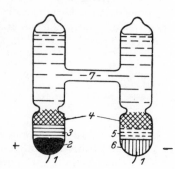

1. *Platinum wire fused in the glass*
2. *Mercury*
3. *Paste of mercurous sulphate*
4. *Crystals of cadmium sulphate*
5. *Small crystals of cadmium sulphate*
6. *Cadmium amalgam containing 12.5% cadmium*
7. *Saturated solution of cadmium sulphate*

Figure 6.15   Weston standard cadmium cell

The e.m.f. of a saturated Weston cell of this form at 20°C is 1.018 59 V and the e.m.f. at a temperature t °C is given by:

$$E_t = 1.018\ 59\ [1 - 0.000\ 0406\ (t{-}20) - 0.000\ 000\ 95$$
$$(t{-}20)^2 + 0.000\ 000\ 01\ (t{-}20)^3] \tag{6.42}$$

Owing to polarisation, no appreciable current may be taken from a standard cell without altering its e.m.f. It is found that the change is not permanent because the cell gradually recovers its original e.m.f.; the cell, however, is unreliable until the recovery is complete. Theoretically, the life of a carefully treated cell is unlimited but actually, owing to the slight drain of current while the potentiometer circuit is being balanced, the cell has a normally useful life of several years. In order to reduce the drain on the cell, and prevent large currents being taken from it while the potentiometer is being balanced, a standard cell is always connected in series with a large resistance (10 000 Ω). When the approximate position of balance is known, the large resistance may be shorted out by a key; this permits the galvanometer detecting the out-of-balance to be used at its maximum sensitivity.

6.3.2   Measurement of electrolytic conductivity

6.3.2.1   CONDUCTIVITY CELLS

In order to simplify the resistance measurement, it is necessary to maintain the resistance of conductivity cells between the limits of 10 and 100 000 Ω. The conductivities of aqueous solutions vary over a very wide range. It is necessary, therefore, to have cells with a range of cell constants from 0.10 to 100.

The minimum electrode area is limited by the permissible polarisation error. Polarisation error depends upon the frequency employed in the measurement and upon the true surface area. In the case of a stainless steel electrode it is given a satinised finish in order to increase the effective area. Increase of area and increase of frequency both reduce the polarisation error.

The construction and appearance of conductivity cells vary with the cell constant and method of use. As the cell constant increases, the length of the conductance path increases and the size of the electrodes decreases.

The conductance C of a liquid of conductivity κ S/cm contained in a cell having electrodes area a cm^2 at a distance d cm apart will be given by

$$C = \kappa \ (a/d) \ \text{S} \tag{6.43}$$
$$\text{or } \kappa = C \ (d/a) \ \text{S/cm} \tag{6.44}$$

assuming the liquid between the electrodes has a uniform cross section. However, owing to the large influence of any change in the geometry of the cell, it is usual to measure the cell constant by measuring the conductance of a standard solution in the cell at a known temperature. Owing to the fact that the value of its conductivity is well established, a solution of potassium chloride having a concentration of 0.01 mol/dm^3 is used. This may be prepared by dissolving 0.7440 g of pure dry potassium chloride in distilled water and diluting to 1 dm^3 at 20°C.

The conductivity of this solution is given in *Table 6.4.*

For very accurate work the conductivity of the dilution water at the given temperature should be added. Solutions at other concentrations may be used provided reliable information is available of its conductivity.

Alternatively the cell constant may be determined by comparing the conductance reading for a series of solutions as taken with the cell under test with those of a standard cell of known constant for the same solutions at the same temperature.

The materials used in cell construction must be unaffected by the electrolyte, and the insulation between the electrodes must be of a high quality and not absorb anything from the process liquid. Glass is therefore used in cells for laboratory work and for industrial measurements on corrosive liquids.

A wide range of materials are at present available covering a wide range of pressures, temperatures and process fluids. The body may be made of epoxy resins, plastics such as p.t.f.e., pure or reinforced, p.v.c., penton or any other material suitable for the application, but it must not be deformed in use by temperature or pressure, otherwise the cell constant will change.

Table 6.4.

Temperature, °C	Conductivity (κ), 10^{-3} S/cm
15	1.143
16	1.169
17	1.195
18	1.221
19	1.247
20	1.274
21	1.301
22	1.328
23	1.355
24	1.382
25	1.409
26	1.437
27	1.464
28	1.492
29	1.520
30	1.548

The electrodes may be parallel flat plates or rings of metal or graphite cast in the tube forming the body, or in the form of a central rod with a concentric tubular body.

One common form of conductivity cell used in power stations and on ships to monitor the quality of boiler feed water is shown in *Figure 6.16*. It is used in particular to measure the salinity of the boiler feed water from the shipboard evaporative distillation system, as the presence of salt in extremely low concentration can cause considerable damage by corrosion. It consists of an inner measuring cell having a cell constant of 0.1, in the form of a satinised stainless steel rod surrounded by a cylindrical stainless steel electrode, having holes to permit the measured liquid to flow freely through the cell. This is surrounded by an intermediate cylinder also provided with holes, and two O-rings which together with the tapered inner end form a pressure tight seal on to the outer body when the inner cell is withdrawn for cleaning, so that the measured solution can continue to flow and the cell be replaced without interruption of the process. The outer body is screwed into the line through which the measured solution flows. The cell can be made of stainless steel throughout or a marine brass version may be used where appropriate. *Figure 6.16(a)* shows the inserted cell as it is when in use, and *(b)* the withdrawn measuring element with the intermediate sleeve forming a seal on the outer body. The cell may be used at 110°C and up to 7 bar pressure.

Another cell is known as the Sproule cell, one form of which is shown in *Figure 6.17(a)* and *(b)*, in which the temperature sensor is located close to the electrodes, giving accurate temperature compensation.

It consists of three annular rings of impervious carbon composition material

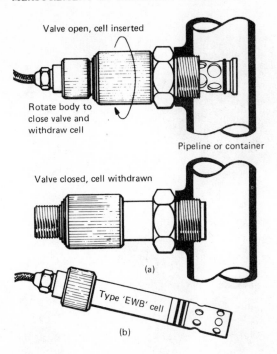

Valve open, cell inserted

Rotate body to
close valve and
withdraw cell

Pipeline or container

Valve closed, cell withdrawn

(a)

Type 'EWB' cell

(b)

*Figure 6.16   Retractable conductivity cell (Courtesy Electronic Instruments Ltd.) (a) Inserted cell as in use
(b) Withdrawn measuring element*

equally spaced within the bore of an epoxy resin moulded body. The tubular
bore is threaded at each end to enable the cell to be mounted vertically as an
integral part of the solution pipeline. Conduction through the solution within
the cell takes place between the central electrode and the two outer rings,
which are connected to the earthed terminal of the measuring instrument; thus
electrical conduction is confined entirely within the cell, where it is
uninfluenced by the presence of adjoining metal parts in the pipe system. This
pattern of cell, because of its exceptional long term stability and freedom from
crevices and projecting features that might restrict the flow of solution and
tend to harbour contaminating matter, is ideally suited to the exacting
requirements of dialysate concentration monitoring in the artificial kidney
machine.

The use of an impervious carbon composition material for the electrodes
substantially eliminates polarisation error and provides conducting surfaces
that do not require replatinisation or special maintenance, other than
periodic, but simple and infrequent cleaning by means of a bottle brush.

The flush nature of the electrodes permits an uninterrupted flow of liquid
and this type of cell is widely used in water treatment plants.

The screw-in pattern, shown in *Figure 6.17(c)*, is used for securing into a pipe
or tank, and models with graphite or stainless steel electrodes are available.

For dipping into a tank such as wash or rinse tanks the version shown in
Figure 6.17(d) is used.

The flow types are suitable for use at 100°C and 7 bar pressure. While all

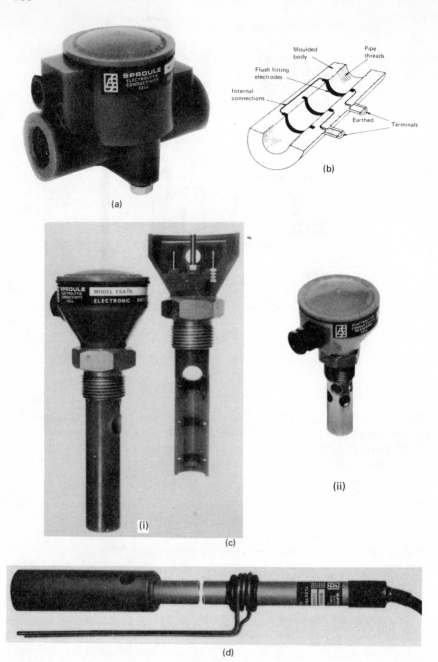

Figure 6.17 Sproule conductivity cells (Courtesy Electronic Instruments Ltd.) (a) Cell assembly with self-contained temperature compensator (b) Section through cell shown in (a) showing arrangement of electrodes (c) Screw-in types (d) Dip-in type

cells may be used at 100°C and 7 bar pressure, that shown in *Figure 6.17(c)(ii)* will withstand 10 bar pressure.

For measurement of the conductivity of highly corrosive solutions such as strong sulphuric or nitric acid, the flanged flow assembly shown in *Figure 6.18* is used. The stainless steel housing is lined with f.e.p. and externally it is protected with chemically resistant paint. A suitable cell having a constant of 25 and a temperature compensating resistance are provided and the assembly is suitable for pressures of 1.5 bar and temperatures of 100°C.

Figure 6.18   Flow cell for highly corrosive liquid (Courtesy Electronic Instruments Ltd.)

Installation and maintenance of conductivity cells

Electrolytic conductivity measuring cells are rugged devices but at the same time they are precise, accurately made items, which form an integral part of a sensitive measuring system and should therefore be handled with care.

Measuring cells should be installed in positions where they are adequately protected from mechanical shock by passing traffic, dampness and extremes of temperature. Where a flow-line cell is connected directly in the electrolyte pipe line, suitable support should be given to the pipes to ensure that the cell is under no mechanical strain, and that the pipe threads in a rigid system are straight and true. Dip pattern cells should be installed such that moving parts in a tank, e.g. agitators, are well clear of the cells.

Attention should be paid to the actual siting in the tank so that localised heating, due to sump heaters, does not allow the recommended maximum temperature for the cell to be exceeded.

Withdrawable cells must be installed where sufficient space for withdrawal of the measuring portion from the assembly is available. The water tight socket must be positioned so that the connecting cable to the cell does not hang against hot or abrasive objects in order to ensure long life and trouble-free operation.

Where measuring cells are installed in pipe-work, it is essential that they are positioned in a rising section of the system to ensure that each cell is always full of electrolyte, and that pockets of air are not trapped. Alternatively, they may be installed in the bottom member of a U formed in horizontal pipe-work. In this case, screw-in cells should be in the top or side of the pipe so that sediment cannot settle in them.

Absolute cleanliness is essential for the measuring cells to perform properly, and for convenience, cells are classified according to material of construction, for the purpose of describing cleaning procedures below.

Mechanical fitting.   Normal thread-sealing practice should be followed to obtain water tight connections between the measuring cell and the pipe-work, with the following precautions being taken.

1. In the case of epoxy bodied cells, sealing compound or tape should be kept to a minimum to avoid damage to the cell by splitting of the threaded portion.

2. The valve assembly of a withdrawable pattern cell should be inserted for one or two threads after cleaning of the threaded boss with a screw-cutting tap. Normal thread sealing practice may then be followed. This ensures that the valve seating does not become fouled during installation.

Electrical connections.   When a screened lead is used to connect any measuring element to an instrument it is essential that the screen be earthed at the instrument end only. It must not be allowed to come into contact with any other conducting surfaces, or a conducting loop will be formed so that if there is any changing magnetic field or changing current flowing in a nearby conductor, a current will be induced in the screen, thus interfering with the measurement.

1. Moulded cells with carbon graphite electrodes are internally connected so that the terminal marked E is the earth one. This should be connected to the blue conductor of the special conductivity cell connecting cable. The central electrode marked C must be connected to the brown conductor, or the inner core of the co-axial conductor. The copper braid of the co-axial conductor has to be trimmed back and not allowed to touch any terminal or earthed part of the system. Temperature compensated cells must have the terminal marked T connected to the conductor.

The temperature sensing element is completely separate from the electrode system and has to be connected to the instrument by a twin core 30/0.20 mm separate cable. Dip-pattern cells are supplied with a cable already connected internally.

2. Stainless steel cells must have their central, insulated terminal connected to the inner core of the co-axial conductor of the cell connecting cable. The copper braid of the co-axial conductor must be trimmed back and not allowed to touch any terminal or earthed part of the system.

The terminal screw tapped into the die-cast body of the cell accepts the negative core of the cell connecting cable.

Cleaning the measuring cell. Although measuring cells are substantially free of contamination when supplied, they should be thoroughly cleaned immediately before installation, as detailed below.

On no account should the bore of an epoxy cell or the electrodes of a stainless steel cell be touched by hand, due to the risk of grease deposit.

1. *Epoxy moulded.* A patented feature of moulded cells is the impervious, carbon graphite, annular electrode allowing a straight through bore in the cell. Although this simplifies the cleaning operation, cleaning must be very thorough to ensure total 'wetting' of the cell.

Cleaning should be carried out with a 50% solution of water/detergent using the bottle brush provided. After thorough brushing with the recommended solution, the cell bore should be rinsed several times in distilled water and then viewed. Looking through the bore towards a source of illumination, the surface should be evenly wetted with no dry patches where the water has 'peeled' away. If dry patches appear rapidly, the surface is not clean, indicating that a thin film of grease is present. Repeated cleaning and rinsing is necessary until the cell bore has the evenly wetted appearance.

2. *Stainless steel and monel.* A patented feature of the stainless steel cell is the 'frosted' appearance of the electrodes which is essential to prevent polarisation. It is most important that this frosting is not polished away by the regular use of abrasive cleaners. This type of cell must be cleaned with a 50% water/detergent solution, and the bottle brush provided.

In the case of screw-in cells the outer electrode may be removed to facilitate cleaning, but on no account should the central electrode be disturbed, as this will impair the accuracy of the electrical constant of the cell.

After cleaning as detailed above, the cell should be thoroughly rinsed in distilled water and viewed. With a source of illumination shining into the electrode system, the interior surface of the outer electrode and the whole of the central electrode should have an evenly wetted appearance. If the surfaces have dry patches where the water has 'peeled' away this is an indication of the presence of grease, and repeated cleaning and rinsing is required until the electrodes are evenly wetted.

3. *Withdrawable pattern.* The withdrawable, measuring portion of the cell should be cleaned as in 2 above, and the same precautions observed. While the cell is being washed, the operator may protect the cable plug from wetting and damage by placing it in a side pocket in his clothing. The plug pins should always be kept clean and dry.

For maintenance purposes it is good practice to have a spare cell available. This should be thoroughly cleaned as previously described and then used to replace the first cell removed for routine cleaning. When the first cell has been cleaned it should replace the second cell to be removed and so on until the work is completed.

Location of measuring cells.   Cells should be completely immersed in the tested solution, the shield should be in place and should be at least 7mm from the wall of the containing vessel; for Bishop type cells this distance should be at least 15 cm. They should be arranged so that no air is trapped in the cell, and where possible the cell should face the flow of liquid so that there is a proper circulation through the cell body. When fitted in a pipe line through which there is an intermittent flow of liquid they should be fitted pointing upwards at the bottom of a U bend in the line so that the electrodes are immersed in liquid when the line is not in use.

Maintenance of cells.   Electrodes must be kept clean; insoluble coatings on the electrodes will affect the sensitivity and accuracy of the conductivity measurements. When only used at intervals, cells should be thoroughly rinsed after use, and if possible stored in distilled water.

The sensitivity of a coated electrode can frequently be restored by treatment in a 10–15% solution of hydrochloric or nitric acid for about two minutes, followed by a rinse. If no improvement is noted the electrode should be replatinised. In use, care should be taken that the surface is not scraped or handled as this impairs the function of the electrodes.

6.3.2.2   MEASURING INSTRUMENTS

The conductivity of a cell may be measured (a) by Wheatstone bridge methods or (b) by direct measurement of the current through the cell when a fixed voltage is applied.

Wheatstone bridge methods.   The actual conductivity of the cell is usually measured by means of a self-balancing Wheatstone bridge of the form shown in *Figure 6.19* and described in detail in Volume 1. This type of instrument gives the greatest accuracy, sensitivity and stability.

The resistance of the arm CD containing the cell is compared with the resistance of the arm AD containing a manual, set or automatic temperature compensating circuit. Any out-of-balance detected by the detector D causes the contact on the slide wire at B to be moved to restore balance, at the same time indicating the conductivity of the cell.

If high accuracy is required, care should be taken to choose the correct frequency and cell constant for the application. The cell constant should be chosen to give a circuit resistance between 100 Ω and 100 kΩ. The higher the frequency the smaller will be the effect of polarisation at the cell, but the greater will be the effect of the capacitance of the cable which is in parallel with the cell. The effect of the cable capacitance can be measured by disconnecting the cell and noting the conductivity. The cable length and conductor area of cross section must be chosen so that the cable resistance is a negligible fraction of the cell resistance, and never runs near enough to power lead to pick up spurious a.c. currents.

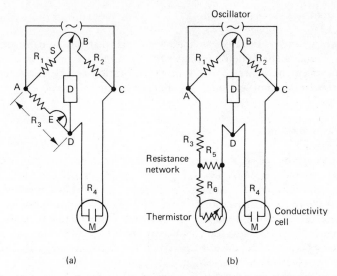

Figure 6.19   Measurement of conductance using Wheatstone bridge (a) Simple circuit (b) Thermistor temperature corrected circuit

Direct measurement of cell conductance.   The conductivity of a cell may be measured directly by the method indicated in *Figure 6.20*. A stable a.c. voltage is applied to the cell and the current flowing is amplified by a stabilised current amplifier. The output is then applied to an indicator and recorder. Temperature compensation is achieved by connecting a manual temperature compensator in the amplifier current, or a resistance bulb may be used to achieve automatic compensation.

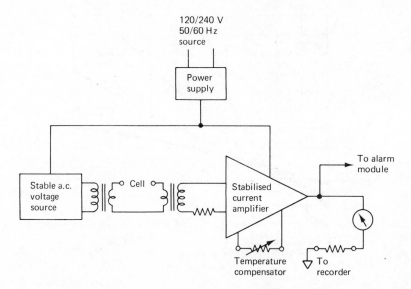

Figure 6.20   Direct measurement of cell conductance

Check of instrument calibration

A check resistance is usually provided to test the instrument calibration. The resistance is such that when it replaces the conductivity cell a definite reading is produced on the instrument. Error in calibration can be corrected by the appropriate method described in the instrument instruction book.

Temperature compensation

The conductivity of a solution is affected considerably by change of temperature, and each solution has its own characteristic conductivity–temperature curve. *Figure 6.21* shows how different these characteristics can be, Q_{25} being the ratio of the conductivity of a solution to its conductivity at 25°C. It is therefore essential to design a different temperature compensator to match each solution, and one company has over 500 manual and 400 automatic compensating circuits available for solutions varying from ultra-pure water to fuming sulphuric acid, at temperatures from −5°C to +150°C.

Manual compensators consist of a variable and a fixed resistor in series. The temperature scale showing the position of the contact on the variable resistance is calibrated so that the resistance of the combined resistors changes by the same percentage of the value of conductivity of the solution at 25°C as does the solution. The scale becomes crowded at the upper end, thus limiting the span of the compensator to about 70°C.

Automatic temperature compensators usually consist of a thermistor

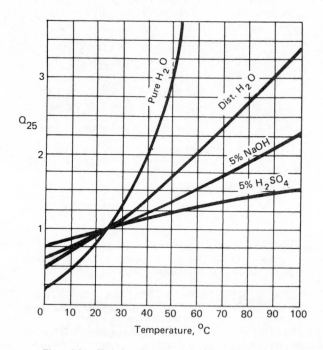

Figure 6.21   Variation of solution conductivity with temperature

temperature sensor having a temperature coefficient of resistance of about -5% per °C. This is connected with a T network of three resistors of negligible temperature coefficient located in the measuring circuit as shown in *Figure 6.19(b)*. This network is arranged so that its temperature characteristic curve matches the solution characteristic so closely that the curves cross at three points. By this means it is possible to provide automatic temperature compensation over a range of 50°C with a maximum departure of less than 1.5% from the selected electrolyte characteristic curve.

It is essential that the temperature sensor is in good contact with the liquid under test, so that it is usually installed in the measuring cell body and the additional connections brought out with the cell connections. Alternatively, a separate compensator consisting of a precision wound nickel element housed in a stainless steel pocket is mounted in the electrolyte as close as possible to the conductivity cell so that both are affected equally by variation of temperature.

6.3.2.3 ELECTRODELESS METHOD OF MEASURING CONDUCTIVITY

The principle of the method is to measure the resistance of a closed loop of solution by the extent to which the loop couples two transformer coils. The liquid to be measured is enclosed in a non-conducting pipe, or a pipe lined with a non-conducting material. Three forms of measuring units are available, as shown in *Figure 6.22*. As the method is most successful with full scale resistances of 10–1000 Ω, relatively large bore pipe may be used, reducing the possible errors due to solid deposition or film formation.

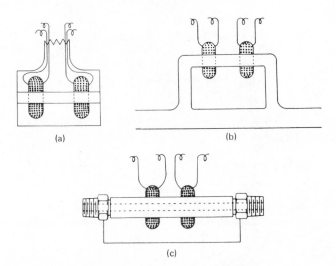

(a)   (b)

(c)

Figure 6.22   Electrodeless conductivity cells

Figure 6.22(a) shows the form used for immersion in a large volume of solution. The two toroids are potted on a single axis which forms an assembly with a cylindrical bore, which with the body of the external solution

constitutes the solution loop linking the transformers. The cell constant is fixed
by the ratio of the length to the cross section of the bore. This type of cell is used
in salinity measurement of sea water.

For measurements on a solution flowing through a pipe the arrangement
shown in *Figure 6.22(b)* is used. P.T.F.E.-lined neoprene hose, glass, p.v.c. and
Kynar pipes have all been used successfully. If the liquid contains suspended
solids or fibres, wide bore non-conducting pipe fitted with metallic end pieces
connected together with a length of wire to complete the circuit may be used if
conditions are suitable *(Figure 6.22(c))*.

The principle of the measuring system is shown in *Figure 6.23. Figure 6.23(a)*
shows the simple circuit which consists of two transformers. The first has its
primary winding, the input toroid, connected to an oscillator operating at 3 or
18 kHz and as its secondary the closed loop of solution. The closed loop of
solution forms the primary of the second transformer and its secondary is the
output toroid. With constant input voltage the output of the system is
proportional to the conductivity of the solution. The receiver is a high
impedance voltage measuring circuit which amplifies and rectifies the output
and displays it on a large indicator. By placing a small resistance in series with
the indicator a millivolt signal is provided for operating a remote potentiometer recorder, which may operate alarm contacts or a controller. Temperature compensation may be manual or automatic.

In order to eliminate effects of source voltage and changes in the amplifier
characteristics a null balance system may be provided as shown in *Figure
6.23(b)*. An additional winding is provided on each toroid and the position of
the contact is adjusted on the main slide wire to restore the system to the
original balanced state by means of the balancing motor operated by the
amplified out-of-balance signal in the usual way.

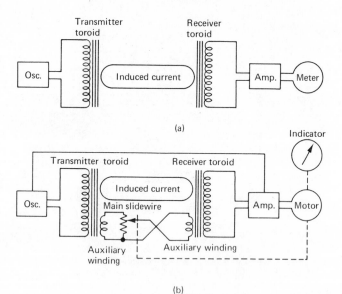

(a)

(b)

*Figure 6.23   Measuring circuits for use with electrodeless cells (Courtesy Beckman Instruments Inc.) (a) Direct
reading (b) Balanced bridge*

6.3.2.4 APPLICATIONS

In addition to checking distilled water for purity (when quantities of electrolytic impurity as little as 0.1 parts per million (p.p.m.) can be measured) conductivity cells are used to measure the steam purity and the purity of feed water in boiler applications. In order to measure the purity of steam entering a turbine, a sample is bled off, cooled and reduced to atmospheric pressure, and passed through a cell having a range of $0-5 \times 10^{-6}$ S with a 0.1 cell constant. The conductivity of feed water is measured after the water has been treated just before it enters the boiler, an instrument with a range of $0-20 \times 10^{-6}$ S and a cell constant of 0.1 being used.

Condensate contamination, especially where sea water is used for cooling purposes, is readily detected by a conductivity measurement.

Comparison of the conductivity of the washing water before and after use readily shows when the washing process approaches completion, for the conductivities of the two water samples become approximately the same. This measurement is used to prevent waste of water in such operations as (a) washing plating and pickling solutions from metals, (b) washing dyestuffs from textiles, and (c) removing excess acids in nitrocellulose manufacture.

In the manufacture of sulphuric acid by the contact process, the sulphur trioxide is absorbed most readily by the acid if the concentration of the acid is maintained at about 98.5% by weight. Conductivity cells are used to give a continuous check of the acid concentration, the measuring instrument being calibrated directly in terms of sulphuric acid concentration.

Instruments measuring electrolytic conductivity may also be used to measure the concentration of a wide range of gaseous contaminants such as acidic gases or hydrogen sulphide in gas or air samples.

Measurement of low concentrations of gas by change of solution conductivity

Sulphur dioxide.   As the problem of air pollution increases the measurement of low concentrations of contaminants becomes more important. A technique used to measure the concentration of sulphur dioxide in air in the parts per hundred million (p.p.h.m.) range is based on the measurement of the change in the conductivity of a reagent before and after it has absorbed the contaminant. The principle of the measurement is to oxidise the sulphur dioxide gas by hydrogen peroxide solution, thus forming sulphate ions which increase the electrolytic conductivity of the absorbing reagent. The main requirement for measurement accuracy is to maintain the reagent flow to within ±0.5% and the sample flow to within ±1% of the rates at which the instrument is calibrated.

The instrument is shown in *Figure 6.24(a)* and *(b)*. Ambient air is sampled through a glass and viton tube at 4.7 dm³/min for the 0–50 and the 0–100 ranges, and at 2.35 dm³/min for the 0–200 p.p.h.m. range, by means of the air pump. This air flows up the glass absorbing column while the reagent flows down. In order to increase the effective area of liquid exposed to the air, a glass spiral is mounted in the column. The column together with the electrolytic conductivity cells, soda lime scrubber for zero checking, and interconnecting pipe-work is enclosed in an insulated temperature controlled analyser section. This is maintained at 49 ±1°C by means of a 200 W heater controlled by a relay and its activating mercury column thermostat. A fan provides continuous circulation of air, and a thermal fuse in the heater line protects the section from overheating. In the section which is not temperature controlled are the reagent metering pump, electronic measuring unit and drain connections.

External to the monitor is a 22 dm³ reagent vessel containing a supply of 2 × 10⁻³ molar solution of hydrogen peroxide and a molar solution of sulphuric acid and a wetting agent, which is delivered to the absorbing column at 1 cm³/min by means of the reagent metering pump. This has a range of 0–160 ml/min, and is provided with a reagent-flow micrometer engraved 0–100, a setting of 37 providing 1 cm³/min. A flow meter is provided in the air sample intake to enable the air flow rate to be checked.

A reference conductivity cell is installed in the reagent intake and a measuring conductivity cell in the line leaving the absorption column. The change of conductivity in the measuring cell is linearly related to the SO_2 concentration and this change is determined by measuring the difference in conductivity of the two cells by means of a solid state detector. An a.c. voltage is applied across both cells and this results in a flow of current through each cell which is proportional to the conductivity of the solution in the cell. An a.c. to d.c. demodulator in series with each cell produces a d.c. output signal from each cell. These d.c. outputs are connected in series opposition and the resulting voltage is directly related to the difference in conductivity of the solutions and hence linearly related to the concentration of SO_2 in the air.

The output is 0–10 mV d.c. and is indicated on a suitable d.c.

(a)

Figure 6.24   The Aeroscan air quality monitor for SO_2 (Courtesy Leeds and Northrup Ltd.)
(a) With front panel removed

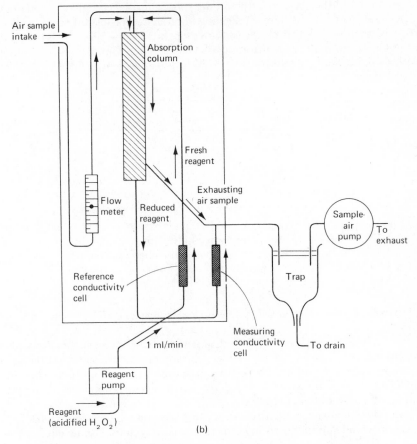

Figure 6.24(b)   Schematic diagram

millivoltmeter and can, if required, be recorded on a suitable recorder. An electronic integrator and many other options such as recording with both integration and sample flow rate and reagent flow rate record with telemetering facilities may be provided. The sensitivity is ±1% of the span and better than 2 p.p.h.m., with a reproducibility of better than 4 p.p.h.m. SO_2.

Zero and range adjustments are provided so that the calibration can be adjusted to the user's standard method. Any accuracy statement must be related to this standard and must be established by a field check. The instrument is suitable for use at ambient temperatures between 4.5 and 37.8°C. The response time for initial response is 45 s, and for 90% of the full scale change 3 min.

The accuracy will of course be affected by other gases present in the sample air, their effects being shown in *Table 6.5*.

Absorber column maintenance—flushing.   Flushing of the absorber column with a wetting agent is of utmost importance in the operation of the monitor. The inner surface of the glass column and the spiral must be completely wetted at all times. If it is not, the flow of reagent will not remain constant and specified sensitivity and stability of measurement cannot be achieved. To permit complete wetting, the glassware must be clean. Therefore, a weekly flushing with a small amount of ethyl or isopropyl alcohol mixed with a 50% solution of

Table 6.5.

Background gas present at 1 p.p.h.m.	SO_2 error, p.p.h.m.
CO_2	0.0
NO_2	0.016
NO	0.009
HCl	0.24
NH_3	−0.26
H_2S	0.02

potassium hydroxide is recommended. This is also necessary whenever the column is permitted to dry; therefore, the flushing is part of the start-up procedure. If a smooth flow of reagent over the entire glass surface does not result, the absorber column must be removed and thoroughly cleaned.

Measurement of contaminants other than gases by measurement of solution conductivity

Salt in crude oil monitor.   This instrument as manufactured by Precision Scientific Development provides a rapid continuous measurement of the salt in crude oil before and after desalting. It samples the stream, performs the analysis and records the result. It will measure concentrations as low as 1.4 kg salt per thousand cubic metre of crude oil, the upper limit being 285 kg per thousand cubic metre, with an accuracy of ±5% and a repeatability of 3% of the average indication. Desalting reduces the corrosion in refining equipment and loss of desalting efficiency causes a large increase in the corrosion rate. However, desalting costs money and the use of a monitor enables the plant to be optimised on cost.

The instrument is based on the measurement of the conductivity of a solution to which a known quantity of crude oil has been added. The sample of crude oil is continuously circulated through a loop in the measurement section of the 'salt-in-crude monitor'. When the test cycle is initiated, 56 ml of solvent (xylene) are introduced from a metering cylinder into the analyser cell. Sample is then automatically diverted from the sample circulating loop into a metering cylinder calibrated to deliver 14 ml of crude oil into the analysis cell.

The electrometric medium (63% n-butanol, 37% methanol, plus 0.25% water) is metered into the analysis cell from a calibrated cylinder that delivers 70 ml.

After the analysis cell contents are thoroughly mixed by a magnetic stirrer, the measuring circuit is energised and an a.c. potential is applied between two electrodes immersed in the liquid. The resulting a.c. current is displayed on a milliammeter in the electrical control assembly, and a proportional d.c. millivolt signal is transmitted from the meter to a suitable recorder. The balancing motor of the recorder is energised only during the measuring portion of the analysis cycle and the recorder shows the salt content.

At the end of the measuring period, a solenoid valve is automatically opened to empty the analysis cell into a drain or sump, completing the analysis cycle. Total minimum cycle time is ten minutes.

With automatic operation a new cycle will start at the end of an adjustable interval (10–60 min). In the 'manual' mode the instrument goes on stand-by condition on completion of an analysis; a subsequent test is initiated by pressing a momentary-contact switch.

The measurement assembly is explosion proof to ANEC Class 1 Group D Division 1 (approx. BS 4683 Group 11A Zone 0), and the control equipment Class 1 Group D Division 2 (approx. BS 4683 Group 11A Zone 2). The sample at the instrument intake may be at a pressure between 4 and 8 bar g and at a temperature between 15 and 93°C. The sample should be filtered by an in-line filter to remove any particles larger than 76 μm, and a flow rate between 60 and 300 cm³/min is required.

Provision is made to introduce a standard sample at any time to check the calibration of the instrument.

Amperometric (polarographic) analysers

Atmospheric pollutants. When two dissimilar metal electrodes are immersed in water, or a suitable electrolyte, and connected together, a small current will flow due to the build-up of electrons on the more electropositive electrode. The current will soon stop, however, owing to the fact that the cell will become polarised.

If, however, a suitable depolarising agent is added, a current will continue to flow, the magnitude of which will depend upon the concentration and nature of the ions producing the depolarisation. Thus, by choice of suitable materials for the electrodes and arranging for the addition of the depolarising agent which is in fact the substance whose concentration is to be measured, amperometric analysers may be made to measure the concentration of a variety of chemicals. In some instruments a potential difference may be applied to the electrodes when the current is again a linear function of the concentration of the depolarising agent.

The sensitivity of the analyser is sometimes increased by using buffered water as the electrolyte so that the cell operates at a definite pH. Amperometric instruments are inherently linear in response, but special steps have to be taken in order to make them specific to the substance whose concentration is to be measured, because other substances may act as depolarising agents and so interfere with the measurement. When the interfering substances are known steps may be taken to remove them.

Where the instrument is intended to measure pollutants in air or gas, the gas to be tested is either bubbled through a suitable cell or arranged to impinge upon the surface of the liquid in the cell. In these cases interfering gases can be removed by chemical or molecular filters in the sampling system.

This form of instrument may be used to detect halogens, such as chlorine, in air and instruments with ranges from 0–0.5 to 0–20 p.p.m. are available measuring with an accuracy of ±2% and a sensitivity of 0.01 p.p.m. By altering the electrolyte the instrument may be changed to measure the corresponding acid vapours, i.e. HCl, HBr HF. When required to measure the concentration of halogen in water, for example chlorine or fluorine in drinking water or water in a swimming pool, the type of instrument shown in *Figure 6.25* is used, which is in fact a chlorine measuring unit.

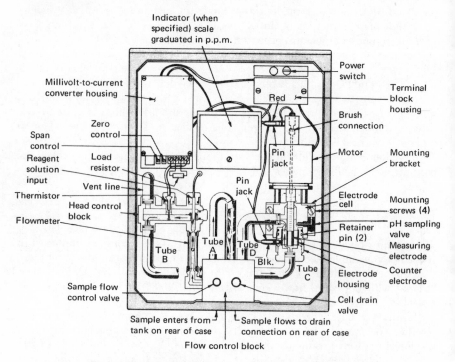

Figure 6.25   Residual chlorine analyser (Courtesy Fischer and Porter)

The sample stream is filtered in the tank on the back of the housing, and then enters the analyser unit through the inlet in the rear of the flow control block. It passes through the sample flow control valve and up the metering tube into the head control block where reagent (buffer solution to maintain constant pH) is smoothly and continuously added by means of a special positive displacement type feed pump assembly.

Buffered sample flows down tube B through the flow control block and up tube C to the bottom of the electrode cell assembly. Sample flow rate is adjusted to approximately 150 cm³/min. Flow rate is not critical since the relative velocity between the measuring electrode and the sample is established by rotating the electrode at high speed.

In the electrode cell assembly, the sample passes up through the annular space between the concentrically mounted outer (copper) reference electrode and the inner (gold) measuring electrode and out through tube D to the drain. The space between the electrodes contains plastics pellets which are continuously agitated by the swirling of the water in the cell. The pellets keep the electrode surfaces clear of any material which might tend to adhere. The measuring electrode is coupled to a motor which operates at 1550 rev/min. The electrical signal from the measuring electrode is picked up by a spring loaded brush on top of the motor and the circuit is completed through a thermistor for temperature compensation, precision resistors and the stationary copper electrode.

The composition of the electrodes is such that the polarisation of the measuring electrode prevents current flow in the absence of a strong oxidising agent. The presence of the smallest trace of strong oxidiser, such as chlorine (hypochlorous acid), will permit a current to flow by oxidising the polarising layer. The amplitude of the self-generated depolarisation current is proportional to the concentration of the strong oxidising agent. The generated current is passed through a precision resistor, and the millivoltage across the resistor is then measured by the indicating or recording potentiometer. This instrument is calibrated to read in terms of the type (free or total) of residual chlorine measured. When measuring total residual, potassium iodine is added to the buffer. This reacts with the free and combined chlorine to liberate iodine in an amount equal to the total chlorine. The iodine depolarises the cell in the same manner as hypochlorous acid, and a current directly proportional to the total residual is generated.

Process oxygen analyser. Another instrument using the polarographic method of measurement is the oxygen analyser used for continuous process measurement of oxygen in flue gas, or inert gas monitoring and a variety of other applications.

The key to the instrument is the rugged sensor shown in *Figure 6.26*. The sensor contains a silver anode and a gold cathode that are protected from the sample by a thin membrane of p.t.f.e. An aqueous KCl solution is retained in the sensor by the membrane and forms the electrolyte in the cell.

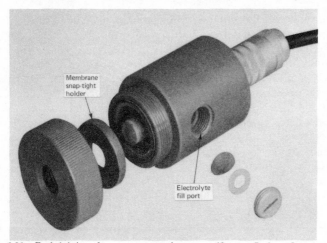

Figure 6.26   Exploded view of process oxygen analyser sensor (Courtesy Beckman Instruments Inc.)

As the membrane is permeable to gases, oxygen will diffuse from the sample to the cathode and the following reactions take place:

Cathode reaction $O_2 + 2H_2O + 4e \rightarrow 4\,OH$

Anode reaction $4\,Ag + 4Cl \rightarrow 4Ag\,Cl + 4e$

With an applied potential between the cathode and anode, oxygen will be reduced at the cathode, causing a current to flow. The magnitude of this current is proportional to the partial pressure of oxygen present in the sample.

The only materials in contact with the process are p.v.c. and p.t.f.e. and the membrane is recessed so that it does not suffer mechanical damage. The cell needs to be recharged with a new supply of electrolyte at 3–6 monthly intervals depending on the operating conditions and the membrane can be replaced easily should it be damaged.

The cell current is amplified by a solid state amplifier which gives a voltage output which can be displayed on an indicator or recorded. The instrument has a range selection switch giving ranges of 0–1, 0–5, 0–10 or 0–25% oxygen and a calibration adjustment. The calibration is checked by using a reference gas, or air when the instrument should read 20.9% oxygen on the 0–25% scale. The instrument has an accuracy of ±1% of scale range at the calibration temperature but an error of ±3% of the reading will occur for a 16°C departure in operating temperature.

When in use the sensor may be housed in an in-line type housing or in a dip-type of assembly, usually made of p.v.c., suitable for pressures up to 3.5 bar g.

6.3.3   Measurement of pH and redox potential

6.3.3.1   MEASURING ELECTRODES

The hydrogen electrode

If in a simple voltaic cell, similar to the one described on page 155, hydrogen is used as one electrode, the potential difference attained between the electrodes will, if everything else is kept the same, be a function of the concentration of the hydrogen ions in the solution in contact with the hydrogen electrode. A hydrogen electrode, *Figure 6.27*, consists in practice of a platinum plate or wire, covered with platinum black, a finely divided form of the metal. When hydrogen is bubbled over such an electrode it is absorbed into its surface and the electrode behaves as a hydrogen electrode. The standard or normal hydrogen potential is that of an electrode in contact with a solution of unit hydrogen ion activity, and this solution is hydrochloric acid having a concentration of 1.228 mol/dm³.

It can be shown that the potential attained by a hydrogen electrode is related to the pH value of the solution by the equation

$$E = E_0 - 0.000\,1984\,T\,\text{pH volts} \qquad (6.45)$$

where T = Temperature, K

E_0 = Constant potential equal to the potential of the electrode when in a solution whose pH value is zero. The electrode becomes more negative relative to the solution with increasing pH value.

The definition of the pH value of a solution is based upon the use of a hydrogen electrode, and the hydrogen electrode is used as the standard with which other electrodes are compared, but it is inconvenient to use in practice. For routine measurements, therefore, other electrodes are used.

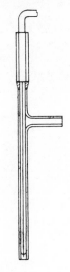

Figure 6.27 Cole hydrogen electrode

Electrodes for routine measurement

There are two types of measuring electrodes used in industrial pH measurement:

The antimony electrode
The glass electrode.

The antimony electrode. The simplest electrode is the antimony electrode. It consists of a piece of pure antimony, usually in the form of a rod or button, mounted in an insulated support and immersed in the solution under test. An electrode of this type is illustrated in *Figure 6.28(b)*.

Owing to the presence of dissolved oxygen in the solution, the metal soon becomes coated with a film of oxide which dissolves slightly in the water, producing in the vicinity of the electrode a solution of antimony hydroxide which dissociates producing antimony (Sb^{+++}) and hydroxyl (OH^-) ions, the degree of dissociation satisfying the equation

$$[Sb^{+++}] [OH^-]^3 = \text{Constant} \qquad (6.46)$$

But the concentration of hydroxyl ions is related to the concentration of the hydrogen ions by the equation

$$[H^+] [OH^-] = K_w$$

The concentration of antimony ions in solution will, therefore, be related to the hydrogen ion concentration of the solution and to its pH value. In becoming an antimony ion in solution, an atom of antimony has acquired three positive charges so that the electrode will acquire a corresponding negative charge. Under ideal conditions the potential E acquired by the electrode is related to the pH value of the solution by the equation

$$E = E_0 - 0.000\ 1984\ T\ \text{pH} \qquad (6.47)$$

where E_0 is, as before, the value of E when the pH value of the solution is zero.

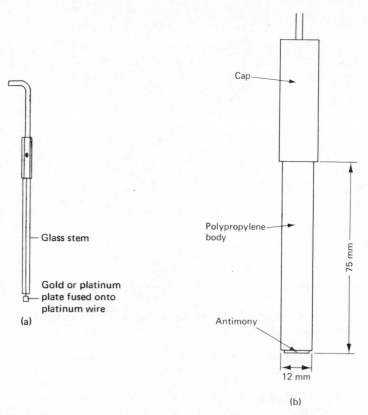

Cap

Polypropylene body

75 mm

Antimony

12 mm

(b)

Glass stem

Gold or platinum plate fused onto platinum wire

(a)

Figure 6.28   (a) Platinum electrode for use in measurement of redox potential (b) Antimony electrode (Courtesy Electronic Instruments Ltd.)

In actual practice, however, the potential of the electrode may be affected by factors other than the pH value of the solution. In order that the electrode may give moderately accurate results, the component upon which the pH value depends must be the only variable constituent of the solution. Even in this case, an empirical calibration is desirable and it must be realised that the calibration for static solutions is different from that of a moving solution of the same composition. Dissolved air or other gases will also affect the calibration. As the oxidation of the electrode takes a certain time to reach a state of 'equilibrium', the electrode must be inserted into the solution some time before a reading is taken.

The electrode cannot be used in solutions containing ions of metals which are electropositive to antimony as these will be deposited on the antimony, upsetting the e.m.f. relationship; neither can it be used in the presence of strong oxidising or reducing agents.

In many circumstances, however, measurement and control to within ±1 pH unit is adequate, as in the neutralisation of acidic or basic effluents, and antimony provides a relatively robust electrode for this purpose. Antimony electrodes are also used in very viscous liquids and in heavy sludges. When antimony electrodes are used for continuous pH measurement, automatic wiping or scraping may be arranged to prevent the accumulation of the corrosion film which causes the potential response of the electrode to pH change to become sluggish. The useful range of the electrode lies between 2 and 12.5 pH.

The glass electrode. By far the most versatile electrode is the glass electrode. It can be made to cover practically the whole of the pH scale and is unaffected by most chemicals except hydrofluoric acid. It may be used in the presence of oxidising or reducing agents without loss of measuring accuracy. The glass electrode consists of a membrane of special low resistance glass, usually sealed to a stem of relatively non-conducting glass (to eliminate errors caused by varying the depth of immersion), separating a solution of constant pH value from the solution under test. If the tested solution has a different hydrogen ion concentration from that of the standard solution, hydrogen ions will diffuse through the glass from the solution of higher hydrogen ion concentration to that of lower hydrogen ion concentration. The solution of greater concentration (lower pH) will therefore lose positive charge and acquire a negative potential relative to the solution of lower hydrogen ion concentration. The value of the potential difference will continue to increase until the electrical forces opposing the transfer of ions exactly neutralises the influence of concentration differences. The actual quantity of hydrogen ion transferred in order to establish equilibrium is negligibly small and leaves the original concentration unaltered.

The potential difference thus developed across the glass membrane has a value which is proportional to the difference in pH values of the two solutions and is measured by putting suitable metallic electrodes into the two solutions. The value of the potential difference set up is given by the same relationship as that for the hydrogen electrode (equation 6.45); the value of E_0 will, of course, be different.

The glass electrode may have a variety of forms, two of which are shown in *Figure 6.29*, but all are basically similar. In the laboratory form the glass bulb is about 0.05 mm thick, but for industrial use more robust bulbs have been developed; these should, however, be handled with reasonable care. Increase in wall thickness results in a very considerable increase in the electrical resistance of the glass wall, which also varies with temperature, as shown in *Figure 6.30(b)*, and requires the use of a d.c. amplifier which will permit a very high input resistance. Insulation resistance of the leads from the electrodes to the amplifier must be extremely high (10^5 MΩ; a 'Megger' test is useless). This is achieved by keeping the leads as short as possible and using the best moisture resisting insulating materials such as polythene or silicone rubber.

The bulb is sealed and contains a suitable buffer solution and chloride ion, the inner electrode being a silver wire coated with silver chloride. When used for measuring the activity of ions other than hydrogen another filling may be used.

6.3.3.2 REFERENCE ELECTRODES

In order to complete the electrical circuit, a second contact with the tested solution is required. The potential difference developed at this second point of contact must be constant. It should be independent of temperature changes (or vary in a known manner), be independent of the pH value of the solution, and remain stable over long periods if the potential difference produced at the measuring electrode is to be accurately measured. Whilst the ultimate reference electrode for pH measurement is a hydrogen electrode in 1.228 mol/dm³ hydrochloric acid, for practical purposes two metal/metal salt solution types of electrode are used. A third type is used occasionally.

1. The silver/silver chloride electrode consists of a silver wire or plate, coated with silver chloride, in contact with a salt bridge of potassium chloride saturated with silver chloride. The concentration of the potassium chloride may vary from one type of electrode to another but a concentration of 1.00 or 4.00 mol/dm³ or a saturated solution are quite common. This saturated type of electrode has a potential of −0.199 V relative to a hydrogen electrode. It has a variety of physical forms which are discussed below.

2. The mercury/mercurous chloride or calomel electrode. The metal used is mercury which has a high resistance to corrosion and being fluid at ambient temperature cannot be subject to strain. The mercury is in contact with either mercurous chloride or in some electrodes with mercurous chloride and potassium chloride paste. Contact with the measured solution is through a salt bridge of potassium chloride whose concentration may be 3.8 mol/dm³ or

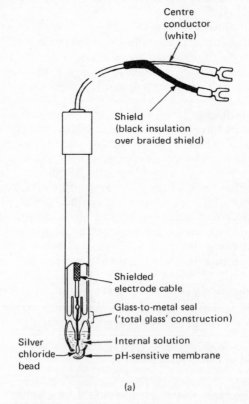

(a)

Figure 6.29   Measuring electrodes (a) (Courtesy Foxboro Ltd.)

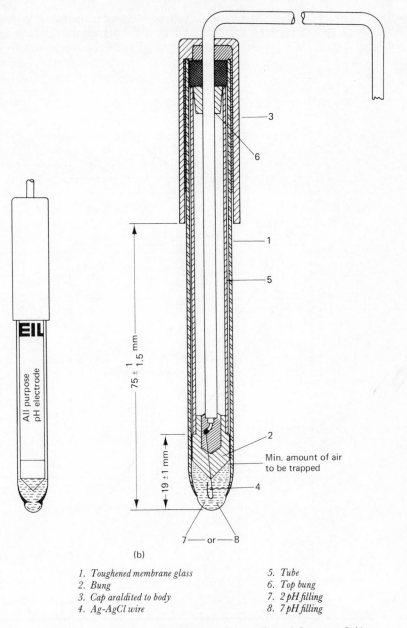

(b)

1. *Toughened membrane glass*   5. *Tube*
2. *Bung*   6. *Top bung*
3. *Cap araldited to body*   7. *2 pH filling*
4. *Ag-AgCl wire*   8. *7 pH filling*

Figure 6.29 (b)   All-purpose industrial electrode (Courtesy Electronic Instruments Ltd.)

other concentration appropriate to the application. Contact with the mercury is usually made by means of a platinum wire which may be amalgamated. The calomel, saturated potassium chloride electrode has a potential relative to the hydrogen electrode of -0.244 V.

3. Where the use of potassium salt is precluded by the condition of use, it

188

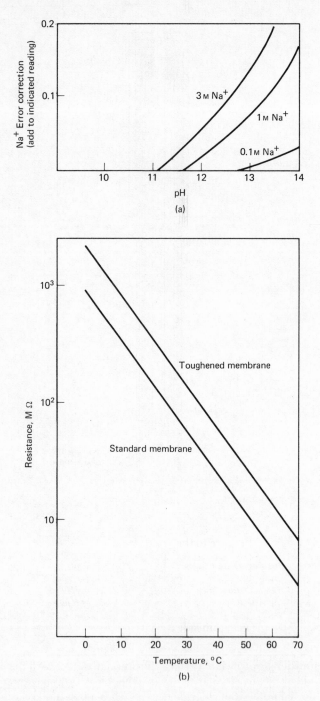

Figure 6.30 *Characteristics of E.I.L. all-purpose glass electrode (Courtesy Electronic Instruments Ltd.) (a) Sodium error–pH relationship at 25°C (b) Variation of pH membrane resistance with temperature*

may be replaced by sodium sulphate, the bridge solution having a concentration of 1 mol/dm³.

Whatever the type of the reference electrode, contact must be made between the salt bridge and the measured solution. Two common methods are through a ceramic plug whose shape and porosity govern the rate at which the salt bridge solution diffuses out and the process solution diffuses into and contaminates the bridge solution. If the plug is arranged to have a small area of cross section relative to its length, the rate of diffusion is very small (say less than 0.01 cm³/day) and the electrode can be considered to be sealed and is used until it becomes unserviceable, when it is replaced by a similar electrode.

Where the application warrants it a high rate of diffusion from the electrode has to be tolerated (say 1 or 2 cm³/day), so the relative dimensions and porosity of the plug are changed, or it is replaced by a glass sleeve which permits relatively fast flow of salt bridge solution, thus reducing the rate and degree of fouling of the junction. In these circumstances, the electrode is refilled on a routine basis, or a continuous supply of bridge solution is arranged into the electrode at the appropriate pressure for the application.

Samples from a wide range of varieties are illustrated in *Figure 6.31*. The notes on the figure are self-explanatory.

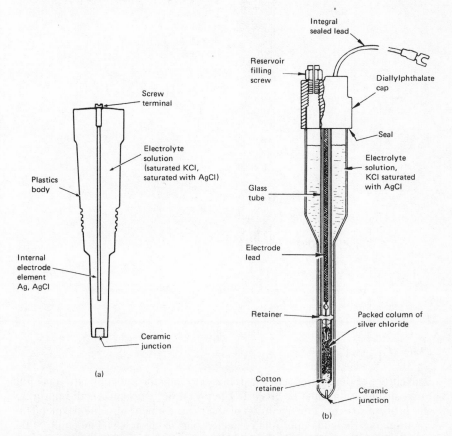

Figure 6.31   Reference electrodes (a) Sealed electrode (b) Flowing type (Courtesy Foxboro Ltd.)

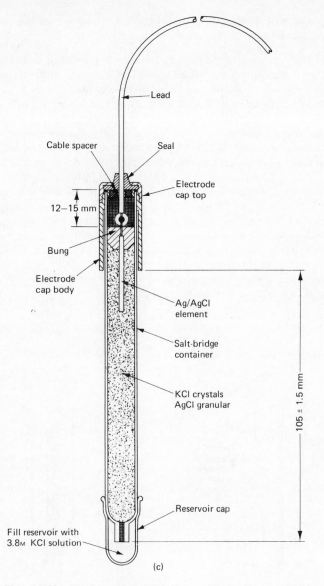

Figure 6.31(c)   Sealed silver/silver chloride (Courtesy Electronic Instruments Ltd.)

Choice of reference electrode

The choice of the appropriate reference electrode for the application is vital, and consideration must be given to the pressure, temperature and nature of the process stream. The accuracy of the measurement and the frequency of maintenance depends upon the correct choice of electrode. The e.m.f. of the reference electrode will only remain constant provided satisfactory contact is made by the salt bridge, so the junction must not become plugged by suspended solids, viscous liquids, or reaction products of the process stream. Where this is a danger, the faster flow type of plug must be used. Many routine measurements can, however, be made with the non-flowing electrode, thus avoiding the necessity of refilling, or arranging the pressured continuous supply. Flowing types of junctions are usually required where an accuracy of ±0.02 pH units (±1 or 2 mV) is required, where frequent or large temperature or composition changes occur, or where the process fluid is such that it is prone to foul the junction.

The temperature of operation will influence the choice of concentration of the filling solutions. Potassium chloride solution having a concentration of 4 mol/dm³ saturates and starts to precipitate solids at about 19°C, and will freeze at −4°C, while if the concentration is reduced to 1 mol/dm³ the solution will freeze at −2°C without becoming saturated. Thus, no precipitation will take place in the solution of lower concentration. Although not damaging, precipitated potassium chloride and associated silver chloride will tend to clog reference junctions and tubes, decreasing electrolyte flow rate, and increasing the risk of spurious potentials. For these reasons, flowing reference electrodes are not recommended for low temperature applications unless provision is made to prevent freezing or precipitation in the electrode and any associated hardware.

When materials such as sulphides, alkali phosphates or carbonates, which will react with silver, are present in the process stream either non-flowing or electrodes containing potassium chloride at 1 mol/dm³ should be used. The diffusion rate of silver can be neglected in the non-flowing type, and the solubility of silver chloride in potassium chloride at a concentration of 1 mol/dm³ is only 1 or 2% of that in a solution at 4 mol/dm³.

High temperatures with wide fluctuations are best handled by potassium chloride solution at 1 mol/dm³.

If one carries out the procedures described in the section on practical specification of a pH scale (page 149) with a given solution at a number of temperatures, one can establish the relationship between e.m.f. and pH, and e.m.f. and temperature, for a given electrode system. These relationships can be shown on a graph of the form shown in *Figure 6.32*. The slope of the graphs will be given by the Nernst equation to the accuracy of industrial measurement. As the graph shows there is a particular value of the pH at which the e.m.f. is independent of temperature. This point, the iso-potential point, is about pH 6 for the electrode system whose characteristics are shown in *Figure 6.32*.

We can therefore express the e.m.f. *(E)* produced at any temperature by the equation

$$E = A - CT(\text{pH}_m - \text{pH}_I) \tag{6.48}$$

where A =   E.M.F. at the iso-potential point
     C is represented by the slope of the graph for temperature T K
   pH_m =   Measured pH
   pH_I =   pH at the iso-potential point.

If this point is arranged to be the locus of the slope of the measuring instrument, a single resistance bulb can be arranged to compensate for the change in sensitivity of the electrode system to pH with temperature, or in the manual instrument, a variable resistance adjusted to a value representing the working temperature of the solution. Thus, when the instrument is set up with a buffer solution the circuit is arranged so that allowance is made for the value of A which may, for a given electrode system and solution, be regarded as being

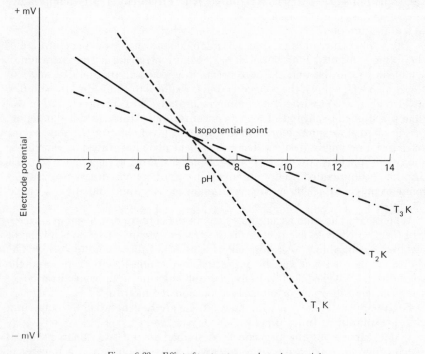

Figure 6.32   Effect of temperature on electrode potential

constant. The circuit is then arranged so that the negative feedback is changed by the temperature compensating circuit so that the instrument compensates for the change in slope of the e.m.f./pH relationship. It is important to realise that the temperature compensation only corrects for the change in the electrode response owing to temperature change. It does not compensate for the actual change in pH of the solution with temperature given in equation 6.27. Thus if pH is being measured to establish the composition of a solution it is preferable to carry out the measurements at a constant temperature.

6.3.3.3   LOW RESISTANCE ELECTRODE SYSTEMS

When the antimony measuring electrode is used, or in the measurement of redox potential, the resistance of the measuring system is relatively low so that potentiometric types of measuring systems of the form described in Volume 1 may be used. *Figure 6.33* shows the principle of such a system. Any difference between the voltage generated at the electrodes and that produced across the

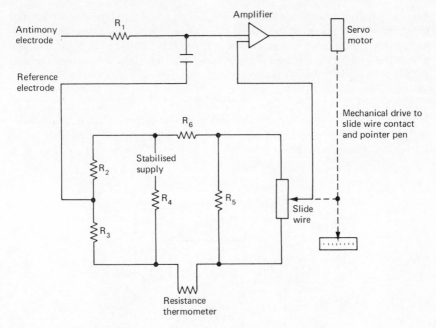

Figure 6.33   Circuit for measurement with low resistance electrodes

potentiometer will be amplified and applied to the servo motor which moves the slide wire contact to restore balance.

6.3.3.4   HIGH RESISTANCE ELECTRODE SYSTEMS

The resistance of a typical glass electrode is as shown in *Figure 6.30,* so that a system consisting of a glass measuring electrode and a reference electrode may have a resistance of several hundred megohms. If an accurate measure is to be made of the e.m.f. developed at the measuring electrode, the measuring system must have an extremely high input impedance. The usual method of measurement is to convert the measured e.m.f. into a proportional current by means of a suitable amplifying system. Several possible systems are available.

The essential requirements in such a system are:

1. A linear relationship between the input potential and the output current of the amplifier.

2. The sensitivity of the amplifier, i.e. (Output current)/(Input voltage), must be constant with time.

3. The zero reading of the instrument must be stable and not vary with time, or be affected by limited variations in voltage or frequency of the electrical supply.

4. The current taken from the electrode must be very small to ensure that polarisation effects and effects due to changes in the electrode resistance may be very small.

These first two needs may be fulfilled by using an amplifier with a very high negative feedback ratio. This means that the greater part of the input potential is balanced by a potential produced by passing the meter current through an accurately known resistor, as shown in *Figure 6.34*. If the p.d., V_0, developed across the feedback resistance is a very large fraction of the measured potential V_1, then the input voltage v is a very small fraction of V_1, and

$$I_0 = (V_1 - v)/R, \text{ approaches } V_1/R$$

With modern integrated circuit techniques it is possible to obtain an amplifier with a very high input impedance and very high gain, so that little or no current is drawn from the electrodes.

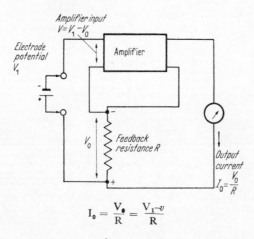

$$I_0 = \frac{V_0}{R} = \frac{V_1 - v}{R}$$

Figure 6.34   Principle of d.c. amplifier with negative feedback (Courtesy Electronic Instruments Ltd.)

Such a system is employed in the pH-to-current converter shown in *Figure 6.35* which employs zener diode stabilised supplies and feedback networks designed to give a high gain, high input impedance diode bridge amplifier.

The d.c. unbalance signal resulting from the pH signal, asymmetry correcting potential and the feedback voltage, changes the output of a capacity balance diode bridge. This output feeds a transistor amplifier which supplies feedback and output proportional to the bridge error signal. Zener diode stabilised and potentiometer circuits are used to provide continuous adjustment of span, elevation, and asymmetry potential over the entire operating range of the instrument.

The input impedance of the instrument is about $1 \times 10^{12}\Omega$ and the current taken from the electrodes less than 0.5×10^{-12} A. An instrument suitable for use in a ANEC Class 1 Group D location (i.e. approximating to B.A.S.E.E.F.A. Zone 0 Group 111A) is available.

The principle of another system which achieves a similar result is shown in *Figure 6.36*, which uses a matched pair of field effect transistors housed in a single can. The principle of the field effect transistor is described below but it is sufficient to mention here that it can have an input impedance in excess of $10^{12}\Omega$.

The principle of the measurement is that the e.m.f. produced by the

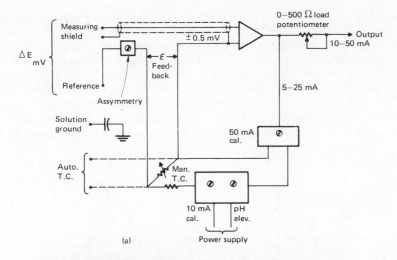

(a)

(b)

Figure 6.35   pH converter (Courtesy Foxboro-Yoxall Ltd.)

measuring electrode is fed to the gate of one of the pair of field effect transistors. The potential which is applied to one side of the high gain operation amplifier will be governed by the current which flows through the transistor and its corresponding resistance R_3. The potential applied to the gate of the second field effect transistor is set by the buffer bias adjustment which is fed from a zener stabilised potential supply. The potential developed across the second resistance R_4 which is equal in resistance to R_3 will be controlled by the current through the second of the pair of matched field effect transistors. Thus the output of the operational amplifier will be controlled by the difference in

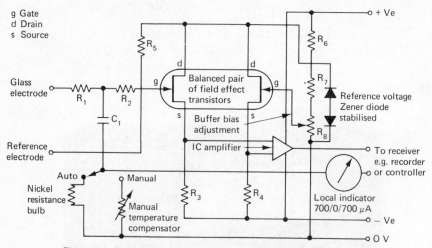

Figure 6.36   Principle of pH measuring instrument for high resistance electrode

the potentials applied to the gates of the field effect transistors, i.e. to the difference between the potential developed on the measuring electrode and the highly stable potential set up in the instrument. Thus, the current flowing through the local and remote indicators will be a measure of the change of potential of the measuring electrode.

The current flowing through the indicator also flows through the manual, or automatic temperature compensating resistor, so that the potential applied to the reference electrode can be arranged to compensate for the change in slope of the pH/temperature relationship, i.e. the gain of the system can be changed by the negative feedback across the temperature compensator so as to match the slope of the pH/temperature relationship. In an actual instrument, the circuit of which is shown in *Figure 6.37(a)*, alarm initiation and manual temperature compensation are provided.

This will be used to illustrate the method of setting up and servicing. The method of setting up the alarms will be found in the maker's handbook.

Circuit description

The circuit may best be understood by division into basic functional areas, i.e. input amplifier, feedback circuit, and power and reference supplies.

197

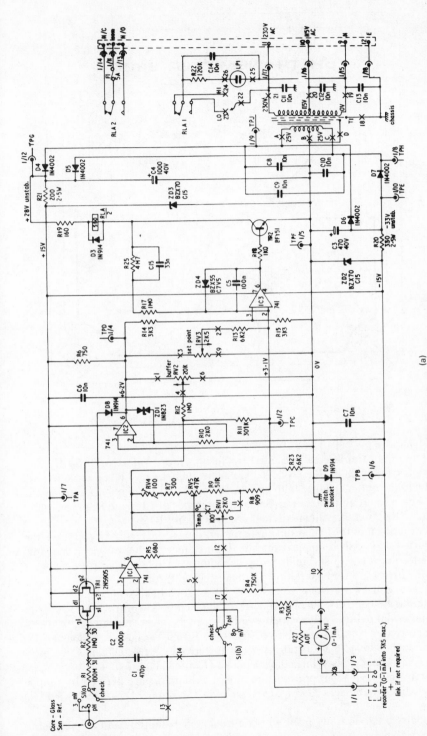

Figure 6.37(a) Circuit diagram of pH transmitter

(a)

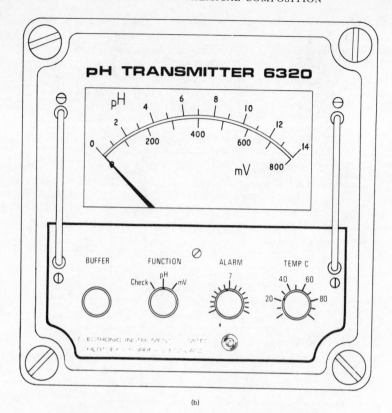

(b)

Figure 6.37 (b) Front panel (Courtesy Electronic Instruments Ltd.)

The input amplifier is preceded by an input filter effective at 50 Hz and above, consisting of R1, R2, Cl, C2. The dual f.e.t. TR1 acts as a high impedance buffer (source follower) to IC1 and these two together act as the high gain input amplifier. The back-off potentials are derived from the buffer control RV2 via the voltage divider chain R11 and R12.

For a given output current (i.e. meter reading), the feedback produces the required potential equal and opposite to the potential from the electrode pair. The feedback is adjustable to compensate for electrode temperature changes for the pH range, and fixed for the redox (millivolt) range.

The feedback network consists of RV4 (to adjust scale length of the temperature control), R8, R9 and RV1 (the Temp. °C control). R23 sets the iso-potential point to approximately pH 7.

The power supplies are derived from a 25-0-25 V mains transformer T1 secondary. The +28 V unstabilised line is derived via D4, D5 and C4, whilst the −33 V unstabilised line comes via D6, D7 and C3.

Stabilised ±15 V supplies for the integrated circuits are derived by simple zener diode stabilisers ZD3 (+15 V) fed via R21, and ZD2 (−15 V) fed via R20.

The reference supply from which all back-off potentials and the set point potential are derived is provided by the temperature compensated reference diode ZD1 in the feedback of the virtual earth amplifier IC2. R10 sets the reference diode current at 7.5 mA. R6 allows substantial current to be drawn from this supply; D8 and D9 protect the indicating meter from overload. C6 to C13 operate as mains-transient and r.f. noise suppressors.

The moving coil indicator M1 is adjusted by shunt resistor R27 to precisely 1 mA f.s.d. Meter assemblies are thus interchangeable as complete units.

6.3.3.5 FIELD EFFECT TRANSISTORS

A field effect transistor differs from a common transistor in that the flow of current between source and drain is governed by the potential on the gate and not the current flowing from the gate. In fact, the gate may be insulated from the rest of the transistor but still apply its controlling effect. Thus, a field effect transistor can provide a current controlling device having an infinitely higher input impedance.

Basically the f.e.t. can be considered as a rectangular block of say p-type silicon with n-type impurities introduced into opposite sides, creating p-n junctions. If the current flow between source and drain contacts is limited to the p-type channel, the conductance of the path will be controlled by the potential on the gate, which will increase or decrease the current by increasing or decreasing the number of effective carriers in the material between the two portions of the gate.

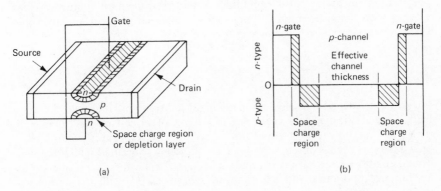

Figure 6.38   Field effect transistors (a) General construction (b) Section at gate showing impurity concentration

Figure 6.38(a) shows the distribution of the impurity through a cross section of the block at the gate at a given junction bias voltage. Since the charges on each side of the junction are the same, the space charge will extend further into the purer region. It is assumed that the concentration in the n regions is uniform and so is the concentration in the p region, and the junction transitions are abrupt. There will exist at each gate channel junction a space charge region from which the free charge carriers have been removed, leaving only nuclei and bound electrons. The width of these space charge regions is a function of the junction potential and the impurity concentration. Applying a reverse voltage to the gate channel junction will cause the conductance of the channel to decrease because of the widening of the space charge region. Thus, the conductance of the channel is an inverse function of the gate-to-channel voltage, i.e. the transverse electric field applied at the gate may be used to control the magnitude of the source-to-drain current.

6.3.3.6   SOURCES OF ERROR AND METHODS OF REDUCING OR ELIMINATING THE ERROR

Sodium ion error

For pH measurement in solutions of pH value below 11, glass electrodes are usually made of sodium glass. In solutions of pH values above 11, ions other than hydrogen ions tend to penetrate the electrode and reduce the indicated pH value of the solution, particularly at higher temperatures. Sodium ions produce the greatest error, lithium ions producing about one half, potassium about one fifth and other ions less than one tenth of the error due to sodium ions.

One method of allowing for this error is to standardise the electrode in an alkaline buffer solution containing a suitable concentration of the appropriate salt.

For use in solutions of high alkalinity and at higher temperatures, lithium and caesium glass electrodes have been developed, and they reduce this type of error considerably. For a given glass at a stated measuring temperature the size of the error can be found from tables provided by the manufacturer so that a correction may be made. The sodium ion errors for the Electronic Instruments electrodes are shown in *Figure 6.30(a)*.

Asymmetry potential

If a symmetrical cell is set up having identical solutions and identical electrode leads on each side of a glass membrane, the e.m.f. of the cell may be expected to be zero. This, however, is found not to be the case, especially when freshly blown glass is used. An e.m.f. of several millivolts is obtained which tends to diminish, and often disappears after some days. This e.m.f. is described as an asymmetrical potential and is probably due to the fact that the two surfaces of the glass may not be in an identical condition of chemical composition or mechanical strain.

Glass electrodes are therefore aged by the manufacturer by being soaked for several days in an appropriate solution so that the asymmetrical potential becomes constant. The electrode is then calibrated by means of suitable buffer solutions so that no assumption is made about the value of E_0 in equation 6.45. A source of variable potential difference, in series with the electrode system, is provided in the measuring system of the pH instrument to allow for the asymmetrical potential and to permit the interchange of measuring electrodes. In this way it is possible to obtain a scale which reads directly in pH units.

Immersion of an electrode in strong acid or alkali may give rise to asymmetrical potential effects. When an electrode has been used in strong acid or alkali it should be soaked in distilled water for 10–15 min before being used in a solution of a different pH value. A dry electrode surface is likely to have an asymmetrical potential, so before use an electrode should be soaked for 24 h in 0.1 mol/dm³ hydrochloric acid, and then washed in distilled water.

Temperature error

In the first place the actual pH value of a solution may change with temperature. The variation of the pH value of a solution with temperature depends upon the nature of the solution. In many solutions of pH value less than 6 and in certain buffered systems the pH value of the solution is roughly independent of temperature. In other circumstances the relationship between pH and temperature is not a linear one. While the effect of temperature variation may be taken into account by the use of a table of corrections, it is often simpler, particularly where the pH value is being measured in order to establish the composition of the tested solution, to determine the pH value at some fixed temperature.

6.3.3.7   INDUSTRIAL ELECTRODE SYSTEMS

Two types of electrode systems are in common use:

1. The continuous flow type of assembly.
2. The immersion, or dip-type of assembly.

Continuous flow type of assembly

The physical form of the assembly may vary a little from one manufacturer to another but *Figure 6.39* illustrates a typical assembly designed with reliability and easy maintenance in mind. Constructed in rigid p.v.c. throughout, it operates at pressure up to 2 bar and temperatures up to 60°C. For higher temperatures and pressures the assembly may be made from EN 58J stainless steel, flanged and designed for straight through flow when pressures up to 3 bar at temperatures up to 100°C can be tolerated. It accommodates the standard measuring electrode, usually of toughened glass.

A reservoir for potassium chloride (or other electrolyte) forms a permanent part of the electrode holder. A replaceable reference element fits into the top of the reservoir, and is held in place by an easily detachable clamp nut. A microceramic plug at the lower end of the reservoir ensures slow electrolyte leakage (up to six months continuous operation without attention is usually obtained). The ceramic junction is housed in a screw-fitting plug, and is easily replaceable.

The close grouping of electrodes makes possible a small flow cell, and hence a fast pH response at low flow rates. An oil filled reservoir built into the electrode holder houses a replaceable nickel wire resistance element. (The temperature compensator is an optional fitment.)

The direction of flow through the cell creates some degree of turbulence and thus minimises electrode coating and sedimentation.

202

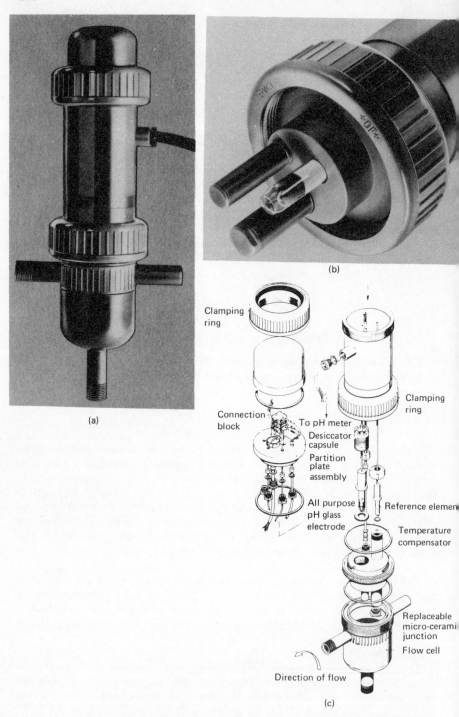

Clamping
ring

Connection
block

To pH meter

Desiccator
capsule

Partition
plate
assembly

All purpose
pH glass
electrode

Clamping
ring

Reference element

Temperature
compensator

Replaceable
micro-ceramic
junction

Flow cell

Direction of flow

(a)

(b)

(c)

*Figure 6.39   Flow type of electrode system (Courtesy Electronic Instruments Ltd.) (a) External view (b) Upper
section detaches for easy buffering (c) Exploded view showing the components*

The integral junction box is completely weatherproof and easily detachable. Electrode cables and the output cable are taken via individual watertight compression fittings into the base of the junction box. A desiccator is included to absorb moisture which may be trapped when the cover is removed and replaced.

Two turns of the lower clamp nut allow the entire electrode unit to be detached from the flow cell and hence from the process fluid. The electrodes can be immersed easily in buffer solution.

Immersion type

Basically this assembly is similar to the flow type except that the flow cell is replaced by a protecting guard which protects the electrode but allows a free flow of solution to the electrodes. Also the upper cap is replaced by a similarly moulded tube which supports the electrode assembly, but brings the terminal box well above the electrode assembly so that the terminals are clear of the liquid surface when the assembly is in the measured solution. Immersion depths up to 3 m are available.

Electrode assemblies should be designed so that the electrodes can be kept wet when not in use. It is often possible to arrange for the easy removal of the assembly from the process vessel so that it can be immersed in a bucket filled with process liquid, water or buffer solution during shut-down.

The design of the assembly is often modified, to suit the use. For example, in measuring the pH of pulp in a paper beater the electrodes and resistance bulb are mounted side by side in a straight line and then inclined down-stream at about 45° from the vertical so that they present no pockets to collect pulp and are self-cleaning.

When the assembly is immersed in a tank, care must be taken in the siting to ensure the instrument is measuring the properties of a representative sample; adequate mixing of the process material is essential. Sometimes it is more convenient to circulate the contents of a tank through a flow type of assembly and then return the liquid to the tank.

The main cause of trouble in electrode assemblies is the fouling of the electrodes. In order to reduce this, two forms of self-cleaning are available and the choice of method is dependent on the application. Where the main cause of trouble is deposits on the glass electrode and mechanical cleaning is required, this may be achieved by the cleaning attachment shown on a dip system in *Figure 6.40(a)*. The pneumatically driven rubber membrane shown in *Figure 6.40(b)* wipes the electrode, providing a simple, reliable cleaning action. It is driven by a spring return pneumatic actuator fed with air at pre-set intervals from a controller which incorporates a programmed timer mechanism which governs the frequency of the wiping action. The cleaning attachment is constructed entirely of polypropylene and 316 stainless steel, except for the rubber wiper which may be replaced by a polypropylene brush type should this be more suitable.

Alternatively an a.c. operated transistorised ultra-sonic generator operating at 25 kHz, which is coupled to a lead zirconate transducer contained in a stainless steel housing and can be fitted to the electrode assembly, may be used. Fitting such a generator to the system greatly increases the periods

(a)

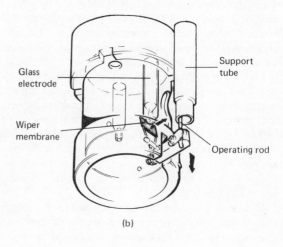

Glass
electrode

Support
tube

Wiper
membrane

Operating rod

(b)

*Figure 6.40   Dip-type assembly with cleaning attachment (Courtesy Electronic Instruments Ltd.) (a) Assembly
(b) Detail of cleaning attachment*

between necessary electrode cleaning. The assembly is usually supplied with 4.5 m of interconnecting cable between the generator and the transducer. Increased lengths are available but the maximum length is limited by the permissible power loss in the cable.

6.3.3.8 INSTALLATION AND MAINTENANCE OF pH METERS

In all cases the instructions provided with the instrument by the maker should be followed.

Electrode cleanliness. Routine cleaning of electrodes should be carried out by rinsing in distilled water and removing any adhering impurities by wiping carefully with cotton wool or soft tissue. More tenacious deposits, particularly of organic origin, may require use of an appropriate solvent. In some cases the installation of an ultra-sonic cleaner may be recommended. For detailed information on the maintenance, cleaning and storage of different types of electrode, reference should be made to the instructional material supplied with the electrode.

6.3.4 Oxygen probes

Just as an electrical potential can be developed at a glass membrane which is a function of ratio of the concentrations on either side, a pure zinconia tube maintained at high temperature will develop a potential between its surfaces which is a function of the partial pressure of oxygen which is in contact with its surfaces. This is the principle involved in the oxygen meter shown in principle in *Figure 6.41*.

The potential developed is given by Nernst's equation

$$E_s = (RT/4F) \; (\log_e \text{[Internal partial pressure of } O_2{}^{4-} \text{ ions]} /$$
$$\text{[External partial pressure of } O_2{}^{4-} \text{ ions])} \tag{6.49}$$

Thus, if the potential difference between the surfaces is measured by platinum electrodes in contact with the two surfaces a measure may be made of the ratio of the partial pressure of the oxygen inside and outside the probe. If dry instrument air (20.9% O_2) is fed into the inside of the probe, the partial pressure of oxygen inside the tube may be regarded as constant, so that the electrical potential measured in a similar manner to that adopted in pH measurement will be a measure of the concentration of the oxygen in the atmosphere around the measuring probe. Thus by positioning the probe in the stack or flue where the temperature is above 600°C a direct measurement of the oxygen present may be made.

In one manufacturer's instrument the probe is maintained at a temperature of 850°C by a temperature controlled heating element. The instrument illustrated can operate from 600 to 1200°C, the reading being corrected for temperature, which is measured by a nickel chromium *v.* nickel aluminium thermocouple located at the probe for temperatures between 600 and 1000°C, or a Pt/Pt 13 Rh thermocouple for temperatures between 900 and 1200°C. The probe is protected by a silicon carbide sheath.

206

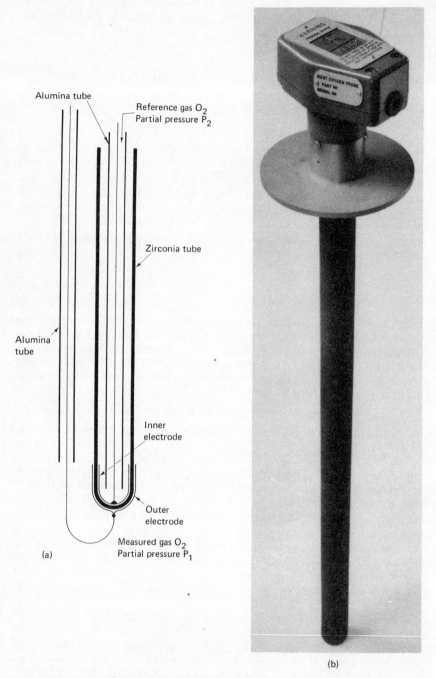

Figure 6.41 Oxygen probe (Courtesy Kent Instruments) (a) Schematic (b) Actual probe

Standard instruments have ranges of oxygen concentration of 20.9–0.1%, 1000–1 p.p.m., 10^{-5}–10^{-25} partial pressure. The instrument can measure the oxygen concentration with an accuracy of better than ±10% of concentration.

The probe is 700 mm long and should be inserted to a depth of 600 mm, either vertically down or horizontally. The output of the converter can be fed to a recorder or indicator or both.

6.4   ANALYSIS OF GASES BY MEASUREMENT OF THERMAL CONDUCTIVITY

6.4.1   Introduction; physical principles

All matter is made up of very small particles called molecules. It is believed that heat is the energy possessed by a body by virtue of the motion of the molecules of which it is composed. The molecules of a solid do not alter their position relative to each other but vibrate about a mean position, and the energy of the vibration increases with increase of temperature. Heat given to a liquid may increase the vibration of the molecules and at the same time cause molecules to move from one part of the liquid to another.

In a gas, the molecules are in rapid motion. Collisions between molecules, and between molecules and the walls of the vessel containing the gas, are frequent, and it is the continual impacts of gas molecules with the walls of the vessel which produce the pressure of the gas upon the walls. The molecules are regarded as being perfectly elastic so that no energy is dissipated by the collisions. Heat given to the gas increases the speed of the movement of the molecules, thus increasing both the kinetic energy of the gas and the pressure upon the walls. According to the well established 'kinetic theory of gases': 'the mean kinetic energy of the molecules of a gas is proportional to the absolute temperature of the gas'.

By using the kinetic theory, Maxwell obtained theoretical verification of:

Avogadro's law.   Equal volumes of all gases having the same temperature and pressure contain equal numbers of molecules.

Dalton's law.   In a mixture of gases each gas exerts a partial pressure which is the pressure it would exert if it alone filled the whole space.

Graham's law of diffusion.   The rate of diffusion of a gas varies inversely as the square root of the density of the gas.

6.4.1.1   THERMAL CONDUCTIVITY OF A GAS

Consider a cylindrical enclosure in a metal block filled with a pure gas. Along the axis of the cylindrical hole a wire is arranged which is at a higher temperature than the metal block.

Molecules of gas will be moving about in the enclosure in a random manner and with a variety of velocities, but the average velocity of the molecules will be characteristic of the temperature of the gas. Some molecules will be moving towards the wire, and when a molecule comes into contact with the wire, heat energy is transferred to it so that its kinetic energy is increased. It will leave the wire with a greater energy than it had when it approached it. It will move across the enclosure with this energy, and give up some of its energy to the metal block which encloses the gas and which is at a lower temperature than the wire. Collisions between gas molecules within the enclosure will not affect this transfer of energy, for when two gas molecules collide, as they are identical and perfectly elastic, they will exchange speeds and directions of motion. The effect, therefore, is the same as if one molecule traversed the path without colliding. Gas molecules will remove energy from the wire and give it up to the metal block; in other words, the gas molecules will conduct heat from the wire to the metal block.

Equal volumes of all gases having the same temperature and pressure contain equal numbers of molecules. For a given temperature and pressure, the cylindrical enclosure will contain the same number of molecules whatever the nature of the gas. Each molecule will transfer the same amount of heat from the wire to the block, but as the mean kinetic energy of the molecules is proportional to the absolute temperature, molecules of a less dense gas will be moving faster than those of a more dense gas. Molecules of a less dense gas will, therefore, cross the gap between wire and block more frequently than those of a more dense gas. Hydrogen, therefore, has a higher thermal conductivity than oxygen or nitrogen.

The higher the temperature of the gas, the greater is the mean kinetic energy and the mean velocity of the molecules. The molecules of a particular gas will, therefore, cross the space between the wire and the block more frequently if the temperature is raised. Hence, the conductivity of the gas will depend upon its temperature. According to the kinetic theory, the thermal conductivity K_t of a pure gas, at an absolute temperature T, should vary with temperature according to the equation

$$K_t = K_0 \, (b + 273/b + T) \, (T/273)^{3/2} \qquad (6.50)$$

where K_0 = Thermal conductivity at 0°C
      b is a constant.

This equation has been verified experimentally between temperatures of −80 and +100°C.

Maxwell also predicted that 'the thermal conductivity of a gas is independent of pressure'. This is found to be true over a wide range of pressures, provided the pressure does not become so high that the gas may no longer be regarded as being a perfect gas. At very low pressure (less than 1 mm of mercury) the conductivity of a gas is proportional to its pressure. This fact is the basis of the Knudsen hot wire manometer or Pirani gauge.

If we take the thermal conductivity of air as 1.00 the conductivities of some gases have the values given in *Table 6.6*.

Table 6.6.

Gas	Conductivity	Gas	Conductivity
Oxygen	1.01	Carbon monoxide	0.96
Nitrogen	1.00	Carbon dioxide	0.59
Hydrogen	7.00	Sulphur dioxide	0.34
Chlorine	0.32	Water vapour	1.30

6.4.1.2   APPLICATION TO GAS ANALYSIS

In gas analysis the conductivities of pure gases are of limited value. It is more important to know how the conductivity of a mixture varies with the proportion of constituent gases. Unfortunately, the relationship between the conductivity of a mixture of gases and the proportion of the constituents is complicated. When collisions occur between molecules of different gases the mathematics of the collisions are no longer simple, and the relationship between the conductivity of the gas mixture and the proportions of the constituents depends upon the molecular and physical constants of the gases and the law of force between molecules during collision. For the purpose of calibrating thermal conductivity instruments it is therefore necessary to establish the required composition–conductivity curves experimentally.

Many forms of thermal conductivity gas analysis instruments have been developed, all of which depend upon the hot wire method of measuring thermal conductivity.

A wire, heated electrically and maintained at a constant temperature, is fixed along the axis of a cylindrical hole bored in a metal block which is maintained at a constant temperature. The cylindrical hole is filled with the gas under test. The temperature of the wire will reach a state of equilibrium when the rate of loss of heat by conduction, convection and radiation is equal to the rate of production of heat by the current in the wire. In practical forms of analysis instruments, conduction is by far the most important source of heat loss. End cooling, convection, radiation and thermal diffusion effects, though measurable, account for so small a part (less than 1 % each) of the total loss that they can be satisfactorily taken care of in the calibration. Convection losses are less when the wire is mounted vertically, so most instruments are designed with the wires mounted thus. Convection losses also increase with the pressure of the gas, so the pressure should be controlled for accurate measurements of conductivity of dense gases. In the usual practical form of apparatus, errors due to gas flow through the apparatus are negligible because the gas does not flow through the cell but enters by diffusion.

Measurement of temperature of the wire

The resistance of the wire depends upon its temperature; thus, by measuring the resistance of the wire, its temperature may be found. In other words, the wire may be employed as the resistance temperature bulb. For convenience, the current used to raise the temperature of the wire may also be used in the measurement of its temperature. The electrical energy (VA watts) supplied to the wire to maintain the excess temperature is a measure of the total heat lost by conduction, convection and radiation. In order to measure the effects due to changes in conductivity of the gas only, the resistance of the hot wire in a cell containing the gas to be tested is compared with the resistance of an exactly similar wire in a similar cell containing a standard gas. This differential arrangement also lessens the effects of changes in the heating current and changes in the ambient temperature conditions. In order to increase the sensitivity two identical measuring and two reference cells are often used.

6.4.1.3 THE BRIDGE CIRCUIT

A katharometer consists of four platinum wires with identical electrical and thermal characteristics arranged in a Wheatstone bridge circuit as shown in *Figure 6.42*. The four wires are enclosed in separate cells within a solid and comparatively massive block. If the four cells are open to the same gas, the four arms are identical and the current through the four arms is the same, the bridge will be in balance, and no current will flow between B and D. However, if the reference cells contain air and the measurement cells contain a gas mixture, such as carbon dioxide and air, less heat will be lost by the filaments to the walls in the measuring cells than those in the reference cells because the conductivity of carbon monoxide is less than that of air. The measuring filaments will be at a higher temperature, and hence have a higher resistance, than the reference filaments. Thus, the potential drop across the measuring filaments will be greater than the potential drop across the reference filaments so that B will be at a higher potential than D, and a current will flow through the galvanometer. The size of the current through the galvanometer, and hence its deflection, will be a measure of the difference in conduction between the cells. Thus, for a specific gas mixture, which can be regarded as a binary mixture, the galvanometer scale can be calibrated in terms of concentration of, say, carbon dioxide in air.

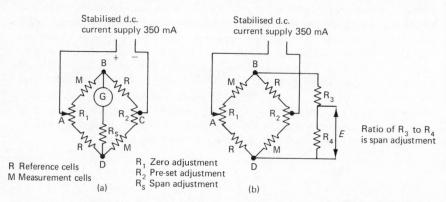

Figure 6.42   Katharometer bridge circuits (a) Direct deflection method (b) Using self-balancing potentiometer to measure E_p

If B and D are connected to R_3 and R_4 as shown in *Figure 6.42(b)* the potential E across R_4 can be measured by a self-balancing potentiometer which can be arranged to indicate or record composition of the measured gas.

If a low range is required, the platinum filaments may be replaced by matched thermistors and the whole assembly housed in a box controlled at a temperature well above ambient so that it is independent of ambient temperature changes. The gas is allowed to reach the measurement temperature before entering the cells and the bridge current accurately controlled so that a high degree of stability is readily achieved. Electronically heated enclosures cannot be used with intrinsically safe instruments.

For direct measurements the reference cells are filled with reference gas and sealed, while the measuring cells are open to the sampled gas. For differential measurements the reference cells are open to the sample gas before treatment and the measuring cells to the gas after treatment.

The simplified mathematical theory of the behaviour of the katharometer bridge is as follows, but it must be appreciated that it is not sufficiently rigid to permit calibrations to be calculated. Calibrations can only be obtained from the behaviour of the actual measured gases. It is assumed all four arms of the bridge have the same initial resistance R_1 when the current is flowing.

Let R_0 = Resistance at ambient temperature
$\quad$ R_1 = Working resistance (i.e. resistance when a current I flows)
$\quad$ I = Current through one wire (i.e. half bridge current)
$\quad$ T = Wire temperature above ambient.

Then, at equilibrium, energy input is equal to heat loss

$$I^2 R_1 = K_1 T \tag{6.51}$$

where K_1 is a constant proportional to the conductivity of the gas if most of the heat loss is by conduction through the gas.

A simple expression for working resistance is

$$R_1 = R_0 (1 + \alpha T) \tag{6.52}$$

where α is the temperature coefficient of resistance of the wire material.

From equations 6.51 and 6.52

$$I R_1 R_0 \alpha = K_1 (R_1 - R_0) \tag{6.53}$$

Then

$$\begin{aligned} R_1 &= K_1 R_0 / (K_1 - I^2 R_0 \alpha) = R_0 + (K_1 R_0 / K_1 - I^2 R_0 \alpha) - R_0 \\ &= R_0 + (K_1 R_0 - K_1 R_0 + I^2 R_0 \alpha / K_1 - I^2 R_0 \alpha) \\ &= R_0 + (I^2 R_0 \alpha / K_1 + I^2 R_0 \alpha) \end{aligned} \tag{6.54}$$

From equation 6.53 if $R_1 - R_0$ is small compared with R_1, K_1 must be large compared with $I^2 R_0 \alpha$ and we can ignore the term $I R_0 \alpha$ so that

$$R_1 = R_0 + (I^2 R_0^2 \alpha / K_1) \tag{6.55}$$

If two measurement filaments have a total resistance of R_1 and the reference filaments of R_2 the output is given by

$$E = I (R_1 - R_2) \tag{6.56}$$

Combining equations 6.55 and 6.56:

$$E = I^3 R_0^2 \alpha [(1/K_1) - (1/K_2)] \tag{6.57}$$

where K_1 and K_2 are proportional to the conductivities of the gases in each pair of cells.

Equation 6.57 shows that the output is proportional to the cube of the bridge current, although in practice this is usually between $I^{2.5}$ and I^3.

For accurate quantitative readings the current must be kept constant. A change of only 1% in this will cause a change of up to 3% in sensitivity (but the zero will not be affected by small changes of current).

The equation shows also that the output is proportional to the difference between the reciprocals of the thermal conductivities of the gases in each pair of cells. This is usually correct for small differences in conductivity but does not hold for large differences, owing to the many approximations made in the calculations.

6.4.2   The design of meters

6.4.2.1   THE SHAKESPEAR KATHAROMETER (ELECTRONIC INSTRUMENTS LTD.)

The katharometer differs from the other forms of thermal conductivity analysis instruments in that the tested gas does not flow through the conductivity cell, but enters the cell by molecular diffusion. To ensure that the composition of the gas in the cell will readily follow any change of composition of the gas outside, the cell is made small and usually has a volume of less than 0.5 cm³. The introduction of the gas into the cell by diffusion makes the measurements independent of the rate of flow of gas, while the compactness of the cell reduces convection effects and enables uniform temperature conditions to be obtained.

Figure 6.43 shows the construction of a typical katharometer cell. The cell, excluding leads, is about 20 mm long and has an outside diameter of about 5 mm. The platinum wire, adjusted to the correct length and resistance, is spot welded to copper leads and drawn into a fine capillary tube. The whole is then heat treated so that the glass fuses on to the wire surface and, on cooling, supports the hot wire and leads. The glass covered wire is bent into 'hairpin' shape A and sealed into an outer glass sheath B; the joints between copper leads and platinum wire being in the pinch seal C. The leads are covered with insulated sleeving. The outer glass sheath is mounted in a metal tube E, the space between B and E being filled with Wood's metal (melting point 65°C). The outer tube is a push fit in the hole in the metal block, but to ensure good thermal contact the top of the tube is soft-soldered to the block.

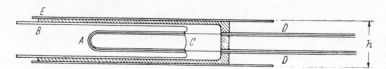

Figure 6.43   Gas cell assembly for katharometer

The reference cell is identical in design except that the tube B is sealed at both ends. If the gas to be tested is dry, a side chamber of the reference cell may contain a drying agent, such as silica gel, so that the standard gas is also dried. If the tested gas is saturated with water vapour the side chamber contains moistened cotton so that the standard gas is also saturated. Any change of temperature in the system will alter the partial pressure of water vapour.

This method, however, will produce equal changes in the temperature of the wires in the two cells only if the conductivities of the rest of the gases in the cells are the same. The presence of vapour will dilute the remaining gases and if the percentage of vapour is large this will cause an appreciable change in the deflection produced by a given percentage of the measured constituent. If the conductivities of the contents of the two cells are very different this method of compensation is useless. For example, the presence of water vapour decreases the conductivity of hydrogen but increases the conductivity of air. If, therefore, one cell contained hydrogen while the other contained air, saturation would produce an increased instead of a decreased error.

The resistance of the wire when cold is usually about 7 Ω rising to about 10.5 Ω when the normal operating current of 350 mA is passed through it. Where a current of this value would produce thermal dissociation (e.g. when ammonia is present) the lower value of 250 mA is used. The normal operating temperature is in the region of 140°C.

The cells are usually arranged in a tinned brass block but p.v.c. may be used where required to resist corrosion, except in intrinsically safe equipment, in sets of four; two, the reference cells RR, are sealed and contain a suitable reference gas and the other two, the measuring cells MM, are open to the tested gas. The four heated elements are connected in the form of a Wheatstone bridge as shown in *Figure 6.42(a)*; the out-of-balance current of the bridge may be measured by the galvanometer G. The bridge units are provided with the resistance coil S which makes them electrically interchangeable, so that any number may be used with the same galvanometer without any change of calibration, and calibrated units may be kept as spares. The resistance S determines the deflection of the galvanometer for a given out-of-balance e.m.f. between B and D and its value will be one of the factors which determine the span of the scale. Increasing this resistance will reduce the size of the deflection for a given difference of composition between tested and standard gas. Varying the value of this resistance is therefore one method of obtaining the correct deflection for a given change in composition. The zero is fixed at the factory by adjusting the position of the connection on R_2.

The bridge is supplied from a steady source of current, stabilised by zener diodes, the size of the current being set by adjustment of the resistance Rh.

In the case of indicating instruments a separate milliammeter is often used to measure the bridge current. In recording instruments a fixed resistance R (or a network of resistances) is included in the circuit, the value of the resistance being such that when the 'Test–Record' switch is turned to the

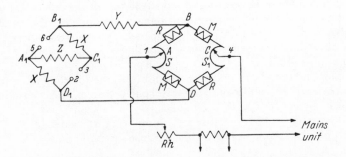

Figure 6.44   Katharometer circuit for use with one or two indicators or recorders

'Test' position, the recorder gives a full scale reading if the value of bridge current is correct.

Many modern E.I.L. katharometers include an arrangement whereby two instruments, either indicating or recording, can be connected to the measuring unit in such a way that either may be removed without changing the reading on the other. The electrical circuit of such an arrangement is shown in *Figure 6.44*, one recorder or indicator being connected between terminals 2 and 3 and the other between terminals 5 and 6. The indicator or recorder used, together with its leads, is arranged to have a fixed total resistance (usually 25 Ω). In order to provide for this, a make-up resistance is provided by the makers which has a resistance equal to that of the leads. When the instrument is set up, a length of wire is removed from the 'make-up' resistance, which has the same resistance as the leads, so that the total resistance of leads and make-up remains constant*.

The characteristics of the indicator or recorder are such that it gives a full scale deflection when a p.d. of 6.25 mV is applied across the instrument and its leads. The katharometer circuit must be such that when a gas corresponding to a full scale reading is passed through the measuring unit, a p.d. of 6.25 mV is obtained across a 25 Ω resistance connected between terminals 2 and 3.

Resistances X each have values equal to the resistance of an indicator and its leads, so that the resistances of all arms of the bridge network $A_1 B_1 C_1 D_1$ are equal. When the measuring bridge is balanced there will be no p.d. between B and D and consequently none between B_1 and D_1, and no current will flow through the indicators.

When the bridge becomes unbalanced and a p.d. exists between B and D, the size of the current through the indicators will be determined by the resistance Y which therefore determines the range of the instrument. As the four arms of the $A_1 B_1 C_1 D_1$ network are equal, there will be no p.d. between A_1 and C_1 when both indicators are in position. When one indicator is taken out of circuit, the p.d. between A_1 and D_1 is no longer zero and a current flows through Z. The value of Z is therefore adjusted so that the reading of one indicator is not influenced by the absence from the circuit of the other indicator, or by its presence in the circuit. Terminals 1 and 4 are connected to two small potentiometers S and S_1 (S may be a tapped resistance in some instruments). The positions of the contacts A and C determine the value of the resistance of the measuring cells at which the bridge will balance, and the potentiometers are therefore the zero balance adjustments. Varying the position of these contacts will therefore alter the starting point of the scale, e.g. will alter the range from, say, 0–20% to 10–30%: but the difference between maximum and minimum readings will remain the same (20%). In order to alter the span of the scale from, say, 0–20% to 0–30%, the resistances Y and Z must be altered. Altering these resistances will change the difference between the minimum and maximum readings, i.e. from 20% to 30%.

This must be borne in mind when calibrating the instrument. The usual procedure is to alter Y and Z until the scale span is correct, and then adjust S or S_1 until the correct zero point is obtained.

The instrument is factory calibrated to an accuracy better than ±1% full scale and has a response time of 5–10 s plus the sampling time.

*See 'Multipoint temperature indicators', Volume 1, page 336.

6.4.2.2 INTRINSICALLY SAFE EQUIPMENT

Katharometers certified by B.A.S.E.E.F.A. as suitable for Group 11A locations are available. In order to render the equipment safe the katharometer is supplied from an intrinsically safe power source, designed so that it can supply a constant current of 350 mA to the katharometer, without the energy available being sufficient to cause ignition. The power unit is mounted in a safe area and all cables leading to the katharometer must be well separated from any non-intrinsically safe circuitry. Owing to the energy limitation, the source is capable of supplying one katharometer only.

Flame traps containing a sintered metal disc must be fitted in the inlet and outlet lines from the katharometer. Zener barrier devices are installed in the line between the katharometers and the measuring instruments in the safe area at the interface between the safe and hazardous areas. Two barriers are used, both of the positive type, one mounted in each signal line.

6.4.2.3 SERVOMEX MICRO-KATHAROMETER

This type of katharometer is used as the detector in gas chromatography. As with other katharometers it consists of a Wheatstone bridge consisting of two measuring and two reference filaments. In general the reference filaments are in the carrier gas and the measuring filaments in the eluted gas, so that changes in conductivity of the eluted gas are rapidly detected and measured. Its main feature is its high response speed and sensitivity.

It consists of two chambers formed by slots cut in a pair of mica gaskets sandwiched between two thick stainless steel discs, each chamber having a volume of 2.6 mm^3. Particular attention is paid to the finish of the edges of the slots, a factor which is very important in minimising 'tailing' effects in the response. One gasket is permanently fixed, and the external connecting wires pass through it and lie on its inner surface in the form of flat tabs. The filaments of 0.008 mm platinum wire are fixed on the surface of the second gasket and are pressed into contact with the tabs when the cell is assembled. The use of two gaskets of equal thickness ensures that the filaments lie in the centre of the two chambers.

The reference and measuring chambers each contain two filaments which together form a complete Wheatstone bridge. Sagging caused by thermal expansion is prevented by three lateral supports of folded platinum iridium strip, 0.005×0.008 mm, welded to each filament.

The thin cross section of the chambers (about the same as that of a 0.5 mm i.d. capillary column) causes the filaments to run cool at relatively high bridge voltages, and higher sensitivity can be achieved. Despite the low cross section, high carrier gas flow rates can be used, and good results are achieved up to 200 cm^3/min. The cell has been used satisfactorily at temperatures up to 300°C.

A significant advantage of the method of construction is that if a filament burns out, a replacement bridge element in the form of a gasket with a complete set of matched filaments can be inserted by the user, the arrangement being such that no special tools are required.

The katharometer is supplied complete with a gas adaptor plate having short lengths of 1.6 mm o.d. stainless steel tube for connections to the measuring cell and reference cells. If it is preferred, this adaptor may be removed and the detector may then be bolted direct to a corresponding flat surface as near to the gas chromatograph column as possible, thus introducing no additional deadspace.

Used with packed or coated capillary columns the katharometer sensitivity can approach that of flame ionisation detectors when used under the same conditions.

When the carrier gas is hydrogen or helium the bridge voltage is 6–8 V supplied from a highly stable source. With nitrogen or argon as carrier gas the voltage should not exceed 4V. If required, platinum iridium, or tungsten filaments are available of about 20–40 Ω, adjacent pairs being balanced to 0.3 Ω or better.

6.4.2.4   THE SIEMENS TYPE

The construction of this form of meter is shown in *Figure 6.45*. All four arms of the bridge are of platinum wire mounted vertically. The wires are kept taut by platinum and iridium springs attached to the ends. Two opposite arms M and M of the bridge are mounted in one metal block and exposed to the gas under test, while the other two arms C and C are in another block and exposed to the standard gas. The standard gas may be sealed in the second block as shown in *Figure 6.45(a)* (which shows the type of instrument used for measuring the carbon dioxide concentration in fruit stores); alternatively, atmospheric air, or some other standard gas, may be aspirated through the second block as shown in *Figure 6.45(b)* (which shows the type of instrument used for measuring the carbon dioxide content of flue gases). Two adjacent arms C and M of the bridge are connected by a short length of manganin wire on which the position of the zero adjuster may be varied as required in order to bring the reading to zero when all wires are exposed to the standard gas. The bridge is connected to the current supply and indicator in the usual way. A current of approximately 0.4 A, sufficient to raise the temperature of the wire to about 100°C, is required, and is supplied by a stabilised mains supply.

It will be noticed that the cells in which the wires are placed form a by-pass to the main stream of gas. The gas in passing through the central passage produces a small difference of pressure between the ends of the by-pass. This pressure difference forces a definite fraction of the gas through the two cells. The dimensions of main passage and by-pass are chosen so as to produce through the cells a flow which is only a small fraction of the main flow. In this way the thermal disturbance within the cells due to variation of flow is made negligibly small while the main flow may be kept large. The comparatively large main flow ensures that the time taken for the gas to reach the instrument from the source is small, so that the response of the instrument to changes in composition is rapid.

As in other forms of the instrument, provision is made for equalising the humidity conditions in the measuring and reference sides of the instrument, and where the gas temperature is very different from that of the meter, provision is made for bringing it to a suitable temperature. The instrument is provided with resistance coils which make the unit electrically interchangeable with the other units of the same type.

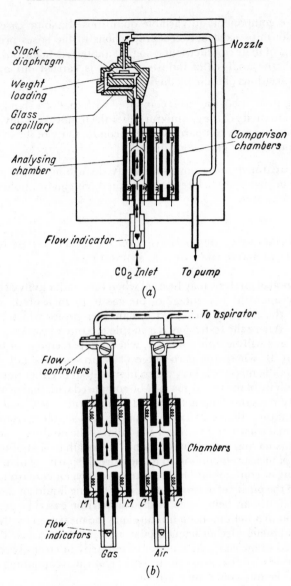

Figure 6.45   Siemens type analyser (MM and CC are the measuring and comparison bridge wires) (Courtesy Siemens Ltd.)

6.4.3   Methods of analysis

The ideal mixture for analysis by the conductivity method is one consisting of two gases having very different thermal conductivities. If the difference in conductivity is small, the accuracy of the measurement will be reduced, and will depend upon the accuracy with which the thermal conductivity can be measured. Unfortunately, industrial gases frequently consist of mixtures of three or more components in variable quantities. In some cases, however, special relationships exist between proportions of the gases present or the relative values of their conductivities, so that analysis is made possible.

In general, the analysis of industrial gases is carried out by two main methods or variations of these methods:

1. The conductivity of the gas is compared with that of a standard gas.

2. The conductivity of the gas mixture after the removal or conversion of the measured constituent is compared with the conductivity of the gas before the removal or conversion of that constituent.

Preliminary treatment to remove or modify disturbing constituents of the mixture may be necessary before the above methods can be applied to certain complicated mixtures.

6.4.3.1 ANALYSIS BY COMPARISON OF CONDUCTIVITY OF THE GAS MIXTURE WITH THAT OF A STANDARD GAS

The first method of analysis may be used when the conductivity of the mixture depends only upon the percentage of the gas to be measured, or upon the percentage of the gas to be measured and another gas for which a correction can be made. Where the tested gas is a simple mixture of two gases, A and B, the standard gas will be either pure A, when the percentage of B present is small, or pure B, where the percentage of A present is small. Where the conductivity of the mixture is very different from that of either pure A or pure B, the conductivity of the tested gas may be compared with that of a gas having approximately the same conductivity and temperature coefficient of conductivity as the mixture. If no such comparison gas is available, a comparison gas having a thermal conductivity greater than that of the mixture is better than a comparison gas having a conductivity which is less than that of the mixture. This method of measurement is used to measure the purity of many gases.

The amount of contamination of electrolytic oxygen containing traces of hydrogen and the purity of oxygen obtained by boiling liquid air are measured by this method, dry air being used as the comparison gas. The percentage of helium or neon in a helium–neon mixture may be measured by the use of an unsymmetrical meter, dry air being used as the comparison gas. The method may be applied to measure the amount of impurity in electrolytic hydrogen containing traces of oxygen, electrolytic chlorine containing traces of hydrogen, and helium containing nitrogen.

Where the mixture of gases contains a third gas C, and the difference between the conductivities of B and C is small in comparison with the difference between the conductivities of A and B, variations in the ratio of the quantities of B and C may be ignored, since the conductivity depends almost entirely upon the percentage of A present. For example, in argon used for commercial purposes, oxygen is usually regarded as the objectionable impurity while the presence of a high proportion of nitrogen may be an advantage. The ratio of the oxygen to nitrogen in the impurity does not seriously affect the analysis for argon, for the difference between the conductivities of oxygen and nitrogen is small compared with the difference between the thermal conductivities of these gases and argon. The analysis is made with an unsymmetrical meter using dry air as the comparison gas. Hydrogen, when mixed with such gases as nitrogen, oxygen and carbon dioxide, which have nearly equal conductivities all very different from that of hydrogen, may be measured by comparison of the conductivity of the mixture with that of a standard gas. This method is used for measuring hydrogen in water gas and in the mixtures used for the fixation of atmospheric nitrogen in the form of ammonia.

Where the gas mixture contains three or more gases and the quantities of the gases other than the measured gas remain in the same ratio, the tested gas may be treated as a simple mixture even where these gases have very different conductivities. For example, any gas mixed with air may be treated as a simple mixture, for although air contains oxygen, nitrogen and argon, it has, when pure, a constant composition and may be regarded as a single gas. The percentage of ammonia in the mixture of ammonia and air used in the production of nitric acid may be measured by comparing the conductivity of the mixture with that of air. The parts of the meter exposed to the ammonia are made of stainless steel, and tin soldering is used for all joints. In the dry-cleaning industry, and in the manufacture of artificial silk, cordite or rubber proofed fabrics, it is often desirable to control the concentration of the vapours of organic solvents such as acetone, alcohol and benzol so as to avoid risks of explosion or any undue loss of expensive solvent. The percentage of vapour in a sample of air may be measured by comparing the conductivity of the sample with that of dry air sealed in the comparison cells.

Where a gas mixture, X, having a complicated but constant composition, is being mixed with another gas mixture, Y, whose composition is also complicated but constant, the percentage of X or Y in the final mixture may be obtained by treating the mixture as if it were a mixture of two simple gases. This method is adopted in the measurements used to control the blending of water gas and coal gas from two gas holders so as to produce a gas of known calorific value.

Analysis is sometimes made possible because a known relationship exists between the quantities of the constituents of the mixture. For example, a gas, A, is produced in the place of a gas B, in a mixture of gases so that the quantity A and B remains constant. The quantities of carbon dioxide, A, and oxygen, B, in flue gases are related in this way.

In the analysis of internal combustion engine exhaust gas a sufficiently definite relationship exists between the quantities of carbon dioxide, carbon monoxide and hydrogen to make analysis for one of these components possible. Air is used as the comparison gas and the meter is often calibrated in terms of air–fuel ratio.

6.4.3.2 ANALYSIS BY COMPARING THERMAL CONDUCTIVITY OF GASEOUS MIXTURE BEFORE A REACTION WITH THERMAL CONDUCTIVITY OF MIXTURE AFTER THE REACTION; DIFFERENTIAL METERS

In certain circumstances the constituent of a gaseous mixture which is to be measured may be easily (a) absorbed by a suitable reagent or otherwise removed by a method which leaves the other constituents unchanged; or (b) caused to react with a constituent which is present in, or is added to, the gaseous mixture, and thereby converted into a gas of a different thermal conductivity, the other constituents of the mixture remaining unchanged.

In mixtures of this kind the measurement may be carried out by comparing the conductivities of the mixture before and after the removal, or conversion, of the measured constituent. The change in the thermal conductivity of the mixture is measured by means of a differential meter. The original gaseous mixture, with an added constituent where necessary, is passed into one half of the meter containing the two reference cells, through the portion of the meter where the absorption or conversion takes place, and then into the second half of the meter containing the two measuring cells. If constituents other than the measured one are varying rapidly, and especially if the variation has a large effect on the conductivity of the mixture (e.g. if one gas in the mixture is hydrogen), the time taken for the gas to flow from one cell of the meter to the other must be made as short as possible, otherwise a large error will occur owing to the fact that the meter will be comparing samples collected at different times.

The differential meter used for measuring the quantity of oxygen in flue gases is shown in *Figure 6.46.*

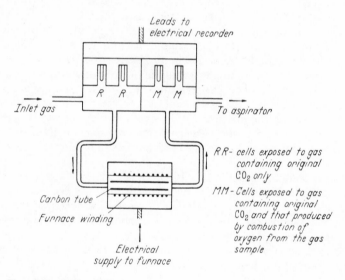

Figure 6.46   Differential katharometer used to measure percentage of oxygen in flue gas

Absorption

This method is used to measure the percentage of carbon dioxide in blast furnace gas when the presence of hydrogen and carbon monoxide precludes the use of other methods. The carbon dioxide is removed by passing the gas through soda-lime. Similarly, the percentage of ammonia gas, produced by synthesis, in a mixture of nitrogen, hydrogen and ammonia may be measured by absorbing the ammonia in dilute sulphuric acid or a suitable solid absorbent.

Conversion

In the measurement of nitrogen purity where the impurity is oxygen, the percentage of oxygen may be measured by causing the oxygen to combine completely with pure hydrogen added for this purpose from an electrolytic cell. The gaseous mixture containing the hydrogen is passed into one half of a differential meter, through a combustion furnace where the oxygen combines with the hydrogen producing water vapour, and then into the other half of the meter. In this way the quantity of hydrogen converted is measured, and as one volume of oxygen combines with two volumes of hydrogen, the quantity of oxygen in the original mixture is known.

The quantity of carbon monoxide in gaseous mixtures which are free from hydrogen may be measured by measuring the change of conductivity when the carbon monoxide is converted into carbon dioxide. The carbon monoxide in the mixture is converted into carbon dioxide by passing the mixture through an electrically heated furnace containing copper oxide. To ensure that all the carbon monoxide is converted into carbon dioxide, a small controlled feed of oxygen is provided.

The quantity of oxygen may be measured in a similar way. The conductivity of the gas mixture is compared with the conductivity of the mixture after it has passed through a furnace containing an electrically heated hard carbon rod at about 700°C *(Figure 6.46)*. The oxygen will be replaced by its own volume of carbon dioxide. The change in thermal conductivity will be a measure of the percentage of oxygen in the original mixture.

In modern steam raising plant the measurement of combustibles is sometimes carried out by measuring hydrogen with a katharometer, while carbon monoxide is measured using infra-red techniques.

6.4.3.3 CALIBRATION OF THERMAL CONDUCTIVITY ANALYSIS METERS

Several methods of calibrating thermal conductivity meters are available; the one chosen depends upon the form of the meter and the particular use to which it is put. In any case it is desirable that some point on the scale, preferably the zero, should correspond to a gas such as air, oxygen, hydrogen, carbon dioxide, etc., which can be obtained readily in a pure state.

1. The meter may be checked under working conditions by comparing the meter reading with that obtained by some other method of analysis. For example, where applicable, a portable chemical absorption type instrument such as an Orsat apparatus may be used to check the instrument reading. It is very important that the comparison should be made when the composition of the gas is fairly constant, otherwise errors may occur owing to the fact that the two instruments are used to compare samples which may be of different composition.

2. A number of mixtures, of compositions which are known approximately and which are distributed at intervals over the range of calibration, may be left in contact with or passed through the meter, until steady readings are obtained and the compositions of the mixtures then found by chemical or other methods of analysis.

In some cases, where the percentage of one constituent is very small, it is difficult to check the composition by direct analysis. In such cases it may be sufficient to calibrate the instrument at a number of higher percentages and interpolate between these points and zero, since calibration curves are usually linear over such short ranges provided the galvo scale or slidewire is uniform.

3. A known gas mixture may be made and this mixture allowed to flow into, or through, the conductivity cell. Whatever the form of the meter, steps must be taken to ensure that all gas initially in the cell is replaced by the gas of known composition. When all gas has been replaced the meter will give a steady reading; this fact may be used as an indication of complete replacement of the gas.

Various methods of making and storing gas mixtures are employed. Where the gas is stored or collected over a liquid, the liquid must be carefully chosen so that the possibility of selective absorption of constituents is avoided. The possibility of selective absorption by cork or rubber, or other organic material, must not be overlooked, especially with mixtures containing gases such as sulphur dioxide or ammonia which are readily absorbed by water or rubber. Mercury is usually used as a sealing liquid.

Minute leaks in the apparatus must be avoided even if the gas mixture is maintained at a pressure which is greater than atmospheric. The less dense components of the mixture will effuse more readily than the more dense constituents, so producing a change in the composition of the mixture. Suitable mixtures may be produced by passing measured quantities of gas into a mercury-sealed gas holder. Care must be taken to ensure that the volumes of gas are measured at the same temperature and pressure or that allowance is made for any difference. Where the volumes of gas to be mixed are similar, they may be measured by the change in height of the gas holder, allowance being made for any change of temperature or pressure which may occur during the mixing.

In all mixing operations sufficient time must be allowed for the gases to mix completely by interdiffusion. The necessary time will be reduced if the pressure of the mixture is increased, and if the more dense components are introduced at the top while the less dense components are introduced at the bottom so that a stirring action is produced by convection.

The number of mixtures required to calibrate a meter will depend upon the shape of the calibration curve of the meter. Where the curve is practically a straight line two or three mixtures only may be necessary.

4. In circumstances where it is difficult to prepare suitable mixtures for checking or calibrating a meter, it may be possible to check the meter indirectly by using a pure gas, or gas mixture, which has a conductivity equivalent to that of the required mixture. Pure gases provide a series of 'fixed points', used in conductivity measurement in a similar way to that in which the melting points of pure metals are used as 'fixed points'* in temperature measurement. Pure oxygen provides a fixed point suitable for calibrating meters used for measuring small percentages of hydrogen, helium, methane, water vapour or ammonia. Mixtures of oxygen and hydrogen may be used for calibration purposes in place of mixtures having a conductivity greater than that of air.

*See Volume 1, page 253.

The mass of gas produced by electrolysis in an electrolytic cell is directly proportional to the current flowing through the cell. If two electrolytic cells are set up to electrolyse acidulated water, and the oxygen from the anode of one is allowed to mix with the hydrogen from the cathode of the other, then by suitable adjustment of the ratio of the currents through the two cells, it is possible to produce any mixture from pure oxygen to pure hydrogen.

Where the variable constituent in the mixture is a vapour, suitable points on the calibration curve may be obtained by applying to the meter the mixture obtained by allowing air, or other suitable gas, to remain in contact with a small quantity of the condensed vapour at a definite temperature until equilibrium is attained. The percentage of vapour in the gas may then be found from the temperature and the vapour pressure–temperature curve of the liquid.

When a meter is being calibrated with water vapour, a mixture of gas and vapour of suitable composition may be obtained by using gas which has been in contact with a suitable mixture of water and sulphuric acid, or in contact with a saturated solution of a suitable salt in water. The vapour pressure of a solution of sulphuric acid in water depends upon the composition and is given in *Table 6.7*. The vapour pressure of the saturated salt solution depends upon the temperature and upon the salt used. Gases having a wide range of percentage humidities may be obtained by the use of a suitable salt solution at the correct temperature.

Table 6.7 VAPOUR PRESSURE OF WATER AND RELATIVE HUMIDITY OF AIR IN CONTACT WITH SOLUTIONS OF SULPHURIC ACID IN WATER UNDER EQUILIBRIUM CONDITIONS

Specific gravity of acid solution	Relative humidity, %	Vapour pressure at 20°C
1.00	100.0	17.4
1.05	97.5	17.0
1.10	93.9	16.3
1.15	88.8	15.4
1.20	80.5	14.0
1.25	70.4	12.2
1.30	58.3	10.1
1.35	47.2	8.3
1.40	37.1	6.5
1.50	18.8	3.3
1.60	8.5	1.5
1.70	3.2	0.6

6.5   ANALYSIS OF GASES BY MEASUREMENT OF HEAT OF REACTION

When combustible gases such as carbon monoxide, hydrogen, methane or acetylene, and combustible vapours such as the vapours of petrol, acetone, alcohol, naphtha, ethylene, etc., are burnt, heat is evolved. Normally a mixture of combustible material and air has to be heated to a certain minimum temperature known as its 'flash point' before the mixture will ignite.

Combustion may be brought about in many cases at a temperature below the flash point by passing the mixture of gas or vapour and air over a suitable catalyst. A catalyst is a substance which facilitates a chemical reaction between other substances, but remains unchanged itself. The amount of heat liberated may be measured by causing the combustion between gas and air to take place at room temperature and measuring the rise in temperature of the mixture by means of a sensitive differential thermocouple. For example, the amount of carbon monoxide in an air sample may be measured by passing the air over a catalyst known as Hopcalite, which is a mixture of several metallic oxides. The amount of heat produced by the combustion is a measure of the proportion of carbon monoxide present.

A more common method of measuring the temperature rise produced by the combustion is to use an instrument which is very similar in construction to the instruments used to analyse gases by measuring their thermal conductivity. The arrangement is shown in *Figure 6.47*. The two measuring arms of the Wheatstone bridge circuit consist of bare platinum wires which are exposed to the gas mixture and heated to such a temperature ($450°C$ for CO and H_2) that the measured gas combines with the oxygen, liberating heat which raises the temperature of the wire by an amount which depends upon the proportion of combustible gas present.

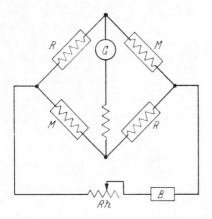

R   Reference cells
M   Measuring cells containing catalytic
     filaments
G   Milliammeter type of recorder or
     indicator
B   Battery or mains unit
Rh   Rheostat to compensate for variation of
     battery voltage

Figure 6.47   Simplified electrical circuit of 'heats
of reaction' type of gas analyser

When used for the measurement of carbon monoxide alone, the instrument is fitted with an activated charcoal filter which removes all heavy hydrocarbon vapours and also protects the platinum wires from deterioration. The usual full scale reading of such an instrument is 4 parts carbon monoxide per 10 000 parts air.

Where the gases contain hydrogen which would render inaccurate the measurement of the carbon monoxide, the hydrogen may be removed by passing the mixture over a catalyst which oxidises the hydrogen only and leaves the carbon monoxide unchanged.

The platinum wires of the measuring arms may in some cases be activated by coating them with a catalyst which facilitates the combustion.

The reference arms of the bridge consist of platinum wires similar to those used in the measuring arms. In instruments which do not use activated measuring filaments, the temperature of the reference arms is maintained below that at which the measured gas reacts with oxygen and the filaments exposed to the gas mixture. Where activated measuring filaments are used, the reference filaments are not activated and may be maintained at the same temperature as the measuring filaments. In another form of the instrument all filaments are maintained at the same temperature and the reference filaments exposed to a standard air sample. This arrangement compensates for changes in the room temperature but not for variations in the thermal conductivity of the gas mixture.

Calibration and adjustment of the range and zero of the instrument are carried out in a similar way to that used for the thermal conductivity instrument.

Figure 6.48 shows a section of the CO + H₂ transmitter. In this instrument one measuring and one reference arm are used; the other two arms of the bridge consist of wire having a very low temperature coefficient. The gas sample after passing through the carbon dioxide meter is mixed with sufficient air for complete combustion; the air is admitted through the nozzle shown.

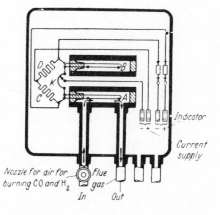

Figure 6.48   Section of CO + H₂ transmitter
(Courtesy Siemens Ltd.)

Figure 6.49 shows the principle of the Methanometer used for measuring the methane content of the air in mines. The air samples pass through a specially designed flashback arrester and flow orifice to the two chambers containing electrically heated platinum filaments. The measuring filament is catalytically activated to cause combustion of any methane present; the second filament is the reference filament. The air sample leaves the instrument through a second flashback arrester, being expelled by the aspirator bulb. The electrical circuit is a Wheatstone bridge; the out-of-balance of the bridge brought about by the burning of the methane on the measuring filament is measured by the milliammeter which is calibrated directly in percentage methane. Other flammable gases are measured in the same way by the 'explosimeter' which is often calibrated in terms of the explosive concentration of the gases for which it is used.

Two further instruments which work on the 'heat of reaction' principle are the Bailey combustible gas and oxygen meters, which may be combined in one unit as shown in *Figure 6.50.*

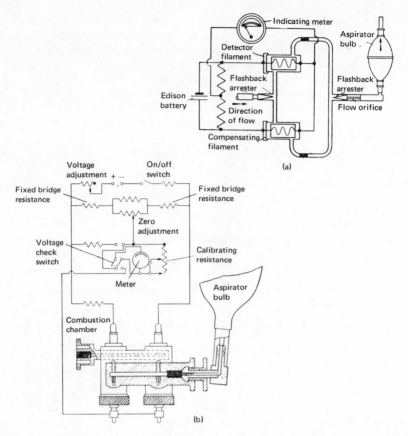

Figure 6.49   Methanometer (Courtesy Mine Safety Appliances Ltd.) (a) Flow and simplified electrical circuit diagram (b) Wiring diagram

Both instruments use a platinum catalyst filament and the temperature of the filament is measured by measuring the potential drop across it by means of a d.c. potentiometer. Out-of-balance is amplified and detected by an electronic amplifier which operates a reversible motor which moves the slidewire contact to restore balance. The recording pen is mechanically linked to the slidewire contact and indicates the percentage of combustibles and of oxygen. As the final temperature of the filament will depend upon the ambient temperature, the instrument case is heated and maintained at a constant temperature by means of a thermostat.

In the combustibles meter a measured quantity of gas sample together with a measured quantity of clean compressed air is passed over the catalyst filament, and the heat liberated by combustion increases the filament temperature by an amount which depends upon the combustibles content of the sample. The instrument is made in a variety of ranges above the minimum range of 5% combustibles.

In the oxygen meter a measured sample of gas and a measured quantity of hydrogen gas are passed over the filament. The heat liberated by combustion raises the filament temperature by an amount which depends upon the oxygen

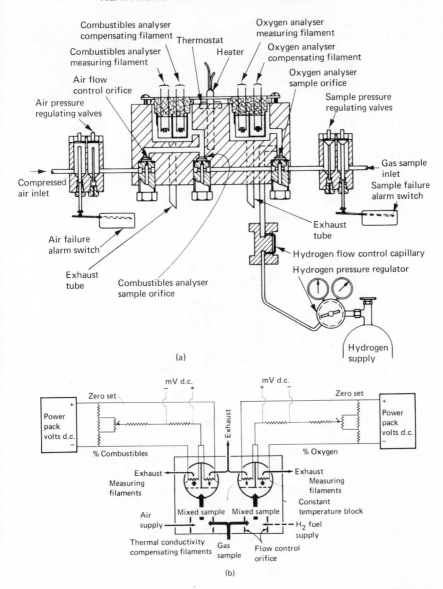

Figure 6.50   Oxygen and combustibles analyser (Courtesy Bailey Meters and Controls Ltd.) (a) Flow diagram (b) Electrical circuit

content of the gas sample. The instrument is made in a variety of ranges between 0–2% oxygen and 0–25% oxygen.

6.5.1   The Katz analyser

Another instrument which is based on the 'heat of reaction' is the Katz analyser used to measure the concentration of carbon monoxide in road tunnels, underpasses and garages and any other place where concentrations of carbon monoxide might accumulate. The standard range, which is 0–400 p.p.m., has been found to be the most useful, as 100 p.p.m. of carbon monoxide by volume in air is regarded as the maximum safe concentration which can be tolerated for long periods; 400 p.p.m. can only be tolerated for 1 h.

The principle of the instrument, shown in *Figure 6.51*, is based on measuring the rise in temperature of a stream of air containing carbon monoxide when passed through Hopcalite catalyst at 100°C. At this temperature the catalyst causes the oxidation of the carbon monoxide to carbon dioxide and the temperature rise as measured by a pair of differential resistance thermometers is proportional to the concentration of carbon monoxide in the air.

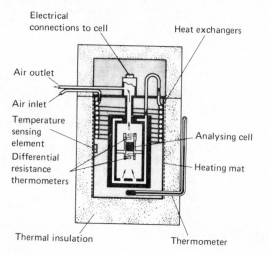

Figure 6.51   Detector of a Katz analyser (Courtesy Electronic Instruments Ltd.)

Sample air is filtered and drawn into the pumping drying unit and cleaning columns, finally entering the detector unit through a flow meter on the front panel. The drying unit consists of two silica gel columns arranged so that one is being regenerated while the other is in use, change-over being automatic. The dried gas is then passed through activated charcoal, soda asbestos and a second activated charcoal column to remove traces of hydrocarbons, or other heavy gases and carbon dioxide. These precautions are found to be necessary to avoid errors on readings and to maintain the catalyst at full activity.

The clean dry gas then passes on to the detector unit. This unit consists of a heat exchanger and the detector cell contained within an enclosure maintained thermostatically at about 100°C. The purpose of the heat exchanger is to ensure that the incoming gas is precisely at the detector cell temperature. The detector cell contains a tube of catalyst and two resistance thermometers, one immediately before and one immediately after the catalyst. The difference between the two temperatures is proportional to the concentration of carbon monoxide in the air.

Power supplies for the detector cell and temperature controls are obtained from a control unit. This consists of printed circuit boards that can be replaced quickly, so that if there is a failure the analyser need be out of action for a few minutes only. A warning lamp on the panel and a remote alarm are provided which indicate failure of the detector unit temperature control, the detector cell circuit, or reduction in gas flow. Simulation of known change in carbon monoxide concentration can be produced by a small heater in the detector cell at will, and checks the whole system except the catalyst. The whole system can be checked only by measuring a known concentration of carbon monoxide, and this check should only be needed after several months' operation.

The stability of the reading is better than ±8 p.p.m., the accuracy at zero ±4 p.p.m., at other points ±5% of the instrument span, and the linearity ±1% of span. The instrument responds to a 90% step change in 5 min and the sampling rate is usually 4 dm^3/min.

The soda asbestos and activated charcoal should be replaced every month but the silica gel lasts several years.

6.6   PARAMAGNETIC OXYGEN METERS

6.6.1   Basic principles

The strength of a magnet is measured in terms of its magnetic moment which is the product of the pole strength of the magnet and the distance between the poles.

When a material, such as a piece of soft iron, is placed in a magnetic field it becomes magnetised by induction, and the magnetic moment of the material divided by its volume is known as its 'intensity of magnetisation'. The ratio of the intensity of magnetisation of the material to the intensity of the magnetising field is called the 'volume susceptibility' (k) of the material. All materials show some magnetic effect when placed in a magnetic field, but apart from substances such as iron, nickel, cobalt and certain alloys such as steel, known as ferromagnetics, the effect shown is very small, and intense magnetic fields are required to make it measurable.

Substances which are magnetised in the direction of the applied field (thus having positive values of k) are called paramagnetics. There are relatively few paramagnetic materials, the most important being oxygen, oxides of nitrogen, the metals from titanium to nickel, platinum and palladium.

Substances which are magnetised in the opposite direction to that of the magnetising field (so that k is negative) are called diamagnetics. Most substances are diamagnetic and the value of susceptibility is usually very small. The most strongly diamagnetic substance is bismuth.

A ferro- or paramagnetic substance when placed in a vacuum or a less paramagnetic medium always tends to move from the weaker to the stronger parts of the magnetic field. A diamagnetic material placed in a vacuum or a medium of algebraically greater susceptibility tends to move from the stronger to the weaker part of the field, but the effect is so small, even in the case of the most diamagnetic substance, that it is difficult to observe. Thus when a rod of ferromagnetic or paramagnetic substance is suspended between the poles of an electromagnet it will set with its length along the direction of the magnetic field. A rod of bismuth, on the other hand, placed between the poles of a powerful electromagnet will set at right angles to the field.

Experiments show that for paramagnetic substances the susceptibility is independent of the strength of the magnetising field but decreases with increase of temperature according to the Curie–Weiss Law:

$$\text{Atomic susceptibility} = \frac{\text{Relative atomic mass}}{\text{Density}} \times \text{Volume susceptibility}$$

$$= C/(T - \theta)$$

where T is the absolute temperature and C and θ are constants.

The susceptibilities of ferromagnetic materials vary with the strength of the magnetising field and above a certain temperature, called the 'Curie Temperature' (1000 K for iron), ferromagnetics become ordinary paramagnetics obeying the Curie–Weiss law.

For diamagnetic substances the susceptibility is practically independent of the magnetising field and the temperature.

6.6.2   Magneto-dynamic instruments

This type of instrument is based on the work of Faraday on susceptibility measurement by measuring the force acting on a diamagnetic body in a non-uniform magnetic field. The size of the force on the deflected body, which usually takes the form of a dumb-bell suspended at the centre from a vertical suspension, is measured in a number of ways and the form of measurement varies from maker to maker.

The dumb-bell may consist of quartz, or in some cases it consists of two glass spheres containing nitrogen, which is diamagnetic, attached to the ends of the suspended arm. A mirror is attached to the middle of the arm which is suspended by a fine strip to an adjustable torsion head.

The dumb-bell and mirror are mounted between specially shaped polepieces of a powerful permanent magnet. The deflecting couple applied to the dumb-bell by the magnetic field will depend upon the magnetic susceptibility of the gas which surrounds it. Since the magnetic susceptibilities of most gases at 20°C are very small (nitrogen, -0.54×10^{-8}; hydrogen, -2.49×10^{-8}; carbon dioxide, -0.59×10^{-8}) while that of oxygen is large ($+ 133.6 \times 10^{-8}$), the susceptibility of the gas surrounding the dumb-bell will depend almost entirely upon the percentage of oxygen present. The deflecting couple applied to the dumb-bell will therefore be a measure of the percentage of oxygen present. The deflection may then be measured by focusing a beam of light on to the mirror, and allowing the reflected light to fall on two photocells located on either side of the zero line. The difference in output from the cells may then be measured and used as a measure of oxygen content.

Alternatively a force balance system may be used whereby the deflection is detected but an opposing force is applied to restore the dumb-bell sensor to the null position.

In the Servomex instrument illustrated in *Figure 6.52(a)* the restoring force is produced by the magnetic field produced in a single turn of platinum wire connected to the rest of the electronics by the platinum suspension wire. The deflection is detected by the twin photocells as shown in *Figure 6.52(b)* and the amplifier produces a current large enough to restore the dumb-bell to the null position, while at the same time giving an output to the recorder.

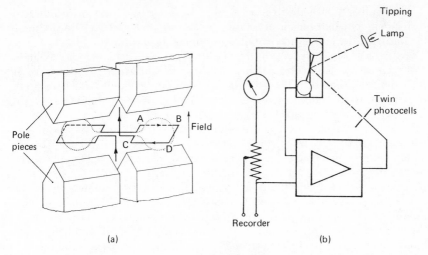

Figure 6.52   Servomex oxygen analyser (a) Dumb-bell unit (b) Principle

In the Bendix instrument shown in *Figure 6.53* the suspension is a quartz fibre, and the restoring force is produced electrostatically by the electrodes located adjacent to the test body, one held at above ground potential and the other below ground potential by the amplifier controlled from the matched photocells upon which the light from the mirror falls.

This type of instrument is not influenced by the thermal conductivity of the measured gas but the susceptibility of oxygen varies considerably with temperature. This may be overcome by maintaining the instrument at a constant temperature above ambient, or the temperature of the measuring cell may be detected by means of a resistance bulb or thermometer, and the appropriate temperature correction applied electronically.

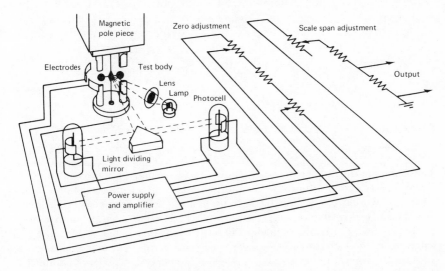

Figure 6.53   Bendix oxygen analyser

The reading obtained will depend upon the barometric pressure but in some instruments the barometric pressure is measured, and compensation achieved by adjusting the temperature of the instrument appropriately.

Instrument ranges from 0–1% to 0–100% full scale deflection are available and intrinsically safe versions may also be obtained. An accuracy of 1% full scale deflection can be achieved, but care should be exercised in setting up the instrument so that the suspension is vertical, and ensuring that no interfering gas such as NO (susceptibility $+59.3 \times 10^{-8}$) is present.

In order to reduce time lags to a minimum a relatively large sample of gas is continuously passed through the instrument but only a small portion of this enters the measuring cell. Provision is made for periodic checking of the zero by passing an oxygen-free gas through the cell. Nitrogen may be used for this purpose or the normal gas sample washed through acid chromous chloride to remove the oxygen. The instrument may be automatically standardised on a mixture of known composition, such as air, every 30 min in order to correct for the effects of changing barometric pressure. Gas samples should be dry, and filtered free of solid particles, especially magnetic particles, and should flow at a steady rate so that dumb-bell movement due to draughts is avoided.

The instrument may be used for estimating oxygen in hydrocarbon gases, combustion products, etc. Since nitric oxide ($k + 60.3 \times 10^{-9}$), nitrogen peroxide and chlorine dioxide are also paramagnetic, they must be removed, if present, before a measurement of oxygen can be successfully made on the sampled gas. Or, if the amounts of these gases in the gas mixture are reasonably constant, the instrument may be zeroed on a gas sample washed in acid chromous chloride, and the oxygen measured in the usual way.

6.6.3   Magnetic-wind type analysers

A common type of instrument depends for its functioning upon two facts:

1. Oxygen being paramagnetic will tend to move from the weaker to the stronger part of a magnetic field, while most other gases being diamagnetic will tend to move from the stronger to the weaker parts of a magnetic field.

2. When oxygen is heated it will become less paramagnetic.

$$\text{Volume susceptibility/Density} = C/(T - \theta) \quad \text{Curie–Weiss law}$$

or

$$\text{Volume susceptibility} = C/(T - \theta) \times \text{Density}$$

But density of a gas α $(1/T)$, where T is the absolute temperature

$$\therefore \text{Volume susceptibility} = C/[T(T - \theta)] = C/(T^2 - \theta T)$$

The principle of the instrument is shown in *Figure 6.54*. The measuring cell consists of a circular annulus with a horizontal by-pass tube on the outside of which are wound two identical platinum heating coils. These two coils form two arms of a Wheatstone bridge circuit to which about 12 V is applied, and are heated by means of the bridge current. It is arranged that one of these windings is between the poles of a very powerful permanent magnet. When a gas sample containing oxygen enters the measuring cell, it will move from the weaker part of the magnetic field to the stronger part so that it will flow into the

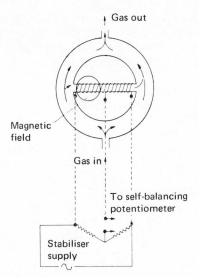

*Figure 6.54   Gas flow and electrical circuit of
magnetic-wind type instruments*

by-pass. Here it is heated so that its magnetic susceptibility is reduced. Thus the force tending to retain the warm mixture in the strong part of the magnetic field will be less than the force tending to attract cool mixture into the magnetic field. Thus there will be a continuous flow of mixture through the by-pass and the amount of gas flowing will depend upon the percentage of oxygen in the mixture. The gas passing through the second winding will be gas which has been heated in the first winding, while that entering the first winding will be cool gas. Thus, there will be a differential cooling of the two windings and the second winding will be at a higher temperature than the first winding. There will be a difference of resistance between the two windings and this difference of resistance is measured by measuring the out-of-balance e.m.f. of the bridge circuit by means of a standard Multelec potentiometer. The measured out-of-balance e.m.f. is proportional to the oxygen content of the sample so that the potentiometer scale can be calibrated directly in percentage oxygen. As both the Wheatstone bridge and the potentiometer are fed from the same voltage regulated supply the instrument is independent of reasonable variations in the supply mains voltage.

Increase in the temperature of the analyser cell causes a decrease in the out-of-balance e.m.f. of about 1½ % for each °C rise in temperature. To offset this effect a resistance thermometer is placed near the analyser cell, and this thermometer forms one arm of another Wheatstone bridge network which is supplied from the same source as the potentiometer. This network is in series with the supply to the potentiometer and adds to or subtracts from the potential applied to the slidewire and automatically compensates for changes in the analyser cell temperature over the range of 0–50°C.

The calibration is also affected by the gas pressure in the cell. The calibration is correct for a stated pressure and correction factors can be applied for departures from this value. In order to obviate the necessity for making the correction, an automatic pressure compensating device is often fitted.

In order to reduce time lags, a comparatively large sample is withdrawn from the process and the small fixed flow required through the instrument controlled by means of a combined flow regulator and indicator.

For accurate analysis the temperature of the gas sample should not exceed 75°C at the analyser inlet, its gauge pressure should be about ±0.05 bar and its composition should not change when it is heated up to 250°C.

6.6.3.1 CARRIER GAS EFFECT

To a first approximation, the out-of-balance e.m.f. of the analyser is given by: $e = kC_0$, where e is the out-of-balance e.m.f. of the analyser for an oxygen concentration of $C_0\%$ and k is a factor which varies with the composition of the 'carrier gas'. The term 'carrier gas' is applied to the gas or mixture of gases other than oxygen. The value of k depends upon the ratio of the volumetric specific heat to the viscosity of the carrier gas.

For a binary mixture of oxygen and one other gas, or oxygen and a mixture of gases of constant composition, the value of k is constant and there is no difficulty. For a ternary or more complex mixture, k varies with the composition of the carrier gas and can lower the accuracy of the measurement, but for a large number of applications large variations in composition of the carrier gas are unlikely and the error is small.

A rough indication of the effect of change in composition of the carrier gas can be calculated from the approximate values of k given in *Table 6.8.*

Table 6.8.

Gas	k	Gas	k	Gas	k
Acetylene	2.65	Ethylene	2.77	Oxygen	0.87
		Helium	0.59	Propane	3.50
Ammonia	2.21	Hydrogen	1.11		
Argon	0.59	Methane	1.94	Sulphur dioxide	1.96
Carbon dioxide	1.54	Nitrogen	1.00	Water vapour	1.14
Carbon monoxide	1.01	Nitric oxide	0.94		
Chlorine	1.52	Nitrous oxide	1.53		

The value of k for a complex mixture can be calculated by summing the partial products:

$$k = (A \% k_A + B \% k_B)/100$$

where $A\%$, $B\%$ are the percentages of components A and B etc., and k_A k_B are the corresponding values of k.

Instruments are produced with standard ranges from 0–2% to 0–100% oxygen in process gases for full scale deflection.

6.6.3.2 E.I.L. ANALYSER

The basic instrument consists of a measuring unit mounted in a temperature controlled box, a unit for controlling the temperature, a set-zero control potentiometer and a gas sampling system. The gas sampling system used depends upon the pressure of the sample gas.

The analyser is built into an instrument case with a glass panelled door and is suitable for wall or flush-panel mounting. The case is provided with pipe connections for gas sample inlet and outlet, and electrical connections for power supplies and up to two read-out channels. Two glass coated platinum filaments (F_1 and F_2 in *Figure 6.55*) are mounted in cavities in a metal block. Both cavities are open to a stream of the sample gas. The two filaments are heated by an electric current and form two arms of a Wheatstone bridge. A magnetic field is directed across the cell containing F_2 in such a way that it is only partly within the heated zone created by the filament when a sample gas containing oxygen passes through the instrument; the oxygen is attracted into the magnetic field. The attraction is greater at the cool edge of the field owing to the higher paramagnetic susceptibility of cool oxygen. The consequent pressure difference across the field induces a flow of gas which cools F_2 in relation to F_1, causing a difference in resistance and imbalance of the bridge. The imbalance is a function of the oxygen concentration.

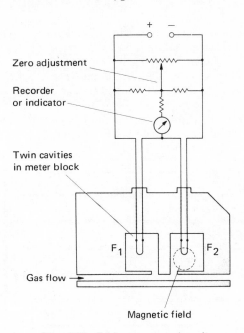

Figure 6.55 E.I.L. oxygen measuring unit

Before oxygen analysis can be carried out the zero must be set. The magnet can be released from its normal position, removing the magnetic field from around F_2 and the instrument therefore behaves as though the gas contained no oxygen, and the zero can be checked. To check the span either a gas containing a known percentage of oxygen can be passed through the analyser, or the instrument arranged to provide a predetermined output when air is passed through the analyser. The sensitivity to oxygen is affected by temperature and barometric pressure. The analyser is automatically compensated for both effects. The unit is thermostatically controlled, but the control temperature is related to barometric pressure. This control is so designed that the shift in sensitivity due to a pressure change is compensated for by the change of sensitivity caused by an equivalent temperature change. For this reason it is necessary to know the altitude at which the analyser is to be installed if above 300 m.

The gas flow through the filament block is approximately 100 cm³/min. The rest of the sample stream, up to a maximum of 500 cm³/min is by-passed.

The filter chamber is filled with cotton or glass wool to remove any dirt from the gas sample. In applications where pulverised fuels are being used, and magnetic dust particles are likely to be present, the filter chamber should be filled with granulated pumice soaked with glycerine.

The normal instrument range is from 0–2 to 0–25% oxygen by volume and the accuracy ±2% full scale deflection and an ambient temperature of 30°C can be tolerated.

6.7   PROCESS CHROMATOGRAPHY

Process gas chromatography is a method of analysing a mixture of gases or vaporisable liquids by segregating it on a time basis into its components and measuring the concentration of each component. The analysis cycle is repeated continuously so that information on trends in the concentration of individual components may be determined so that the process operation may be optimised.

One principle used to segregate the components of the mixture of gases or volatile liquids is the fact that the rate at which a component is swept through a

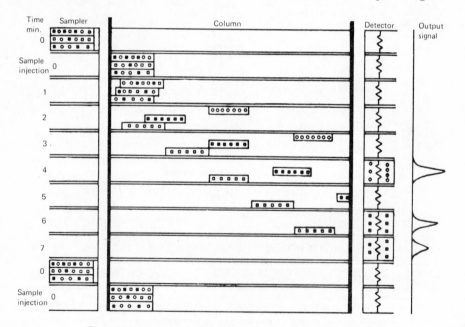

Figure 6.56   Chromatographic separation (Courtesy Foxboro-Yoxall Ltd.)

packed column of a high surface area granular solid coated with a thin film of non-volatile liquid is dependent upon its relative solubility in the non-volatile liquid, so that the least soluble reaches the end of the column first. The time taken for a given component to emerge or 'elute' from the column under a given set of conditions is defined as the retention time. *Figure 6.56* illustrates pictorially the separation of a three-component mixture. The sample is introduced into the column and is transported through the column by the 'carrier' gas. The components will elute from the column in order of their solubilities in the film of liquid on the packing material, the least soluble appearing first.

Because the carrier gas is flowing continuously and components are eluting at different times, the gas leaving the column will alternate between pure carrier gas and a binary mixture of carrier gas plus a component. This effluent is passed through a detector where the 'arrival' of each component is detected. The resultant detector output is a function of the concentration of each component and, when recorded on a suitable instrument, provides a visual record of the analysis, referred to as a chromatogram. This particular type is known as a partition column. It is used in the chromatographic method known as gas-liquid chromatography, in which the liquid film is the stationary phase and the carrier gas is the moving phase.

The elements of the basic chromatograph are illustrated in *Figure 6.57*. These elements and their functions are:

A carrier gas supply for transporting the sample through the analyser.
A sampling means for measuring and injecting a quantity of sample to be analysed.
A chromatographic column for separating the components of the sample.
A detector for sensing the presence of components in the sample.
A constant temperature enclosure housing the column, sampler, and some types of detectors.
A programmer to actuate various time-sequenced operations.
A read-out device for recording the results of analysis.

Carrier gas system

The primary factors that determine which carrier gas to use are the effect of the gas on component resolution and detection sensitivity. The latter is of greater importance since the desired resolution can be achieved by correct column design. The carrier gas and type of detector are chosen so that eluted components generate large signals. For this reason, helium is generally used with thermal conductivity cells because of its high thermal conductivity. Hydrogen has a higher thermal conductivity than helium, but because of precautions necessary when using hydrogen, helium is preferred where suitable.

Specific properties of each carrier gas are exploited with other types of detectors, such as argon with the beta ray detector, and air with the catalytic combustion detector.

In special instances a carrier gas other than that normally associated with a particular detector will be used for other reasons. For example, to measure hydrogen in trace quantities using a thermal conductivity detector, it is necessary to use a carrier gas other than helium because both helium and hydrogen have high thermal conductivities. Accordingly, argon or nitrogen is used because either has a much lower thermal conductivity than hydrogen, resulting in a larger difference in thermal conductivity and hence a greater output.

The rate of flow of carrier gas has two effects on analysis. The first is its effect on signal amplitude and the second its effect on retention time. Accordingly, the flow rate, once selected, must be maintained constant during successive analyses.

Carrier gas is supplied from a conventional bottled supply. A pressure reducing valve is used to reduce the pressure of the carrier gas to a level compatible with the flow control equipment.

Either of two methods is normally used to control the flow rate of the carrier gas. The first is a precision pressure regulator which maintains a constant pressure upstream of the column and reference side of the detector. The second is a differential pressure regulator which maintains a constant pressure drop across a variable restriction.

For operator observation, a rotameter is provided to indicate carrier gas

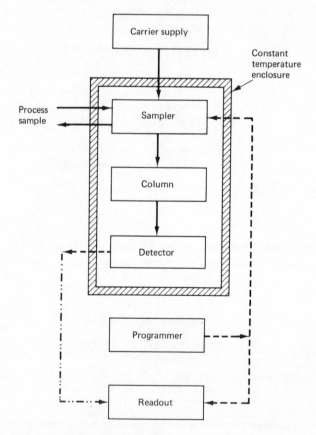

Figure 6.57   Basic process chromatograph (Courtesy Foxboro-Yoxall Ltd.)

flow. However, this is used as a 'rough' indication since the best indication of correct flow is the analysis record itself.

Sampling system

The sample, suitably prepared if necessary, is fed to the instrument by a fast sampling loop. It is then fed into the instrument by a sampling valve of the form shown in *Figure 6.58* for liquids, and *Figure 6.59* for gases.

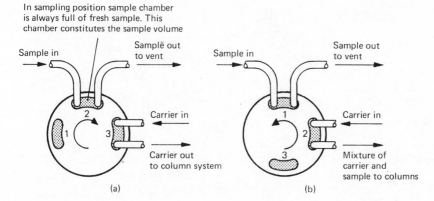

Figure 6.58   Liquid sample valve (Courtesy Foxboro-Yoxall Ltd.) (a) Valve de-energised (b) Valve energised

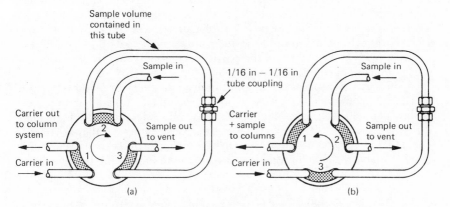

Figure 6.59   Gas sample valve (Courtesy Foxboro-Yoxall Ltd.) (a) Valve de-energised (b) Valve energised

It is essential that the sample size should be constant for each analysis and that it is introduced into the carrier gas stream rapidly as a slug. Further, the sample valve should be designed continuously to circulate the sample during the injection to minimise transportation lag. The valve should have the minimum number of moving parts for reliability, be constructed of materials that will not contaminate the sample, require no lubrication, have no leakage of sample and carrier, and have no dead volume that can result in contamination of successive samples. The valve should be capable of injecting samples as small as 1 mm³.

In multi-column systems a similar valve is required to switch columns *(Figure 6.60)*.

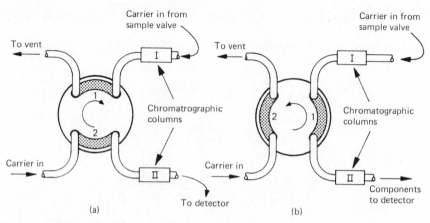

Figure 6.60 Column switching valve (Courtesy Foxboro-Yoxall Ltd.) (a) Valve de-energised (b) Valve energised

Chromatographic column

A typical partition column consists of a suitable length of 3 or 6 mm i.d. tubing wound into a helix for convenient housing and packed with finely ground firebrick which has been coated with a silicone oil. The granular material is referred to as the solid support and the coating as the partitioning liquid or liquid phase. The versatility of the partition column is due to the extremely large number of partitioning liquids available.

To.illustrate the separation capabilities of a partition column, it is possible to separate a mixture of benzene (boiling point 80.1°C) and cyclohexane (boiling point 80.7°C). It would be practically impossible to separate them by distillation, because their boiling points are so close. However, they are readily separated in a chromatographic column by selection of the correct partitioning liquid. In fact, a choice of liquids can be made to permit the benzene to be eluted either before or after the cyclohexane *(Figure 6.61)*. This is accomplished by using the difference in physical properties of benzene and cyclohexane. Because benzene is slightly polar, selection of a polar partitioning liquid will retard the benzene more than the cyclohexane, and cyclohexane will elute first. If a non-polar liquid is chosen, the reverse will be true.

Any partitioning liquid must have a low vapour pressure at operating temperature so that it will not be depleted too rapidly at the operating temperature. The liquid is also chosen for a particular analysis because of its selectivity in separating the components of a sample. Apart from its ability to resolve components, it must not react with the tubing material, the solid support, the sample or the carrier gas. The weight/percent ratio of liquid to solid is varied to achieve desired results and is usually in the range of 1–40%.

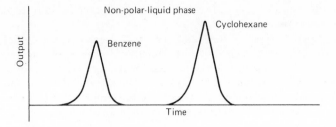

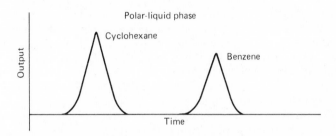

Figure 6.61   Effect of partitioning liquid (Courtesy Foxboro-Yoxall Ltd.)

The primary purpose of the solid support in a partition column is to 'hold' the liquid in the column. Its main requirement is that it be inert and have ability to be coated by a partitioning liquid. All solid supports are finely ground (125–500 μm) materials such as firebrick, 'Celite' or, in special cases, granulated synthetic materials.

Another type of column frequently used is an adsorption column. In the adsorption column, components are separated by their differences in adsorption which can be considered as their tendency to adhere to the adsorbent. Packing materials used in the adsorption column are surface-active solids such as activated alumina, charcoal, silica gel and synthetic zeolites. These materials are usually packed dry, i.e. not impregnated with a liquid.

Molecular sieve columns are another type, most of which are packed with materials which separate components on the basis of their molecular size, slowing down the larger (heavier) molecules more than the smaller (lighter) ones. Both the adsorption column and molecular sieve column are used in the chromatographic method known as gas-solid chromatography.

In general, although relatively simple separations are made with a single column, more complex samples require two or more column materials. Multiple-column arrangements are also used to minimise column contamination that can result from certain components passing through a particular type of column and to reduce analysis time, where only a partial analysis is made for selected components.

Detectors

The desirable characteristics of a chromatograph detector are that it have fast response, linear output over wide ranges of concentration, be reproducible and have high detection sensitivity.

Several different types of detectors are used in gas chromatography and each operates on a completely different principle. However, all detectors 'zero' on the carrier gas and respond to the components. The type of detector most commonly used operates on the basis of differential thermal conductivity. If a constant current is passed through a filament, the temperature of the filament, and hence its resistance, will vary with the rate at which heat is conducted away by the surrounding gas.

In a typical detector, four identical thermal conductivity cells, two for reference and two for measuring, are used in a Wheatstone bridge configuration as in a katharometer. Only pure carrier gas plus components flow through the measuring cells. When no components are being eluted, carrier gas only flows through both cells and the voltage drop across each is the same and bridge output is zero. When carrier gas plus a component passes through the measuring cell, the bridge becomes unbalanced due to the varying thermal conductivity of the mixture and a bridge output results. Thus, the resultant bridge output is a function of the analysis.

The type of detector next in importance is the flame ionisation detector, which offers much greater sensitivity than the thermal conductivity type and is ideal for trace analysis of combustible components.

This detector, *Figure 6.62,* uses a small flame which results from the combustion of hydrogen in the presence of oxygen. The basis of operation is the difference between the number of ions present in a clean H_2–O_2 flame and the number present when a combustible compound containing carbon is added to the flame. With the addition of carbon, the number of ions increases greatly. An electrode in close proximity to the flame collects the ions and produces an electrical output. This output is at a very high impedance so that a high impedance amplifier is necessary to use the signal for read-out purposes.

Several variations of flame ionisation detector can be used. In one type,

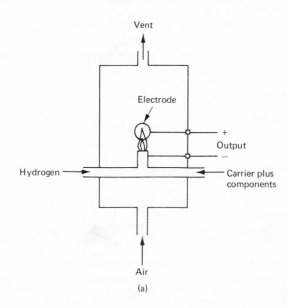

(a)

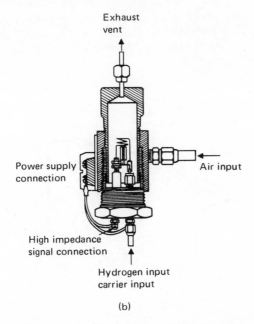

Exhaust
vent

Power supply
connection

Air input

High impedance
signal connection

Hydrogen input
carrier input

(b)

Figure 6.62   H₂ flame ionisation detector (Courtesy Foxboro-Yoxall Ltd.) (a) Schematic (b) Actual

hydrogen is used as the carrier gas and subsequently burned at the jet tip to provide the ionising flame. In another type, hydrogen is supplied separately to the burner while carrier gas (which can be almost any gas) and elutants pass through the flame. Oxygen to support combustion must be provided either from a bottled supply or from clean, hydrocarbon-free instrument air.

Constant temperature enclosure

Two general methods are used to distribute heat within the analyser to maintain the temperature sensitive elements at constant temperature ($\pm 0.1^\circ$C or better) and to minimise temperature gradients. One uses an air bath, and the other metal-to-metal contact (or heat sink). The former depends upon circulation of heated air by means of some form of circulator and the latter upon thermal contact of the temperature sensitive elements with heated metal. There are advantages and disadvantages to both types.

An air bath has inherently fast warm-up and comparatively high temperature gradients and offers the advantage of ready accessibility to all elements within the temperature controlled compartment without creating an explosion hazard.

On the other hand, metal-to-metal contact has slower warm-up but has relatively low temperature gradients. However, it has the disadvantage of explosion hazard, requiring housing of the entire analyser in an explosion proof housing with inherent limited accessibility to elements. In the latter case, in order to service any part of the analyser it is necessary to break into the explosion proof housing.

An analyser designed to use the advantages of both methods and minimise the disadvantages isolates the non-hazardous elements from the hazardous so that they are separately accessible. *Figure 6.63* is a schematic illustration of how this is achieved in one design.

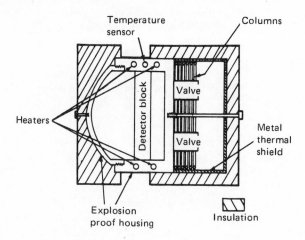

Figure 6.63   Constant temperature explosion proof housing (Courtesy Foxboro-Yoxall Ltd.)

The heaters are nichrome wires imbedded in the aluminium casting. A high sensitivity thermostat is thermally close-coupled to the heaters and thermodynamically located at the point of heat loss. It is evident that if the thermostat senses the loss at the only point that it can occur and controls the heat input to balance this loss, the temperature throughout the enclosure will reach equilibrium and be maintained constant.

The detector, which in many analysers has caused a hot spot, is thermally shunted directly to the heated aluminium casting. This results in the detector supplementing the heaters as a source of thermal energy. By correct design of the casting and detector block, thermal distribution can be controlled and thermostatic action attenuated, resulting in uniform temperature control of the detector block, column and sample valve.

Gradients across the column(s), sample valve and column switching valve(s) are avoided by placing a highly conductive metal shield directly in contact with the heated casting and over the entire volume housing the column and valve(s). The column(s) and valve(s), which present no explosion hazard because they require no electrical connections, are accessible without opening the explosion proof housing.

The above design thus uses the advantages of metal-to-metal contact and retains the accessibility of components realised with an air bath.

Programmer

The programmer of a process chromatograph, frequently referred to as a 'control unit', has two modes of operation—automatic and manual. In the automatic mode the programmer initiates all time-sequenced operations of the chromatograph such as sample injection, component signal attenuation, automatic zero adjustment, column switching, stream selection, peak selection and read-out. For manual operation the programmer has switches, push-buttons and knobs to permit a human operator to initiate these functions. Manual operation is necessary for start-up, maintenance and calibration.

Chromatographic read-out

The output signal of a chromatograph, if continuously recorded, would appear as a series of 'peaks'. This type of display is the basic form of chromatographic record and is referred to as a chromatogram. A typical chromatogram is shown in *Figure 6.64*. This chromatogram is of no value until the chromatograph has been calibrated with samples of known composition and concentration. Once the chromatograph has been calibrated, a chromatogram identifies the components (qualitative analysis) by the time required for a component to elute under specified conditions; the area under each peak is a measure of concentration (quantitative analysis) of each component.

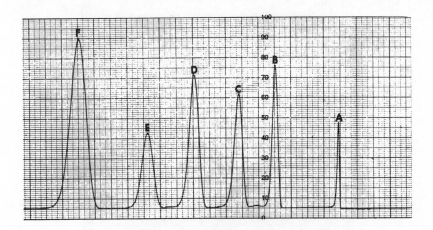

Figure 6.64   Actual chromatogram of six-component stream (Courtesy Foxboro-Yoxall Ltd.)

To facilitate routine calibration the programmer has provision for initiating the injection of a standard sample and the record is displayed in full chromatograph form. In order that the record can be kept on scale and allow calibration directly in percent concentration, in spite of the wide variation in concentration of components and variation of sensitivity of the detector to different components, means are provided to attenuate the signal produced by each component.

All detectors operate on the principle of zeroing on the carrier gas and responding to the components. So that all measurements can be made from the same reference, provisions are included to balance or zero the detector. This is attained by a combination of a manually operated attenuator provided in the programmer and an automatically inserted external biasing voltage.

Frequently peak height is taken as a sufficiently accurate indication of the concentration, and may be displayed as a bar chart for a number of components.

The most useful form of read-out for process application is the continuous step trend record, *Figure 6.65*. With this form of read-out, individual pens on multi-pen recorders are used to record changes in concentration for each component of interest. To obtain this type of record, a 'peak picker' is used to sense and store the peak signal representing each component. During each analysis each peak signal is compared to the corresponding signal stored during the preceding analysis and the recorder pen associated with that component moves only if a change has occurred. The continuous step trend read-out yields a record similar to that which an operator is accustomed to using and, in addition, has the advantage of a continuous signal available for automatic control, data logging or process computers for each component of interest.

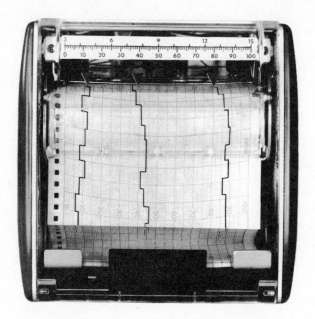

Figure 6.65   Three-component trend record (Courtesy Foxboro-Yoxall Ltd.)

6.7.1   Process chromatograph

Figure 6.66 illustrates the analyser of a typical process chromatograph used when it is required to measure the concentration of a number of components of a process stream.

The analyser section is housed in the upper half and views of the interior of the weatherproof enclosure are shown in *Figure 6.67*. *Figure 6.67(a)* shows the

*Figure 6.66   Analyser on pedestal
(Courtesy Foxboro-Yoxall Ltd.)*

equipment from one side where the column is seen. *Figure 6.67(b)* shows the detector area which is seen from the other side. The covers of the explosion proof enclosure have been removed. The equipment is designed to be explosion proof to be used in American National Electrical Code Class 1 Group D Division 1 areas which are similar to, but not identical with, BS 4683 Zone 1 Group 11A.

Basically this unit houses the temperature controller section, sample valves, filled columns and detector. These are mounted together with the carrier gas and air supply pressure regulators. The pressure and flow of the carrier gas are indicated together with the temperature of the analyser section.

A cut-away section of the sample valve in the sampling position is shown in *Figure 6.58(a)*. The carrier gas and sample flow through the valve is as indicated. The sample port in the slide is accurately machined to trap an exact volume of sample. For gas streams, sample volumes vary from 0.1 cm³ up to several cubic centimetres. For liquid samples, ports are sized to handle samples as small as 1 mm³. On command from the programmer, air pressure applied to the operator rotates the seat and the sample is carried to the analyser column. In the meantime, the sample stream continuously circulates through the valve, reducing transportation lag and ensuring that an up-to-date sample is always available.

The time required for injecting the sample is very short. After injection, the programmer vents the operator and the slide is returned to its original position by a restoring spring. The only moving part in the valve is the slide, ensuring a high degree of reliability. Since the slide and all parts in contact with the sample are either p.t.f.e. or stainless steel, no lubrication is required, eliminating a potential source of sample contamination. Elimination of any dead volume prevents contamination of successive samples and ensures reproducible sample volume.

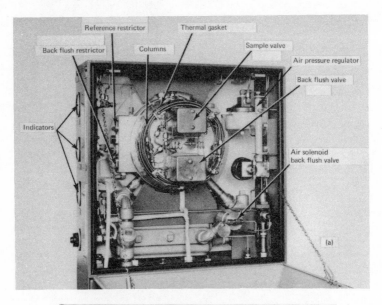

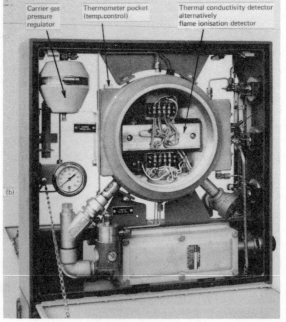

Figure 6.67   Interior of analyser section (a) Enclosure and column area (b) Enclosure and detector area (Courtesy Foxboro-Yoxall Ltd.)

The sample valve, being located outside the explosion proof detector housing, is readily accessible. In order to decrease the time taken for a given analysis, two columns may be used so that one column is being used while the other is back-flushed. Frequently, when the component of interest is eluted early in the cycle the forward flow is discontinued, the detector disconnected, and the remainder of the sample flushed backwards through the column until the column is free of sample. The column is then ready to be used for a further analysis. When this technique is used a multi-port valve of the form shown in *Figure 6.60* is required.

6.7.1.1   READ-OUT

The output signal of the chromatograph analyser depends on the type of detector used and dictates the equipment required to provide a useful signal for recording and control.

When using a thermal conductivity detector, the output is determined by the nature of the excitation source. In this chromatograph a separate 1000 Hz oscillator power supply is used to excite the thermal conductivity detector bridge. The use of 1000 Hz eliminates all thermal e.m.f. effects, especially in the attenuator potentiometers, and yields a higher signal-to-noise level when compared to a d.c. excitation of the bridge, thus allowing smaller concentration of samples to be measured. It also allows the use of a high gain a.c. amplifier resulting in a sensitive, stable system. The use of 1000 Hz also eliminates 50 Hz pick-up.

To ensure reproducible analysis, each chromatograph has some provision for automatically balancing or zeroing detector output. In operation the programmer initiates automatic zero adjustment when no components are being eluted, and the bridge output, if any, is fed directly into a transducer. The transducer can accomplish auto-zero adjustment by periodically servo-positioning a slidewire to develop a voltage in opposition to the drift voltage. In the Foxboro Chromatograph this function may also be accomplished by the Chromatographic e.m.f.-to-Current Converter (Chromoverter). The Chromoverter is a completely solid state millivolt-to-milliampere converter, and is available with or without automatic zero adjustment. The Chromoverter converts the usually narrow span millivolt output of the detector into a linear 10–50 mA signal.

The current output may be recorded or fed to a current-to-air converter, and this pneumatic output can then be fed to a pneumatic Peak Selector Memory Unit (p.s.m. unit). The purpose of this unit is to sense, retransmit and store the pneumatic signals corresponding to the component peaks.

The standard form of final read-out used with the Foxboro Chromatograph is a continuous trend record. This is accomplished by using individual pens on multi-pen pneumatic Consotrol recorders to record each analysed component. The inputs to the Consotrol receivers are from the p.s.m. unit. During each analysis cycle, a pneumatic signal corresponding to each component peak height to be recorded is transmitted to the Consotrol receivers and 'locked in' assigned receiving bellows. If, during a successive analysis, a component concentration changes, the value of the pressure in the receiving bellows will change and the pen will assume a new position. The resultant record of the concentration of a component will be a continuous line with changes in concentration appearing as 'steps'. The continuous trend record is similar to the type of record an operator is accustomed to using and offers the added advantage of a continuous signal available for automatic control.

A chromatogram display of a standard sample is essential for calibration. Accordingly, provisions are included to permit an operator to select a chromatogram form of display when desired. This is accomplished by placing the chromatogram switch on the programmer in the 'On' position. In this position a three-way solenoid valve in the transmission line to one pen in the trend recorders connects the output of the transducer directly to the receiving bellows of the chromatogram pen, by-passing the p.s.m. unit. This results in the selected pen continuously recording the output of the transducer. The signal from the p.s.m. unit that would normally be recorded by this pen is vented to atmosphere. The pen selected for recording the chromatogram is usually a pen recording the least important component. If desired, a separate recorder with a fast chart speed can be used for chromatogram recording. If a pen on a trend recorder is used to record a chromatogram, a switch in the recorder permits selection of the 38 mm/min speed, instead of the normal 19 mm/h speed.

6.7.1.2   SAMPLE PREPARATION

The purpose of sample preparation is to take a representative sample of the process stream and prepare it for introduction into the chromatographic column. Because the nature and conditions of process streams vary widely it is necessary to design each preparation system for the application. While the equipment varies with the application, it is designed in modular units to provide a clean, up-to-date sample at the desired pressure and flow rate.

Sample preparation systems furnished with the Foxboro Chromatograph are of two basic types depending on whether the sample is a liquid or a gas. A typical schematic flow diagram of the gas type is illustrated in *Figure 6.68*.

Many applications require analysis of two or more process streams with one analyser. In these instances a sample line from each stream is piped to the analyser and sample lines are sequentially switched through solenoid valves to the sampling valve. When multi-stream analysis is involved, inter-sample contamination must be prevented. Contamination of respective samples can occur through valve leakage and inadequate flushing of common lines. To ensure adequate flushing, capacity of common lines is kept to a minimum and stream selection valves are timed so that while the sample from one stream is being analysed, the sample from the next stream is flowing through all common lines.

Prevention of inter-sample contamination from valve leakage is accomplished by locating valves with respect to pressure drops so that any leakage will flow to vent rather than intermix in common lines. A typical flow arrangement for multi-stream application is shown in *Figure 6.69*.

In some applications additional conditioning of the sample is required. Typical of these would be steam tracing to maintain a sample in a gaseous state, vaporisation to change a liquid to a gas and elimination of stream contaminants by mechanical or chemical means.

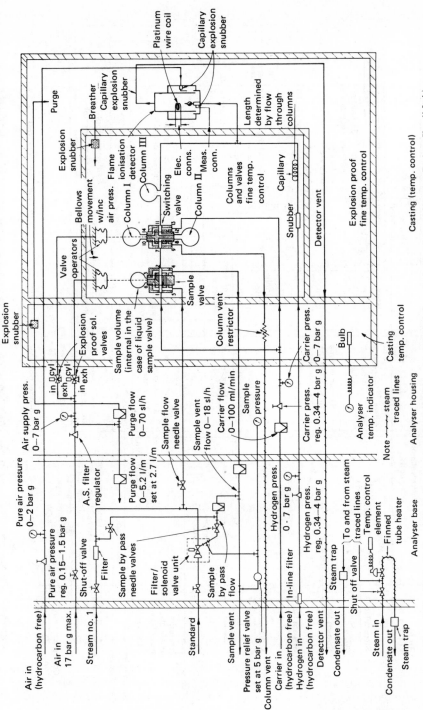

Figure 6.68 Typical schematic flow diagram of single-stream chromatograph with flame ionisation detector (Courtesy Foxboro-Yoxall Ltd.)

252

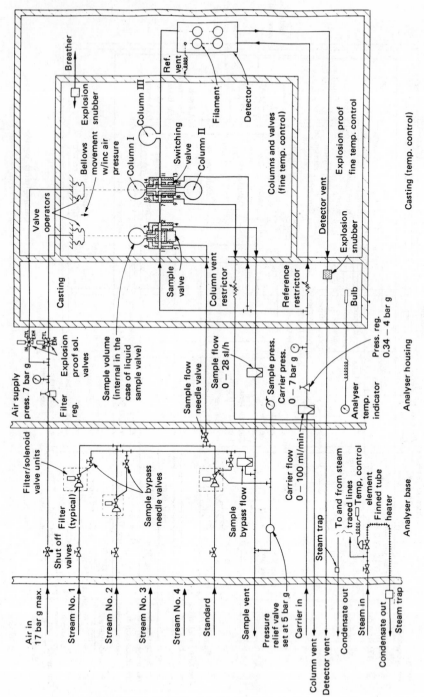

Figure 6.69 Typical schematic flow diagram of multi-stream chromatograph with thermal conductivity detector (Courtesy Foxboro-Yoxall Ltd.)

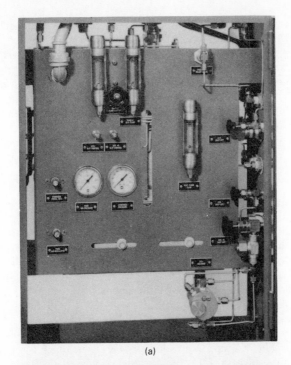

(a)

(b)

Figure 6.70   Typical pedestal arrangement (Courtesy Foxboro-Yoxall Ltd.) (a) Face of panel (b) Back of panel

For most applications, all sample preparation equipment is integrally mounted within the pedestal. For applications requiring complex sample preparation and switching, the additional equipment is mounted outside the pedestal on which the analyser can be mounted. When mounted in the pedestal the arrangement of the equipment is as shown in *Figure 6.70*. This equipment is designed to ensure that the sample and other supplies are delivered to the analyser at the correct flow rate and pressure. A pressure relief valve is fitted to protect the sampling system (i.e. sample valve) from excessive pressure. Shut-off valves are fitted internally on all services, excepting bottled gas lines.

6.7.2   Compact process chromatograph

This chromatograph, shown in *Figure 6.71*, is a single-stream instrument designed for high speed on-line measurement of the concentration of a single component, or group of components. In effect it is a quality transducer designed as with transducers of other parameters for monitoring or controlling a process plant. It consists of an analyser, a processor, and a power unit suitable for use in IEC Zone 1 areas.

The analyser unit is shown in *Figure 6.72* and contains those parts of the system required for sample handling and separation, and detection of the components. The column and detector are enclosed in a temperature controlled unit at the top of the unit and the associated electronics in the lower half. The packing and length of the small bore column are chosen to suit the application, and the carrier gas regulator has been specially designed for high stability under low flow conditions.

The sample injection and column switching valves have seats and slides of hard-wearing ceramic material. Mating faces are precision ground and channels in the faces prevent cross contamination between the ports. All connections are within the small ceramic manifold, reducing the length of connections to a minimum.

The small volume thermal conductivity type detector uses thermistor elements to produce the output signals with high speed and stability. The electronic circuit modules mounted in the lower half of the main case control the oven temperature, power the detector and amplify its output, and provide power pulses to operate the valve solenoids.

The processor contains the electronic circuits which control the sequential operation of the total system. It times the operation of the simple injection and column switching valves, selects and integrates a chromatographic peak, and up-dates the trend output signal.

The power unit provides the low voltage regulated supplies for the analyser and the processor and may be mounted up to 3 m from the processor.

6.7.2.1   PRINCIPLE OF OPERATION

The operation of the chromatograph can be either on the conventional fixed-time basis or the ratio-time basis. In fixed-time operation the sample injection is the start of the time cycle. At pre-set times the 'integration window'

(a)

(c)

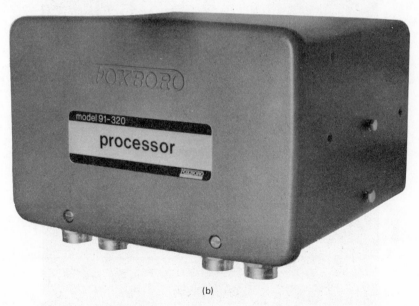

(b)

*Figure 6.71   The Compact Chromatograph (Courtesy Foxboro-Yoxall Ltd.) (a) Analyser (b) Processor
(c) Power unit*

is opened and closed, to coincide with the start and finish of the emergence of the components from the column. While the window is open the detector signal is integrated to give a measure of the concentration of the component. Other operations such as column switching and automatic zeroing are similarly timed from the sample injection. For fixed-time operation to be reliable, pressure and flow rate of carrier gas, and temperature and quantity of stationary phase in the column must be closely controlled.

Many of the problems associated with fixed-time operation may be avoided by use of ratio-time operation. In this mode of operation the retention time of components is measured from an early reference peak (corrected retention time, see *Figure 6.73*) instead of from the time of sample injection. The ratio of two corrected retention times (retention ratio) is less affected by changes in the critical column parameters. The corrected retention time for an early trigger peak is used to predict the time when the component of interest will be emerging, that is, the integration window.

Figure 6.72   Analyser internal view (Courtesy Foxboro-Yoxall Ltd.)

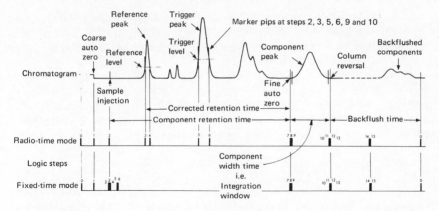

Figure 6.73   Typical chromatograph showing logic steps (Courtesy Foxboro-Yoxall Ltd.)

For the system to be able to operate in the ratio mode, it is necessary to have two specific peaks in the chromatogram in advance of the peak of the component of interest *(Figure 6.73)*.

Reference peak

The reference peak is due to the first component eluted from the column, with a very low retention time (such as air), and is used as the start point for the ratio timing. If a suitable component is not consistently present in the process sample, one can be injected into the column at the same time as the sample, by using the second loop of the sample valve.

Trigger peak

The trigger peak must appear on the chromatogram between the reference and component peaks. It must be self-evident by virtue of size, and it must be consistent in height and width. As with the reference peak it can be from a component of the process sample, or injected separately. Alternatively it can be a negative peak derived by using a doped carrier gas. The logic circuits measure the time between reference and trigger peaks and use this, together with the pre-set ratio value, to compute the time for the start of the integration window. Similarly the trigger peak width is used to define the width of the window. At the start of integration the value of the signal level is stored. The integrator then measures the area under the component peak for the period of the window opening. At this point the signal level is again measured and compared with the stored start value to determine whether any baseline shift has occurred. The integration is corrected for any baseline shifts as described below.

The final value of the integration is stored and used to give an output signal which represents the concentration of the component. As this signal is up-dated after each analysis the output shows the trend of the concentration.

After the completion of integration, the column is back-flushed in order to remove any later components, the duration of the back-flushing being ratioed from the analysis time. Alternatively, for those applications requiring a measurement such as 'total heavies', the peak of the total back-flushed components can be integrated.

There are some applications where the ratio-time mode cannot be used. Typically, the measurement of a very early component, such as hydrogen, precludes the existence of earlier reference and trigger peaks. Operation of the various functions is then programmed using the fixed-time mode. Selection of the required mode is made using a switch on the processor.

6.7.2.2 SYSTEM OPERATION

In any mode of operation of the system the analyser needs to be at its control temperature, with the carrier gas and the sample flowing.

The following description details the step-by-step operation of the sequence. *Figure 6.73* shows a chromatogram and the related logic steps in both fixed- and ratio-time modes and *Figure 6.74* shows the basic analogue and logic connections between circuit boards.

The logic circuits in the processor are stepped from one state to the next by signals which are generated within the various function circuits. There are 16 steps. The changes from Step 0 to 1 and Step 14 to 15 are made by signals generated in the logic circuit. Two clock-pulse generators, on the logic circuit board, ensure the correct timing of the operational sequence.

The automatic mode of operation results in a succession of analyses which continue until the 'halt' button is operated. In the manual mode one analysis is made and the logic stops at Step 15, with 'halt' and 'ready' indicators glowing, until a further analysis is initiated by operation of the 'action' push-button.

Automatic operation in ratio-mode

The sequence of operation is initiated by pressing the 'action' push-button, which activates the logic circuit. The sample valve is switched to the 'fill' position, and the column is switched for forward operation. After a short delay, the logic moves to Step 1. At this stage, the output of the thermal conductivity detector is due to the carrier gas only, and this signal is zeroed by the coarse auto-zero circuit. The 'sample' lamp is energised.

As the logic circuit moves to Step 2, the sample valve operates to inject the measured volume of sample into the column. At the same time ·the backflush-time circuit starts to count up, measuring the time for the backflush operation, which occurs at a later stage in the sequence. The output from the thermal conductivity detector is fed, via the coarse auto-zero circuit, to the level detector. When the pre-set reference peak detection level is sensed, the logic moves to Step 3, the 'sample' lamp is extinguished, the 'reference' lamp is energised, and the retention time circuit starts to count up. Subsequently, the reference peak falls to the detection level on its trailing edge, whereupon the level detector commands the logic to move to Step 4.

The retention time circuit continues to count up until the detection level on the leading edge of the trigger peak is sensed by the level detector. This moves

259

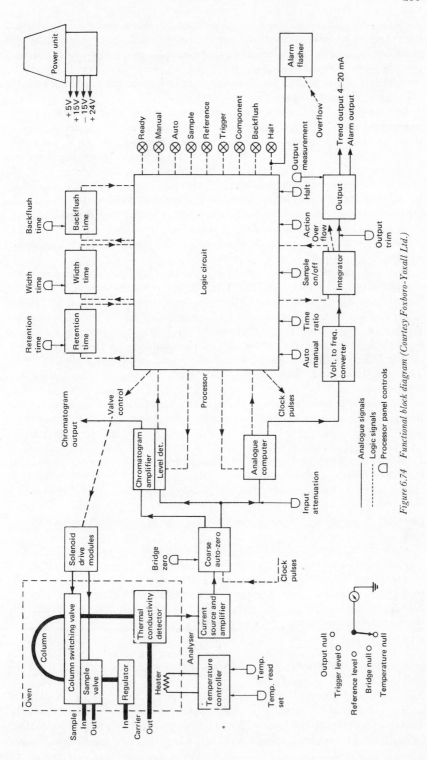

Figure 6.74 Functional block diagram (Courtesy Foxboro-Yoxall Ltd.)

the logic to Step 5, when the operation of the retention time circuit is reversed, the 'trigger' lamp energised and the 'reference' lamp extinguished. At the same time the width time circuit starts to count up, to measure the duration of the trigger peak. When the trailing edge of this peak falls below the detection level, the logic is moved to Step 6 and the width time circuit stops counting, the count being retained for future use.

The retention time circuit continues to count down (at a rate set by the 'retention ratio' dial) until zero count is reached. This commands the logic to move to Step 7, to initiate the fine auto-zero operation within the analogue computer circuit. The value of this correction is stored in the analogue computer circuit until required for correction of the integration. Once the information is stored the logic is moved to Step 8. The width time circuit starts to count down at a rate set by the ratio of trigger to component peak widths, this ratio having been previously set on a dial on the front of the panel. At the same time a logic input to the retention time circuit causes it to count up as a 'slave' to the width time circuit to memorise the duration of the 'integration window'.

The logic is moved to Step 9, in readiness for the emergence of the component peak from the column. The 'trigger' lamp is extinguished and the 'component' lamp is energised. The logic command causes the integrator to count the pulses from the voltage-to-frequency convertor circuit, whilst the width time circuit continues to count down. When it reaches zero count, a signal is fed via the logic circuit to stop the counting by the retention time circuit. When this has occurred an 'enable' signal moves the logic to Step 10. The stored count in the retention time circuit represents the duration of integration.

The computer circuit memorises the value of the final baseline signal before the logic moves to Step 11. The logic input to the computer circuit transfers the sum of the two baseline values into the fine auto-zero circuit memory, and the 'component' lamp is extinguished. The backflush-time circuit starts to count down at a rate governed by the backflush ratio potentiometer, so that the backflush duration is ratioed from the analysis time. An input from the logic circuit is fed to the computer circuit, to select the final value of the voltage required for baseline correction. At the same time the computer circuit provides a signal to clamp its input from the coarse auto-zero circuit to zero.

As the 'backflush' lamp is energised, the logic is moved to Step 12. The column switching valve is operated to reverse the column connections, for backflushing. The retention time circuit starts to count down, to duplicate the integration window time, during which the integration is corrected for baseline variations. The logic then moves to Step 13. When the retention time circuit reaches zero count, the integrator stops and the correction of the peak area measurement is thus completed. The logic then moves to Step 14.

The final enable signal is generated within the logic circuit to transfer the digital count of the integrator to the analogue store. The output from the analogue store is converted to a proportional current trend signal. The backflush-time circuit drives to zero digital count, whereupon the 'backflush' lamp is extinguished and the 'ready' lamp is energised. This completes the total cycle, returning the logic to Step 0, and sequence recurs without further operation of the 'action' push-button.

Automatic operation in the fixed-time mode

This mode of operation is used when reference and trigger peaks are not available, and hence the logic circuit is stepped by internal timers instead of by the peak signals. The following description highlights the differences between the two modes of operation.

Steps 0 and 1 are the same as in the ratio mode, but the timing of logic steps 2 to 5 is controlled by internal clock pulses. In Step 2, the retention and backflush-time circuits start counting in accordance with front panel dial settings. The logic steps through to Step 6, where it waits until the retention time circuit reaches maximum count, which then advances the logic to Step 7. As with the ratio mode, Step 7 is the fine auto-zero operation. On Step 8 the width timer starts to count up, and integration starts as in the ratio mode, but Step 9 is completed when the width time circuit reaches maximum counts, stopping integration. Steps 10 to 15 continue as previously described for the ratio mode of operation.

Manual operation

This mode of operation, selected by the 'auto/manual' switch on the front panel, provides a single analysis which is followed by column backflushing and the normal 'halt' condition. Single analyses are initiated by operation of the 'action' push-button, provided that the previous analysis has been completed. This mode of operation is used during initial programming or servicing.

6.7.2.3 METHOD OF INTEGRATION

All integrators respond to any signal which is above zero during the

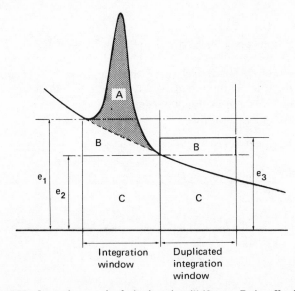

Figure 6.75 Integration correction for 'peak-on-the-tail' (Courtesy Foxboro-Yoxall Ltd.)

integration period, whether it be a peak or some baseline disturbance such as drift, offset, or noise. These baseline variations cause errors in the peak area measurement. Conventional integrators ignore these errors, but the circuits specially designed for this chromatograph correct for any change in baseline during the integration, whether due to a zero shift or the tail of a large component (see *Figure 6.75*).

The method of integration correction is the same in both the fixed-time and ratio-time modes of operation. At the start of integration the signal level (e_1) is stored in the analogue computer circuit for later use, and for the duration of the integration window, the integrator measures and holds the area ($A + B + C$). At the end of this period the final signal level (e_2) is measured, and the average value (e_3) of e_1 and e_2 is determined by the computer circuit. The integrator is operated for a duplicated integration window, during which the integrated value of e_3, which represents the area ($B + C$), is subtracted from the initial integration. The resultant value is the area A, which represents the concentration of the component.

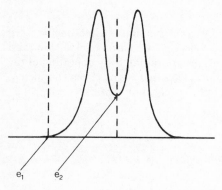

Figure 6.76   Integration correction for two adjacent peaks (Courtesy Foxboro-Yoxall Ltd.)

A switch on the computer circuit board permits the selection of alternative modes of correction for those instances in which the difference between e_1 and e_2 does not represent a baseline change (e.g. partially resolved peaks, see *Figure 6.76*). Instead of e_3 being the average of e_1 and e_2 it can be made equal to either e_1 or e_2 according to the application requirements.

7
MEASUREMENT OF VISCOSITY

The magnitude of the forces brought into play when one portion of a fluid moves relatively to another portion was first discussed by Newton in his *Principia*. He assumed that the force required to maintain a difference of velocity between two planes in a liquid is proportional to their relative velocity divided by the distance between them, i.e. the velocity gradient. If, for example, a plane of area A m² is situated parallel to and at a distance of d m from a fixed plane which is at rest, and the space between the planes is completely filled with a fluid, the force F N required to move the plane area A at a velocity v m/s in its own plane relative to the fixed plane is given by:

$$F = \eta \, A(v/d) \tag{7.1}$$

where η is defined as the dynamic viscosity of the fluid between the planes.

Thus the dynamic viscosity in SI units will be given by:

$$\eta = (F/A) \, (d/v) \ \text{Ns/m}^2$$

However, for general application dynamic viscosity is often expressed in centipoise (cP) where $1 \text{ cP} = 10^{-2} \text{ P} = 10^{-3} \text{ Ns/m}^2$.

For work in connection with flow, the ratio of the dynamic viscosity to the density of a fluid is often required. This is then known as the 'kinematic' viscosity.

Kinematic viscosity at t^0C

$= $ Dynamic viscosity at t^0C/Density at t^0C

$= (\text{Ns/m}^2) \, (\text{m}^3/\text{kg}) = (\text{kgms m}^3/\text{s}^2\text{m}^2\text{kg}) = \text{m}^2/\text{s}$

Again for general application the kinematic viscosity is often expressed in centistokes (cSt) where $1\text{cSt} = 10^{-2} \text{ St} = 10^{-6} \text{ m}^2/\text{s}$. Many tube viscometers, particularly those for determining viscosity relative to some standard liquid, measure kinematic viscosity. The oil industry has for many years been concerned with the kinematic viscosity of liquids. For these reasons the British Standards Institution now specifies kinematic viscosities.

Occasionally, particularly in the study of colloids, the term 'fluidity' is used. This is the reciprocal of the viscosity in poises.

Laboratory methods of determining viscosity are largely based upon equation 7.1 or upon Poiseuille's law for the volume Q discharged in a unit time from a tube of length l and radius a, i.e.

$$Q = \pi P a^4/8\eta l \tag{7.2}$$

where P is the pressure difference between the ends of the tube and η the dynamic viscosity. This equation also forms the basis of a continuous on-line viscometer in which Q is constant and P is measured. This relationship holds only if the flow is streamlined or laminar, i.e. if the Reynolds number* is less than the limiting value.

Viscosity measurement may also be based upon the measurement of the drag upon a stationary cylinder when placed in a concentric rotating cylinder containing the liquid to be tested, or upon the drag on a rotating cylinder when placed in a stationary concentric cylinder. In modern industrial instruments used for continuous measurements on the processes, other methods of measuring the force required to produce relative motion in a liquid are also used.

Non-Newtonian liquids

Newton's equation (7.1) is based upon the assumption that the force required to maintain a difference of velocity between two planes in a liquid is proportional to the velocity gradient in the liquid between the planes. In many industrially important materials such as paint, printing ink, chocolate and other food products, starches, adhesives and many other emulsions, suspensions and colloidal dispersions, it is found that the viscosity depends upon the velocity gradient and such substances are called 'non-Newtonian'. In general, the viscosity of non-Newtonian liquids decreases as the velocity gradient increases so that the volume discharged in a unit time from a capillary tube is not simply proportional to the pressure but generally increases at a more rapid rate than the pressure. Likewise, in the concentric cylinder apparatus, the couple is not proportional to the relative angular velocities of the cylinders but increases less rapidly than for a normal or Newtonian liquid.

If the viscosity of a substance depends on both velocity gradient and time it is said to be 'thixotropic'. A thixotropic substance possesses an internal structure which breaks down (i.e. the viscosity decreases) when the substance is subjected to shear, but which will rebuild itself in time if allowed to rest. It is therefore necessary to measure the 'apparent viscosity', which is equal to the viscosity of a normal liquid which would produce the same rate of flow or deflection of a cylinder under identical conditions in the particular apparatus used. For example, the apparent viscosity of a non-Newtonian paint at rest in a tank may be greater than when flowing under the influence of a paddle stirrer. The paint will break down still further if it is pumped through a pipeline at an even higher mean shear rate. Similarly, the measured viscosity is a function of the shear rate conditions imposed by the measuring system, and the most consistent results are obtained by subjecting the material to a substantially constant rate of shear which should match the shear rate in the process.

Thixotropy is but one of several flow properties which influence the quality and uniformity of many industrial products. Since these properties are dependent upon velocity gradient (or rate of shear) it is necessary to make measurements over a wide range of shear rates in order to assess the flow properties completely. Where the products are structurally too complex to allow continuous viscosity measurement at a single rate of shear to be used for process control, quality may be controlled from the laboratory where rotational viscometers of the cone and plate type† may be used. The

*Volume 1, page 176.

†Cone and plate viscometer with automatic flow curve recording, Ferranti Ltd.

conventional coaxial cylinders are replaced by a flat plate, above which rotates a slightly conical disc so designed that the entire measured sample is subjected to a uniform rate of shear and shear stress. The cone is driven by a variable speed motor through an electro-mechanical torque dynamometer which measures the drag on the cone. The instrument records the stress/shear rate curves automatically and thus enables a rapid assessment of the flow characteristics of the product to be made.

Techniques are also in use for measuring important flow properties such as plasticity and yield value which give the tack to printers' ink and the 'mouldability' to pottery clay, and the thixotropic properties which allow brush marks to flow out of paint. Other characteristics such as shear rate thinning of rubbers and resins, and the dilatancy (work hardening) of certain pastes may also be studied from stress/shear rate flow curves.

Effect of temperature

In specifying the viscosity of a liquid it is vital that the temperature should be stated because the viscosities of liquid decrease very rapidly with increase in temperature, and the rate of decrease is generally larger for the more viscous liquids. In water for example (dynamic viscosity 1.79 cP at 0°C), the temperature coefficient at 0°C is about 3.5% per °C rise in temperature, while at 100°C the temperature coefficient falls to about 1% per °C rise in temperature. For castor oil at 20°C (dynamic viscosity 986 cP) the temperature coefficient is 8.4% per °C in temperature; while for pitch at 20°C (dynamic viscosity 330×10^6 P) the temperature coefficient is greater than 30%.

The viscosity of a gas on the other hand increases with rise in temperature but the change is small, e.g. air: viscosity 170.9 μP at 0°C, 195.1 μP at 50°C, 217.5 μP at 100°C (1 μP $= 10^{-6}$P).

In all forms of apparatus used to measure viscosity it is therefore necessary to maintain the sample at a constant temperature. In a control system, however—e.g. to control the viscosity of fuel oil delivered to burners—variation of temperature may be used to control the viscosity.

Laboratory methods of measuring viscosity are described in many textbooks. In this section, therefore, only instruments which have been applied to continuous measurements on processes will be described under the following headings:

Measurement of pressure drop across a capillary tube.
Measurement of drag on a stationary member due to moving fluid.
Measurement of the force or energy required to move a member at a constant rate in the fluid.

Measurement of the viscosity of the fluid in the process vessels or mains has several advantages. It is not necessary to remove the sample to the laboratory so that time is saved and readings may be obtained continuously. When a sample is removed from the process, it is sometimes difficult to maintain the sample in the original condition owing to changes of temperature, pressure, the evaporation of volatile constituents or the absorption of moisture by hygroscopic fluids. When viscosity control is required continuous measurement is essential.

7.1   MEASUREMENT OF VISCOSITY BY MEASURING PRESSURE DROP ACROSS CAPILLARY TUBE WHEN LIQUID IS FLOWING AT CONSTANT RATE

This method may be applied to the continuous on-line measurement of the dynamic viscosity of Newtonian liquids or non-Newtonian liquids if a viscosity determination at one shear rate will provide adequate information.

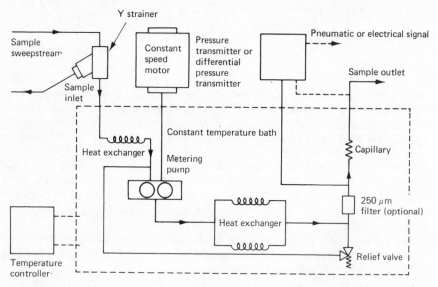

Figure 7.1   Continuous on-line viscometer, schematic flow diagram (Courtesy G.E.C.—Elliott Process Instruments Ltd.)

Figure 7.1 shows a schematic diagram of the instrument. The externally mounted filter (supplied with the viscometer as standard equipment) is a large capacity Y strainer of 150 μm aperture width that provides a filtered sample to the instrument. A constant sample flow rate is achieved with the precision metering pump driven by a synchronous motor. The sample fluid then passes through a heat exchanger. It should be noted that the pump and capillary tube, as well as the heat exchanger, are immersed in a constant temperature oil bath. The temperature of this bath is regulated to ±0.005°C. The sample fluid, now at constant temperature and constant volume, is forced to flow at a constant rate through a capillary tube. The pressure drop across the capillary tube is converted to a pneumatic or electrical signal that is a linear function of dynamic viscosity (centipoise). The filter having an aperture width of 250 μm in front of the capillary tube (an optional part) is to protect the capillary against coke particles that might form in the heat exchanger. A relief valve protects the flow system against excessive pressure that might occur due to blockage of the capillary, etc.

The choice of capillaries and transmitters permits measurements to be made over a range of from 0 to 2500 cP at the bath temperature. After installation and adjustment the viscometer requires very little attention, and an accuracy of better than $\pm 1\%$ has been obtained on plant application.

The oil bath and the electronic controls are each housed in light weight aluminium explosion proof boxes having a group classification equivalent to BS 4683:1971 Group 11A. The oil bath cover and box are insulated with Maranite and fibreglass enclosed in a steel housing.

The precision metering pump delivering a constant 64 cm^3/min and bath stirrer are driven by an explosion proof synchronous motor mounted on the oil bath cover. The bath stirrer consists of two hollow blade stirrers which cause the bath oil to flow radially out through the blades with a high velocity as well as in directions normal to, and tangential to, the blade surfaces.

The stainless steel heat exchanger has sufficient capacity to bring the sample to the required temperature for the viscosity measurement. A stainless steel cooling coil is also provided in the oil bath for constant circulation of cooling water if the desired control temperature is near ambient, or if the inlet sample temperature is greater than the bath temperature.

The maximum viscosity range which may be measured is 0–2500 cP. The capillary is selected to measure the viscosity of the liquid over a particular range at the measurement temperature. The range covered by each capillary tube is determined by the range of the differential pressure transmitter used. Each tube is calibrated and marked at the factory, and an approximate calibration curve provided. The capillary assembly is designed so that it can be readily changed without the need for special tools.

A stainless steel relief valve is set to open when the pressure exceeds 8 bar, permitting flow from the capillary tube inlet to the pump inlet, to protect the instrument against excessive pressure owing to low temperature, clogging of the system or the use of the wrong capillary tube.

The differential pressure across the capillary tube is measured by means of a differential pressure transmitter, which may be pneumatic or electric depending on the user's preference. The ratio of maximum value for a particular capillary tube can vary from 1.09:1 to infinity, with the maximum range of 0–2500 cP depending upon the span of the differential pressure transmitter.

In general, the impulse lines are fitted with a diaphragm seal and the pressure applied to the pressure measuring element by a gas and vapour free liquid filled system. The sealed system is recommended for most samples, but is essential where the sample is of a wax or pitch base, or any other substance which would congeal in the impulse lines.

The bath temperature is detected by means of a resistance thermometer having a response time of 0.8 s, which through a proportional plus integral action controller capable of controlling the bath temperature to $\pm 0.005°C$ controls the input to a tubular type immersion heater of 1 or 2 kW capacity. The temperature set point may be selected by means of a ten-turn potentiometer, or if desired a decade switch which permits the selection of five fixed temperature set points can be provided. In general, the oil bath temperature range is ambient to 116°C but models for use up to 177°C are available.

7.2   MEASUREMENT OF DRAG ON A STATIONARY MEMBER
DUE TO MOVING FLUID

7.2.1   The Ferranti portable viscometer

The Ferranti viscometer, designed for use under industrial conditions, consists of a rotating outer cylinder driven by a small two-phase motor of high torque, with a second cylinder mounted coaxially with it. These cylinders are immersed in the liquid under test, and the rotation of the liquid by the outer cylinder causes the liquid to exert a viscous drag on the inner cylinder. This cylinder is suspended from a jewel bearing and is free to rotate against a calibrated spring and is therefore deflected an angular distance which is proportional to the viscosity of the liquid. This deflection is indicated by a pointer which moves over a scale calibrated directly in viscosity units. The instrument is designed to eliminate the 'end effect' on the inner cylinder, and for the investigation of the anomalous behaviour of non-Newtonian liquids a wide range of shear rates is obtainable. This is achieved by the combined use of a three- or five-speed gear box and a set of three or more interchangeable inner cylinders, which also give the standard instrument a measuring range from a few centipoises to several thousand poises.

When required for continued use on a process the viscosity measuring head may be robustly designed to allow a continuous flow of liquid through the measuring annulus, and it may be permanently installed at a suitable point in a process. It is arranged to provide a continuous electrical signal proportional to viscosity, capable of actuating standard recorders and controllers. The equipment will operate at temperatures up to 200°C where corrosive fumes are not present.

7.2.2   The Fischer-Porter Viscorator

The effect of the 'float' shape upon the flow coefficients in the area type of flowmeter has been discussed in detail in Volume 1. When these effects were being investigated the indicated flows of two floats in the same flow stream, one float designed for maximum susceptibility to viscosity changes and the other designed to be immune to viscosity effects, were compared and it was found that, at any given condition of temperature, the relative heights of these two floats within a tapered tube are a direct measure of the viscosity of the fluid flowing. From this basic principle industrial viscometers capable of measuring continuously the viscosity of liquid having viscosities as high as 10 000 P were developed. The Viscorator may be installed in the line carrying the liquid or in a by-pass, so that the viscosity may be measured under full line pressure and the actual line conditions of temperature, etc., thus facilitating viscosity control.

Several forms of Viscorator are available but the basic principle is the same in all forms; the flow is set at a definite rate and the position of the viscosity sensitive float is a measure of the viscosity of the fluid. In the two-float Viscorator, illustrated in *Figure 7.2(a)* a viscosity-immune float is used as an indicator of flow, and the flow adjusted by means of the manually operated control valve to the desired value. The value of the viscosity is then indicated

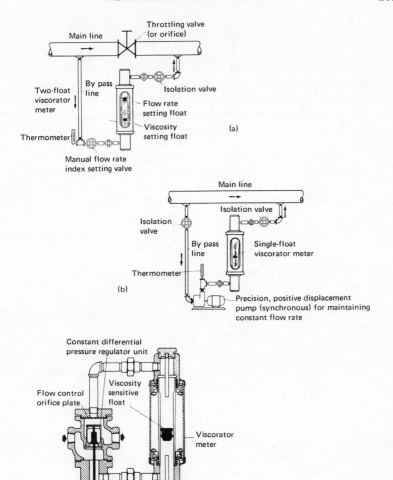

Figure 7.2 The Fischer-Porter Viscorator (Courtesy Solway Flowrators Ltd.) (a) Two-float (b) Single-float (c) Auto-sampling

by the position of the lower float relative to the viscosity graduations. When the Viscorator is installed in a by-pass, an orifice plate or throttling valve is installed in the main line in order to create a differential pressure which ensures a reasonable flow through the by-pass in which the Viscorator is installed.

In the single-float instrument, the use of which is illustrated in *Figure 7.2(b)*, the flow rate is maintained constant by a continuous displacement type of pump driven by a constant speed motor. The position of the float is then an indication of the viscosity of the liquid flowing.

In the auto-sampling form of the instrument illustrated in *Figure 7.2(c)* a weight-loaded float, a tapered tube, and an orifice are used to maintain a constant differential pressure across the instrument connections so that a constant sampling rate is obtained. This system is used with transmitting types of instruments used with recorders and controllers; the methods used for transmitting float position to the outside of the tube have already been discussed*.

Temperature compensated instruments which provide continuous indication, recording and control of fluid viscosity to a base reference temperature over a wide range of sampling temperature are also available; they have a sample temperature indicator in addition to the viscosity pen. Temperature compensation over the full viscosity range is accurate to ±1% for a temperature span of ±5°C or ±2½% for a temperature span of ±14°C.

7.2.3   Pneumatic force-balance viscosity transmitter

In this instrument the torque produced on the stationary disc by the fluid between it and the rotating disc is measured by pneumatic force-balance as shown in *Figure 7.3(b)*. The liquid whose viscosity is to be measured passes upwards between the discs housed in the line shown in *Figure 7.3(a)*.

The disc (2) which is rotated at a constant speed is provided with radial slots where one edge of each slot is bent outwards. These wings continuously draw in a new supply of the liquid to be measured and force it into the gap between the two discs. The stationary disc (4) is affected by a torque, which is proportional to the viscosity and the width of the gap between the two discs. The gap is adjustable for measured span adjustment. The torque is transmitted to a transducer, which by means of a force-balance system delivers a pneumatic output signal proportional to viscosity change.

On increase in viscosity, the flapper (10) approaches the nozzle (11). As supply air is continuously being supplied, the pressure increases at the nozzle and in the feedback bellows (7) until balance has been obtained between the measuring moment and the feedback moment from the bellows. Both bellows are of the same dimension. One bellows is stationary and the other is adjustable (9). By moving this bellows the measuring span can be changed. The span decreases—sensitivity increases—with decreasing distance between the bellows.

The starting value of the measured span—'zero point'—can be adjusted by changing the tension in the spring (12). The output signal (0.2–1 bar) is a linear function of the measured moment which in its turn also is linear in relation to the viscosity.

The instrument has a range of up to 15 P absolute viscosity, the span 18 cP minimum to 300 cP maximum being set and calibrated to the user's requirements. The sampled fluid flows at 13 m³/h, and can be up to 60 bar in the standard model or 90 bar if desired, at a temperature up to 180°C. The temperature of the measurement is indicated on the thermometer on the transmitter. The housing is cast steel but the measuring parts in the

*Volume 1.

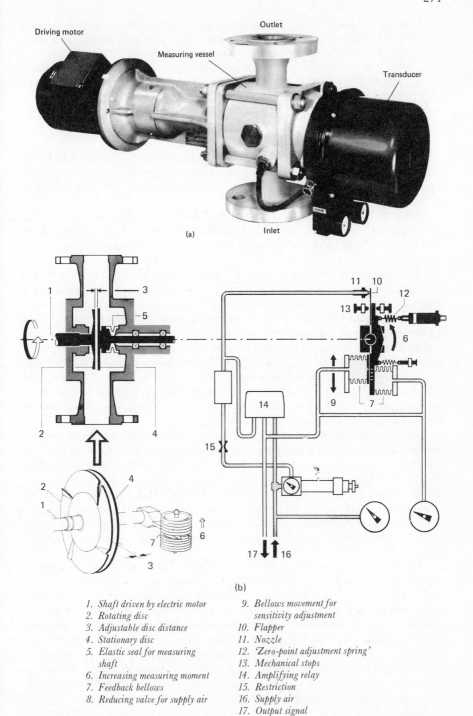

(a)

(b)

1. Shaft driven by electric motor
2. Rotating disc
3. Adjustable disc distance
4. Stationary disc
5. Elastic seal for measuring shaft
6. Increasing measuring moment
7. Feedback bellows
8. Reducing valve for supply air

9. Bellows movement for sensitivity adjustment
10. Flapper
11. Nozzle
12. 'Zero-point adjustment spring'
13. Mechanical stops
14. Amplifying relay
15. Restriction
16. Supply air
17. Output signal

Figure 7.3   Pneumatic force-balance viscosity transmitter (Courtesy Eurocontrol GB Ltd.) (a) Principal parts (b) Measuring principle

appropriate stainless steel. The instrument supply is at 1.4 bar and the output 0.2–1 bar. The measuring accuracy is better than ±1 % of the measured span.

7.3   MEASUREMENT OF THE FORCE OR ENERGY REQUIRED TO MOVE A MEMBER AT A CONSTANT RATE IN THE FLUID

7.3.1   Contraves viscometer

The construction and design of this type of viscometer is illustrated in *Figure 7.4*. A dip type is also available in which the measuring bob and outer cylinder are carried on an extended shaft and supports so that they can be immersed in a vessel of the fluid to be measured.

The external appearance is shown in *Figure 7.4(a)*. If it is required the measuring cell can be enclosed in a jacket through which a heat exchange fluid can be passed to enable the viscosity measurement to be made at a constant temperature.

The principle of the measurement is that a cylindrical measuring bob is rotated at a known speed in the liquid to be measured, thus producing a uniform shear stress. The torque required to maintain this shear stress depends upon the viscosity, and is measured by measuring the torque reaction on the driving system from the twist produced in the suspension system.

The structure of the instrument is shown in the section in *Figure 7.4(b)*. A synchronous motor and drive train, which can include a three-speed gear box, is mounted inside the aluminium casing and suspended from a torsion wire which allows 340° rotational motion. Speed changing is manual by a knob on the instrument, and for measurements on very viscous liquids additional step-down gears ratio 1:10 or 1:100 can be fitted.

The torque required to rotate the measuring bob depends on the viscosity of the substance, so that the suspended driving unit experiences a torque reaction which is measured by a calibrated spring. The suspended system turns until, at equilibrium, the angle through which the system has turned is proportional to the torque on the measuring bob. By means of a 200 Ω linear potentiometer the torque deflection can be translated into a proportional electrical signal, thus allowing remote indication, recording and control. According to the pointer position on the dial, a corresponding resistance value is measured between 0 and 200 Ω.

In order to protect the sensitive torque measuring system from the process stream, the measuring cup is rotated by means of a magnetic coupling.

The housing of the in-line system is suitable for pressures up to 200 bar and temperatures up to 350°C. All materials in contact with the measured substance are made of 18/8 M stainless steel, whereas the measuring bob bearings are made of stainless steel, silver, Teflon or sapphire, depending on the type of instrument. For special cases ruby bearings can be supplied. Measuring bobs of different diameters are available for each type of measuring cell. Each measuring bob is accompanied by the corresponding characteristic curve to allow a simple graphical determination of the viscosity.

An explosion proof version is available in which the potentiometer is connected to an intrinsically safe circuit, and the motor housed in an explosion proof case designed to German and Swiss authorities approval.

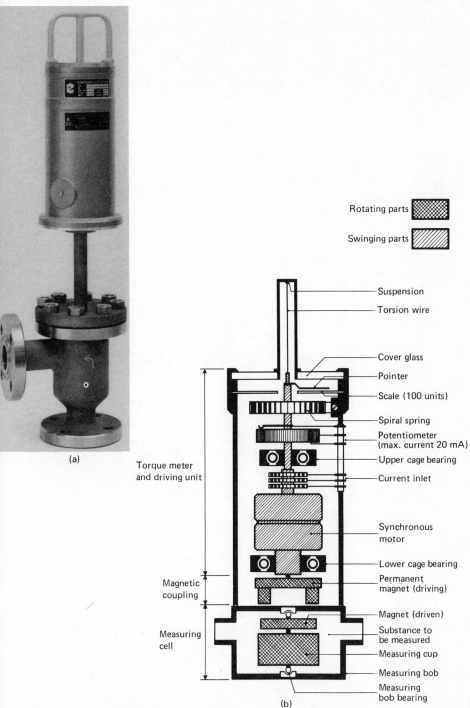

*Figure 7.4   Contraves in-line viscometer (Courtesy Contraves Industrial Products Ltd.) (a) In-line instrument
(b) Section showing measuring system*

7.3.2   The Bendix Ultra-Viscoson

In this instrument a thin alloy steel blade mounted on the end of a probe of suitable length is set vibrating longitudinally, with an amplitude of the order of 1 μm, by a short electrical impulse. This blade produces ultrasonic shear waves in the material surrounding the blade, causing relative motion between the layers of material near the blade. The amount of energy required to produce the vibrations of the blade is measured by an electronic computer which converts this measurement into viscosity readings which may be indicated or recorded by a suitable 0–50 mV instrument or used to actuate a controller. The temperature of the liquid under test may be measured and recorded at the same time, or the output of the temperature measuring bulb fed into the computer so that the viscosity referred to some fixed temperature may be indicated or recorded. Instruments are available with ranges of 0–50, 0–500, 0–5000, 0–50 000 cP.

If the blade is immersed in a substance having suspended particles of size greater than 1 μm low readings will be obtained which will be close to the viscosity of the parent liquid, since the amplitude of vibration is insufficient to subject the suspended particles to adequate shearing stresses.

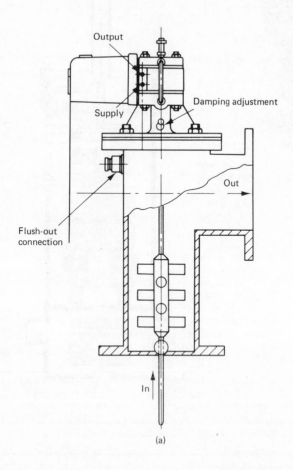

(a)

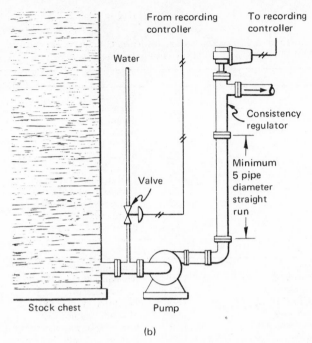

From recording
controller

To recording
controller

Water

Consistency
regulator

Minimum
5 pipe
diameter
straight
run

Valve

Stock chest

Pump

(b)

Figure 7.5   Paper consistency measurement (Courtesy Fischer and Porter Ltd.) (a) Section (b) Typical installation

7.4   PAPER CONSISTENCY MEASUREMENT

A property akin to viscosity is the consistency of paper stock. It is important to measure and control this property if the quality of a paper is to be maintained, as it is a measure of the fibre length of the stock and its degree of 'wetness'. The instrument measures on an arbitrary scale but enables an operator to know whether he is reproducing a condition of the stock which he knows has been successful.

The paper stock flows through a high tee *(Figure 7.5(a))* housing a cylindrical stainless steel shaft, guided top and bottom, from which stainless steel fingers project. The drag on these fingers as the stock flows by is measured by a modified design of force-balance transmitter similar to that in a differential pressure transmitter (Volume 1), the force on the sensor being counterbalanced by the force produced on a bellows system. The output of the transmitter is arranged to give an output of 1.0–0.2 bar with increasing consistency. The transmitter is provided with the usual zero and span adjustments. It is suitable for line pressures up to 7 bar g and temperatures up to 50°C.

The output is recorded and it may be used to control the water addition to paper stock before it is fed on to the paper making machine by an installation of the form shown in *Figure 7.5(b)*.

APPENDIX

Table A1. pH VALUES OF ACIDS AND BASES AT 25°C AT CONCENTRATIONS IN mol/dm³
UNLESS OTHERWISE STATED

Acids

Hydrochloric, 1.0	0.1	Formica, 0.1	2.3
Hydrochloric, 0.1	1.1	Lactic, 0.1	2.4
Hydrochloric, 0.01	2.0	Acetic, 1.0	2.4
Sulphuric, 1.0	0.3	Acetic, 0.1	2.9
Sulphuric, 0.1	1.2	Acetic, 0.01	3.4
Sulphuric, 0.01	2.1	Benzoic, 0.01	3.1
Orthophosphoric, 0.1	1.5	Alum, 0.1	3.2
Sulphurous, 0.1	1.5	Carbonic (saturated)	3.8
Oxalic, 0.1	1.6	Hydrogen sulphide, 0.1	4.1
Tartaric, 0.1	2.2	Arsenious (saturated)	5.0
Malic, 0.1	2.2	Hydrocyanic, 0.1	5.1
Citric, 0.1	2.2	Boric, 0.1	5.2

Bases

Sodium hydroxide, 1.0	14.0	Ammonia, 1.0	11.6
Sodium hydroxide, 0.1	13.0	Ammonia, 0.1	11.1
Sodium hydroxide, 0.01	12.0	Ammonia, 0.01	10.6
Potassium hydroxide, 1.0	14.0	Potassium cyanide, 0.1	11.0
Potassium hydroxide, 0.1	13.0	Magnesia (saturated)	10.5
Potassium hydroxide, 0.01	12.0	Sodium sesquicarbonate, 0.1	10.1
Sodium metasilicate, 0.1	12.6	Ferrous hydroxide (saturated)	9.5
Lime (saturated)	12.4	Calcium carbonate (saturated)	9.4
Trisodium phosphate, 0.1	12.0	Borax, 0.1	9.2
Sodium carbonate, 0.1	11.6	Sodium bicarbonate, 0.1	8.4

Table A2. RELATIVE HUMIDITY AS A FUNCTION OF WET-BULB DEPRESSION

Dry-bulb temperature, °C	Wet-bulb depression, °C										
	0.5	1.0	1.5	2.0	2.5	3.0	3.5	4.0	4.5	5.0	5.5
	Relative humidity, %										
10	94	88	82	76	71	65	60	54	49	44	39
12	94	89	83	78	73	68	63	57	53	48	43
14	95	90	84	79	74	70	65	60	56	51	47
16	95	90	85	81	76	71	67	62	58	54	50
18	95	91	86	82	77	73	69	65	60	56	52
20	96	91	86	83	78	74	70	66	62	59	55
22	96	92	87	83	79	76	72	68	64	61	57
24	96	92	88	84	80	77	73	69	66	62	59
	6.0	6.5	7.0	7.5	8.0	8.5	9.0	9.5	10.0	10.5	11.0
10	34	29	24	19	14	9	5	—	—	—	—
12	38	34	29	24	20	16	11	7	3	—	—
14	42	38	33	29	25	24	17	13	9	5	2
16	46	41	37	34	30	26	22	18	15	11	8
18	49	45	41	37	34	30	27	23	20	16	13
20	51	48	44	41	37	34	30	27	24	21	18
22	54	50	47	44	40	37	34	31	28	25	22
24	56	52	49	46	43	40	37	34	31	28	26

Table A3. HUMIDITIES OVER SATURATED SALT SOLUTIONS

Saturated solutions of various salts in water are used to obtain known relative humidities of air circulated in sealed enclosures which are maintained at a uniform and constant temperature

Saturated salt solution	Temperature, °C										
	0	5	10	15	20	25	30	35	40	50	60
	Relative humidity, %										
Potassium sulphate	99	98	98	97	97	97	96	96	96	96	96
Potassium nitrate	97	96	95	94	93	92	91	89	88	85	82
Potassium chloride	89	88	88	87	86	85	84	83	82	81	80
Ammonium sulphate	83	82	82	81	81	80	80	80	79	79	78
Sodium chloride	76	76	76	76	76	75	75	75	75	75	75
Sodium nitrite	—	—	—	—	66	65	63	62	62	59	59
Ammonium nitrate	77	74	72	69	65	62	59	55	53	47	42
Sodium dichromate	60	59	58	56	55	54	52	51	50	47	—
Magnesium nitrate	60	58	57	56	55	53	52	50	49	46	43
Potassium carbonate	—	—	47	44	44	43	43	43	42	—	—
Magnesium chloride	35	34	34	34	33	33	33	32	32	31	30
Potassium acetate	25	24	24	23	23	22	22	21	20	—	—
Lithium chloride	15	14	13	13	12	12	12	12	11	11	11
Potassium hydroxide	—	14	13	10	9	8	7	6	6	6	5

Tables A2 and *A3* courtesy of Kaye, G. W. C., and Laby, T. H., *Tables of Physical and Chemical Constants,* 14th ed., Longmans.

INDEX